edited by E.L.Cripps · London papers in regional science 4 · a pion publication

space-time concepts
in urban and regional models

p Pion Limited, 207 Brondesbury Park, London NW2 5JN

ISBN 0 85086 044 X

Set on IBM 72 Composers by Pion Limited, London.
Printed in Great Britain by J.W.Arrowsmith Limited, Bristol.

Preface

This volume contains the papers which were presented at the fifth Annual Conference of the British section of the Regional Science Association, held in London in August 1972. All of the papers deal with aspects of the spatial organisation of cities and regions, and a considerable number of them deal with the development of spatial systems in time. The papers are organised into five parts. The first contains papers which examine the notion of space-time developments in regional science. The second part is concerned with developments in more conventional models of regional economies. The third and fourth parts of the collection are both concerned with models of urban growth and structure. They are distinguished largely by the style of model building of the authors of each paper. Part 3 is comprised of papers on abstract models which rely mostly on theory and analytical methods for their solution, and are continuous in their variables. Part 4, on the other hand, deals with the development of more operational models, discrete in form, and which tend to have a larger empirical content. Part 5 has a different focus from the four previous sections and, though it has in part a concern with the spatial organisation of cities and regions, its major focus is on the methodology of urban design and planning.

The volume will provide useful material for academic regional scientists, economists, geographers, sociologists, and planners, as well as practitioners in these fields.

ELC
Institute for Transport Studies, University of Leeds.

Contributors

J. C. Amson	*The Mathematical Institute, The North Haugh, University of St. Andrews, St. Andrews, KY16 9AJ*
R. Barras	*Centre for Environmental Studies, 5 Cambridge Terrace, Regents Park, London NW1 4JL*
T. A. Broadbent	*Centre for Environmental Studies, 5 Cambridge Terrace, Regents Park, London NW1 4JL*
E. Casetti	*Department of Geography, The Ohio State University, Columbus, Ohio 43210*
M. Cordey-Hayes	*Centre for Environmental Studies, 5 Cambridge Terrace, Regents Park, London NW1 4JL*
P. C. Forer	*Tourism and Recreation Research Unit, Department of Geography, Edinburgh University, High School Yards, Edinburgh EH1 1NR*
N. J. Glickman	*Department of City and Regional Planning, University of Pennsylvania, Philadelphia, Pennsylvania 19104*
I. R. Gordon	*Centre for Research in the Social Sciences, University of Kent at Canterbury, Canterbury*
B. Harris	*Department of City and Regional Planning, University of Pennsylvania, Philadelphia, Pennsylvania 19104*
W. Isard	*Department of Regional Science, University of Pennsylvania, Philadelphia, Pennsylvania 19104*
P. Liossatos	*Peace Research Unit, Department of Regional Science, University of Pennsylvania, Philadelphia, Pennsylvania 19104*
H. W. Richardson	*Centre for Research in the Social Sciences, University of Kent at Canterbury, Canterbury*
M. L. Senior	*Department of Geography, University of Leeds, Leeds LS2 9JT*
A. G. Wilson	*Department of Geography, University of Leeds, Leeds LS2 9JT*

Contents

Transport Rate and Pollution as Basic Variables in Space-Time Development†

W.ISARD
University of Pennsylvania
P.LIOSSATOS
Cornell University

1 Introduction

In a previous manuscript (Isard and Liossatos, 1973) we developed an elementary model to set forth space-time as a single general concept, unifying the notions of both space and time. Both space and time were treated on an equal basis and concomitantly to depict development. Interconnected with this advance was the use of field theory, which permitted us to circumvent the typical criticisms levelled at techniques treating discrete sets of single-point space-economies. Our model, though elementary, pertained to continuous space, and was found to yield the traditional basic principles governing investment and the spatial pattern of welfare prices.

In this paper we wish to improve our elementary model in several important directions so that it can be said to correspond more closely to reality. In section 2 we introduce labor into the model as a second factor of production. In section 3 the transport rate is taken to be a basic variable, and in section 4 differential fertility is considered. In section 5 pollution is introduced as a key variable which influences the pattern of space-time development. In section 6 we take into account the diffusion and decay of pollution, and examine some implications for rent analysis.

2 The introduction of labor as a factor

The first improvement of our simplified model involves the introduction of labor as a basic factor of production. We now postulate for any space-time point the production function:

$$Y(x,t) = F[K(x,t), L(x,t)] , \tag{1}$$

where
Y is the output of our single commodity,
K is the capital stock, and
L is the amount of labor employed in production,
the available labor at any space-time point being unbounded. We take

$$\frac{\partial F}{\partial K}, \ \frac{\partial F}{\partial L} > 0 ; \ \text{and} \ \frac{\partial^2 F}{\partial K^2}, \ \frac{\partial^2 F}{\partial L^2} < 0 ,$$

† Research supported by the Environmental Protection Agency, grant E.P.A.800289, and the National Science Foundation.

namely conditions of positive marginal productivity in the use of any
factor, and diminishing marginal productivity with increase in the use of
that factor. We posit welfare W, at any space-time point, as a function of
both consumption C and labor L, given by:

$$W(x,t) = f[C(x,t)] - v[L(x,t)] . \tag{2}$$

Here $f(C)$ is a utility function, and $v(L)$ is a disutility function. Therefore
we may view $-v(L)$ as a negative utility function. We take

$$\frac{df}{dC}, \frac{dv}{dL} > 0 ; \quad \frac{d^2f}{dC^2} < 0 ; \quad \text{and} \quad \frac{d^2v}{dL^2} > 0 ;$$

that is positive marginal utility in consumption, positive marginal disutility
of labor, diminishing marginal utility with increase in consumption, and
increasing marginal disutility with increase in labor, respectively. As
before, consumption is equal to production Y, *less* the goods allocated for
capital investment $(1+n)\dot{K}^{(1)}$, *less* the net exports $\overset{x}{U}$, *less* the amount of
goods σU used up in effecting the flow U of goods, that is in transporting
the U amount of goods going through any point. So

$$C(x,t) = Y(x,t) - [1+n(x)]\dot{K}(x,t) - \overset{x}{U}(x,t) - \sigma U(x,t) . \tag{3}$$

The objective again is to maximize welfare W over both the space interval
$[0, B]$ and the finite time period $t = 0$ to $t = t_1$, that is to determine
$K(x,t)$, $L(x,t)$, and $U(x,t)$ as twice continuously differentiable functions
in such a way that

$$\overline{W} \equiv \int_0^B \int_0^{t_1} W \, dx \, dt \tag{4}$$

is maximized, subject to appropriate initial and boundary conditions.
    With labor introduced we now have three Lagrange equations (Euler
conditions of optimality):

$$\frac{W_C}{1+n} \frac{\partial F}{\partial K} = -\frac{\partial(W_C)}{\partial t} , \qquad K\text{-equation} \tag{5}$$

$$\sigma W_C = \frac{\partial(W_C)}{\partial x} , \qquad U\text{-equation} \tag{6}$$

$$W_C \frac{\partial F}{\partial L} = \frac{dv}{dL} , \qquad L\text{-equation} \tag{7}$$

where $W_C = df/dC$, the marginal utility of consumption. As indicated
elsewhere, when we multiply both sides of equation (5) by dt and

---

(1) $\dot{K}$ is the realized addition to capital stock. n is a positive and increasing function
of x, reflecting the increasing difficulty of investment with increase in distance from
the initial point of development, $x = 0$.

integrate from 0 to t_1, we obtain the basic investment principle:

at any space-time point, goods should be invested as capital up to the point where the marginal utility foregone, from not consuming the required units of goods in order to put one unit of capital in place at that space-time point, just equals the cumulative sum (over the remaining points of time in the relevant planning horizon) of the utility from the additional products due to that unit of capital, plus the utility that is saved by not having to use up consumption goods at the end of the planning horizon in order to have that unit of capital then.

When we multiply both sides of equation (6) by dx and integrate from x_1 to x_2, we obtain the basic spatial flow (interregional trade) principle:

at any and every time point, the difference in the marginal utility (welfare price) of a good at two locations in space must equal the social transport cost between these points, this cost being the cumulative sum of the utilities foregone in providing transport for a unit of good through each location in the space interval $[x_1, x_2]$ over which the good is transported.

Our new L-equation (7) simply states the basic labor allocation principle:

at any and every space-time point, the utility of the marginal product from an additional unit of labor must equal the disutility of that labor.

From equation (7) we have

$$W_C = \frac{dv}{dL} \bigg/ \frac{\partial F}{\partial L} . \tag{8}$$

Since W_C declines with time at a given location, as follows from equation (5), so must this ratio. That is

$$\frac{\partial}{\partial t}\left(\frac{dv}{dL} \bigg/ \frac{\partial F}{\partial L}\right) < 0 . \tag{9}$$

Further, since W_C increases with x for any fixed time-point, as follows from equation (6), so does the ratio $(dv/dL)/(\partial F/\partial L)$, or

$$\frac{\partial}{\partial x}\left(\frac{dv}{dL} \bigg/ \frac{\partial F}{\partial L}\right) > 0 . \tag{10}$$

Now by differentiating equation (6) with respect to time, and equation (5) with respect to space, we obtain respectively:

$$\frac{\partial^2 W_C}{\partial t \partial x} = \sigma \frac{\partial W_C}{\partial t} , \tag{11}$$

$$\frac{\partial^2 W_C}{\partial x \partial t} = -\frac{\partial W_C}{\partial x} \frac{1}{1+n} \frac{\partial F}{\partial K} - W_C \frac{\partial}{\partial x}\left(\frac{1}{1+n} \frac{\partial F}{\partial K}\right) . \tag{12}$$

Using equations (5) in (11), and (6) in (12), and bearing in mind that $W_C(x, t)$ is twice continuously differentiable, we can collect equations (11) and (12) to obtain

$$-\frac{\sigma W_C}{1+n}\frac{\partial F}{\partial K} = -\frac{\sigma W_C}{1+n}\frac{\partial F}{\partial K} - W_C\frac{\partial}{\partial x}\left(\frac{1}{1+n}\frac{\partial F}{\partial K}\right).$$ (13)

After cancellation, we have

$$W_C\frac{\partial}{\partial x}\left(\frac{1}{1+n}\frac{\partial F}{\partial K}\right) = 0.$$ (14)

Since $W_C > 0$, it follows that

$$\frac{\partial}{\partial x}\left(\frac{1}{1+n}\frac{\partial F}{\partial K}\right) = 0$$ (15)

which implies that

$$-\frac{dn/dx}{(1+n)^2}\frac{\partial F}{\partial K} + \frac{1}{1+n}\frac{\partial}{\partial x}\left(\frac{\partial F}{\partial K}\right) = 0.$$ (16)

Since $n > 0$, $dn/dx > 0$ and $\partial F/\partial K > 0$, we obtain

$$\frac{\partial}{\partial x}\left(\frac{\partial F}{\partial K}\right) > 0.$$ (17)

Equation (17) states that the marginal product of capital increases with distance from the spatial reference point $x = 0$. Further, if we assume that the marginal product of one factor increases as the use of the other increases, relation (17) is also consistent with capital stock and labor input, and thus production, falling with distance from the spatial reference point $x = 0$[2].

Also from equation (15) we can obtain the solution of equations (5) and (6)[3], namely:

$$W_C(x,t) = W_C(0,0)\exp\left(\sigma x - \frac{1}{1+n}\int_0^t\frac{\partial F}{\partial K}dt\right).$$ (18)

In this section we implicitly assume that population comes to exist (instantaneously and without cost) at locations as labor is required. In a later manuscript we shall examine population as an independent variable.

---

[2] Carrying through the differentiation of equation (17) yields

$$\frac{\partial^2 F}{\partial K^2}\overset{x}{K} + \frac{\partial^2 F}{\partial L\partial K}\overset{x}{L} > 0 \quad \text{or} \quad \frac{\partial^2 F}{\partial K^2}\overset{x}{K} > -\frac{\partial^2 F}{\partial L\partial K}\overset{x}{L}.$$

By assumption,

$$\frac{\partial^2 F}{\partial K^2} < 0 \quad \text{and} \quad \frac{\partial^2 F}{\partial L\partial K} > 0.$$

Hence if $\overset{x}{L} < 0$, $\overset{x}{K} < 0$; and from function (1), $\overset{x}{Y} < 0$.

[3] See Isard and Liossatos (1973) for the steps required to reach this solution. For convenience we take $t_0 = 0$.

3 Transport rate as a variable over time

Equation (18) draws attention to the fact that at time $t = 0$ we must assume a spatial pattern of consumption which yields a pattern of marginal utility given by

$$W_C(x, 0) = W_C(0, 0)\exp(\sigma x) .\qquad(19)$$

In reality when an initial development is effected, at least as has been observed historically in many cases, the transport rate σ may be taken to be very high, so that a concentrated pattern of consumption around a reference point $(x = 0)$ can be assumed[4]. But with time, as development proceeds and roads are constructed, σ may be best viewed as declining. Hence we now wish to consider σ as a function of time. In doing so, the Lagrange equations (5), (6), and (7) remain unchanged. However the solution to these equations is now

$$W_C(x, t) = W_C(0, 0)\exp\left[\sigma(0)x - \frac{1}{1+n}\int_0^t \frac{\partial F}{\partial K}dt\right],\qquad(20)$$

where

$$\frac{\partial}{\partial x}\left(\frac{1}{1+n}\frac{\partial F}{\partial K}\right) = -\frac{d\sigma}{dt} ,\qquad(21)$$

and is no longer zero as it is in equation (15). Note that, from equation (21), $\frac{1}{1+n}\frac{\partial F}{\partial K}$ is a function of $\frac{d\sigma}{dt}$; and equation (20) may be rewritten to indicate explicitly the dependence of W_C on $\sigma(t)$ as:

$$W_C(x, t) = W_C(0, 0)\exp\left[\sigma(t)x - \int_0^t \frac{\partial F}{\partial K}\bigg|_{\text{at } x = 0} dt\right].\qquad(22)$$

The significance of the relation (21) is best seen by reference to figure 1. In figure 1a, for which $\sigma(0)$ is large and $d\sigma/dt = 0$, we see how consumption falls sharply at the initial point of time and continues to do so at subsequent points of time. Correspondingly we may imagine that the flow of goods rises and then falls sharply in the initial point of time and continues to do so in subsequent points of time. In figure 1b, which pertains to a situation where the transport rate falls with time, that is $d\sigma/dt < 0$, the decline of C becomes less and less sharp as time passes. Correspondingly we may imagine that changes in flows over space are less sharp and that the region of positive net exports increases. Similar changes occur in the graphs of the other variables as σ changes. In short the resistance to spatial spread of development is reduced, and consequently the space-economy expands more rapidly with time.

[4] In accord with equation (19), consumption falls with distance since it depends upon $\exp(-\sigma x)$; and if σ is large, consumption is practically zero for $x \geqslant 10/\sigma$. Strictly speaking, however, consumption is always nonzero, though it may be negligible for large x.

Note also that since we have defined mass density ρ [see Isard and Liossatos (1973)] as

$$\rho = \sigma(1+n) \tag{23}$$

at each space point, the mass density at each point x decreases with time. Similarly the mass associated with the system decreases with time.

Generalizing further, we may allow σ to depend also on U (the volume of flow), where $\partial\sigma/\partial U < 0$ (reflecting economies of scale in transport); but where the scale economies from volume, that is $(\partial\sigma/\partial U)U$, do not exceed the transport rate σ subject to such economies. Accordingly the Lagrange equation (6) changes [equations (5) and (7) remain unchanged] to read

$$\sigma + \frac{\partial\sigma}{\partial U}U = \frac{\partial}{\partial x}W_C \ . \tag{24}$$

Since $\sigma + (\partial\sigma/\partial U)U > 0$, W_C increases with x, C declines with x, and the behavior of other magnitudes are as generally depicted by our various figures in this and the preceding paper. Note again that the concept of mass density changes. We now have

$$\rho = \left(\sigma + \frac{\partial\sigma}{\partial U}U\right)(1+n) \ . \tag{25}$$

Since $U > 0$, and $\partial\sigma/\partial U < 0$, the mass density ρ at any space–time point (x, t) is decreased as a consequence of this generalization.

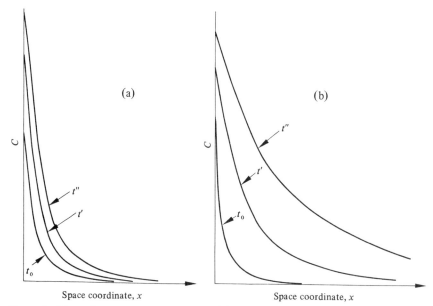

Figure 1. Plots of consumption over space (a) for $\sigma(0)$ large and $d\sigma/dt = 0$, (b) for $\sigma(0)$ large and $d\sigma/dt < 0$.

On the other hand, if we assume that after a point congestion and diseconomies appear such that $\partial\sigma/\partial U > 0$, the tendency, loosely speaking, is for mass density ρ to increase.

4 Differential fertility

It is of interest to investigate the significance of differential fertility of agricultural soil upon the optimal path of development. To simplify our analysis we assume that the most dense point of initial agricultural development (which corresponds to $x = 0$, $t = 0$) is also the point of highest fertility (the location of the most fertile soil), and that fertility falls off regularly with distance from that point. Accordingly we may let output be a function of capital, labor, and soil fertility, S, where $S = S(x) > 0$ with $dS/dx < 0$. Thus we have

$$Y = F(K, L, S) . \tag{26}$$

With this general formulation the Lagrange equations (5), (6), and (7) remain unchanged in form, but the significance of the terms $\partial F/\partial K$ and $\partial F/\partial L$ changes. The form of the solution (18) remains unchanged, but the content of this solution, as well as of relation (15), changes because of the changed significance of $\partial F/\partial K$. Also the mass of the system remains the same, but the driving force changes because the significance of $\partial F/\partial K$ changes.

It is instructive to examine a more specific dependence of production on fertility. Let

$$Y = \varphi(x)F(K, L) , \tag{27}$$

where $\varphi(x)$ represents the fertility variable with $\varphi(x) > 0$ and $d\varphi/dx < 0$ on the interval $[0, B]$. With this specific formulation the Lagrange equation (6) remains unchanged, while equations (5) and (7) change to become respectively:

$$\frac{W_C\varphi(x)}{1+n}\frac{\partial F}{\partial K} = -\frac{\partial}{\partial t}(W_C) , \tag{28}$$

$$W_C\varphi(x)\frac{\partial F}{\partial L} = \frac{dv}{dL} . \tag{29}$$

The solution (18) is modified and now reads:

$$W_C(x, t) = W_C(0, 0)\exp\left[\sigma x - \frac{\varphi(x)}{1+n}\int_0^t \frac{\partial F}{\partial K}dt\right] , \tag{30}$$

and we replace equation (15) by

$$\frac{\partial}{\partial x}\left[\frac{\varphi(x)}{1+n}\frac{\partial F}{\partial K}\right] = 0 \qquad \text{for } \sigma \text{ constant} . \tag{31}$$

Note that the definition of mass changes to become

$$\rho = \frac{\sigma(1+n)}{\varphi(x)} .$$ (32)

When $\varphi(x)$ becomes small it implies a very large mass—which is consistent with the fact that the values of W_C and consumption C propagate very slowly.

Finally we observe that where our wave model involves time-dependence of n, $\varphi(x)$, and σ, equation (30) must be appropriately revised [5].

5 Pollution as a basic variable affecting space–time development
In accord with our previous models on pollution, we now introduce the pollution variable R. We may consider it in several different ways. Let us first posit that all pollution produced at a time point is also consumed at that point. Later we shall allow pollution to be stored as a stock. In both cases society produces abatement goods, either by taking goods out of current consumption to use directly as abatement goods or to construct capital facilities which produce abatement goods. We also may assume that all points of the space-economy are subject to such heavy pollution that at all points it is desirable to abate it. Later we relax this assumption.

We take $R(x, t)$ to measure the level of pollution (a 'bad' commodity) present at any space–time point. We specify the welfare function as:

$$W = f(C) - g(R) - v(L) ,$$ (33)

with

$$\frac{\partial W}{\partial R} \equiv W_R \equiv -g_R < 0 \quad \text{and} \quad \frac{\partial^2 W}{\partial R^2} \equiv W_{RR} \equiv -g_{RR} < 0 \qquad \text{for } R > 0. [6]$$

We take R at any space–time point to be a function of (1) the level of production, Y, of the desired economic good, and (2) the level of

---

[5] When n, $\varphi(x)$, and σ are time-dependent as well as x-dependent, the solution takes the form

$$W_C(x, t) = W_C(0, 0) \exp\left[\int_0^x \sigma(x, 0) \, dx - \int_0^t \sigma(x, t) v(x, t) \, dt \right] ,$$

where the wave velocity $v(x, t)$ is given by

$$v(x, t) = \left[\varphi(x, t) \frac{\partial F}{\partial K} + \frac{\partial n}{\partial t} \right] \bigg/ \sigma(1 + n) ,$$

and where the assumption of twice continuously differentiable W_C requires that

$$\frac{\partial(\sigma v)}{\partial x} = -\frac{\partial \sigma}{\partial t} .$$

[6] We could use a more general welfare function, $W = h(C, R) - v(L)$, but doing so would require additional assumptions about the second derivatives in order to specify the behavior of C and R over time and space from a knowledge of W_C and W_R.

abatement represented by the amount, J, of the economic good diverted from consumption and investment, and directly converted to abatement goods[7]. Thus we have

$$R = R(Y,J) .\tag{34}$$

Accordingly we revise the consumption equation (3) to read

$$C = Y - (1+n)\dot{K} - \overset{x}{U} - \sigma U - J .\tag{35}$$

Since in our first model all pollution produced at any point of space-time is also consumed at that point, no stock of pollution carries over to the next point of time. For this model we let relation (34) take the specific form

$$R = \alpha Y - J ,\tag{36}$$

where $0 < \alpha < 1$, and where R is a magnitude per unit of time per unit of length the same way as Y, J, and C are. In this model we also assume that goods taken out of consumption are used directly as abatement goods, and are not invested in capital facilities to produce abatement goods.

For the maximization of welfare over space and time, we have an additional Lagrange equation, the J-equation. The Lagrange equations are:

$$W_C \frac{\partial F}{\partial L} + W_R \alpha \frac{\partial F}{\partial L} = \frac{\mathrm{d}v}{\mathrm{d}L} , \qquad L\text{-equation} \tag{37}$$

$$W_C \frac{\partial F}{\partial K} + W_R \alpha \frac{\partial F}{\partial K} = -(1+n)\dot{W}_C , \qquad K\text{-equation} \tag{38}$$

$$\sigma W_C = \overset{x}{\dot{W}}_C , \qquad U\text{-equation} \tag{39}$$

$$W_C \frac{\partial C}{\partial J} + W_R \frac{\partial R}{\partial J} = 0 . \qquad J\text{-equation} \tag{40}$$

By considering equations (35) and (36), equation (40) becomes

$$W_C = -W_R .\tag{41}$$

We may now interpret equation (37). First we recognize that the production of any additional unit of output also involves the concomitant production of an α fraction of a unit of pollution. Thus the net utility of a unit of production is the gross utility of that unit of output, W_C, less the disutility of the α fraction of pollution, $-\alpha W_R$—that is, net utility is $W_C + \alpha W_R$. Hence the net utility from the marginal product of labor, $\partial F/\partial L$, is $(W_C + \alpha W_R)(\partial F/\partial L)$, which equation (37) equates to $\mathrm{d}v/\mathrm{d}L$, the disutility of labor. Also observe that given equation (41) we may rewrite

---

[7] In this first model, we assume no capital is required for the production of the abatement good.

equation (37) as

$$(1-\alpha)W_C\frac{\partial F}{\partial L} = \frac{dv}{dL} . \tag{42}$$

Similarly we may revise our interpretation of equation (5) to obtain an interpretation of equation (38) wherein W_C is gross utility, and $W_C + \alpha W_R$ is the *net* utility, which by equation (37) is also equal to $(1-\alpha)W_C$. Equation (39) is to be interpreted as before.

Equations (40) and (41) simply state that at the margin the last unit of output transferred from consumption to abatement involves a foregone utility, which is equal to the marginal disutility avoided by the use of that unit for abatement. Since in equation (38) $W_C + \alpha W_R = (1-\alpha)W_C > 0$, and $\partial F/\partial K$, $(1+n) > 0$, we have

$$\dot{W}_C < 0 . \tag{43}$$

Further, from equations (41) and (43),

$$\dot{W}_R = -\dot{W}_C > 0 . \tag{44}$$

Still more, from equations (39) and (41)

$$\overset{x}{W}_R = -\overset{x}{W}_C = -\sigma W_C < 0 . \tag{45}$$

From equation (43) it follows that consumption at any fixed point in space grows with time, that is $\dot{C} > 0$—an expected finding. From equation (44) it follows that the production (and consumption) of pollution at any fixed point in space declines with time, that is, $\dot{R} < 0$, an unexpected finding. From equation (45) it follows that at any time point consumption declines with distance, that is $\overset{x}{C} < 0$, an expected finding; and that production (and consumption) of pollution increases with distance, that is $\overset{x}{R} > 0$, another unexpected result.

These unexpected results are unexpected because, in reality, we observe that the pollution to which a population is exposed increases with time, whether it is pollution per unit of time (which we consider in this model) or a stock of pollution (which we consider in the next model). Also in reality we usually observe that the pollution to which a population is exposed generally decreases with distance from an initial point (center) of an agricultural–urban–industrial development. However, the fact of the matter is that, as development proceeds, reality increasingly diverges from the optimal path. Clearly once pollution mounts to a level where it becomes desirable to abate it—that is, where the utility foregone, by taking one unit out of consumption and devoting it to abatement, becomes equal to and then becomes smaller than the disutility from pollution which can be avoided—abatement should take place. But as development continues, consumption grows still more and the marginal utility foregone by releasing a unit of y for abatement continues to decline. Concomitantly as Y, the production of the economic commodity, increases, there is no tendency for the level of pollution (and thus the marginal disutility of pollution) to decline. Rather the level of pollution emission, αY, increases with the increase of production. Thus, over time, the decline at the margin in utility foregone because of abatement, coupled with a tendency (if not combatted) for pollution disutility to mount, makes it increasingly desirable to effect abatement. It becomes increasingly desirable to produce more abatement goods, and sufficiently more so that the level of pollution, R, falls in consistence with condition (41). Thus our optimal path, given our assumptions, necessarily yields $\dot{R} < 0$.

Correspondingly we observe that the optimality implication, that $\overset{x}{W}_C > 0$, implies that, at the margin at any time point, the utility foregone in releasing a unit of y for abatement increases with distance. Therefore on this count the desirability of abatement decreases with distance. This then suggests that $\overset{x}{R} > 0$, and this must be so since for optimality $W_C = -W_R$, and thus $\overset{x}{W}_C = -\overset{x}{W}_R$. Since $\overset{x}{W}_C > 0$, then $-\overset{x}{W}_R > 0$. But by our assumption we can have $-\overset{x}{W}_R > 0$ only if $\overset{x}{R} > 0$.

We now consider a second model in which R can accumulate or decay over time as a stock. Here, R, like capital, is a magnitude per unit of length. Its change per unit of time, as given by $\dot{R}$, is related to current production, Y, of the economic good and of the level, J, of economic goods devoted to the production of abatement goods. Accordingly we replace equation (36) by

$$\dot{R} = \alpha Y - J . \tag{46}$$

With this new equation we may now rewrite (35), the basic consumption equation, as

$$C = (1 - \alpha)Y - (1 + n)\dot{K} - \overset{x}{\dot{U}} - \sigma U + \dot{R} . \tag{47}$$

Note that here the independent field variables are K, L, U, and R. J becomes an auxiliary variable which is determined by equation (46).

Accordingly the Lagrange equations become:

$$(1 - \alpha)W_C \frac{\partial F}{\partial L} = \frac{dv}{dL} , \tag{48}$$

$$(1 - \alpha)W_C \frac{\partial F}{\partial K} = -(1 + n)\dot{W}_C , \tag{49}$$

$$\sigma W_C = \overset{x}{W}_C , \tag{50}$$

$$W_R = \dot{W}_C . \tag{51}$$

Equations (48) and (49) are to be interpreted as equations (37) and (38), except that net utility is now given *directly* by $(1 - \alpha)W_C$ instead of by $W_C + \alpha W_R$. Equation (50) is to be interpreted as before.

Equation (51) states that the negative of the marginal disutility of pollution must equal the time rate of change in marginal utility. Its meaning is better seen if we multiply both sides of it by dt and integrate from t to t_1 to obtain

$$W_C\bigg|_{\text{at } t} = -\int_t^{t_1} W_R \, dt + W_C\bigg|_{\text{at } t_1} . \tag{52}$$

This equation states that the utility foregone by devoting one unit of y to abatement rather than to consumption must be equal to the sum of two terms. The first term represents the cumulative sum of disutility avoided or utility gained, over the time points from t to t_1, by having at each of these time points a stock of pollution decreased in size because at year t an additional unit of y was taken out of consumption and used for abatement. The second term indicates the amount of utility not foregone at year t_1, in order to have at t_1 a stock of pollution decreased by the same amount in size, because in year t we had devoted an additional unit of y to abatement. This utility not foregone in year t_1 thus represents another gain (a saving) from foregoing a unit of consumption in year t. For convenience we shall designate the sum of the two terms on the right-hand side of equation (52) as an *adjusted cumulative sum* of utility gained.

In this model it also follows that $\dot{C} > 0$, $\overset{x}{\dot{C}} < 0$, $\dot{R} < 0$ when $\dot{K} > 0$, and $\overset{x}{\dot{R}} > 0$.[8] We have not yet been able to demonstrate that $\dot{K} > 0$.[9] Graphically we have the situation shown in figure 2.

We now wish to relax the assumption that abatement takes place at all points of the space-economy at all points of time. Actually at a sufficiently early stage of development we may imagine a situation where no abatement takes place at any space point. Subsequently, as development proceeds differentially at the several space points, we may imagine that abatement begins first at that space point of greatest production and consumption, and in time spreads to all other space points. For example, prior to some time $\tilde{t}$ for some $\tilde{x}$ we may imagine that abatement is not justifiable, because both consumption and production are so small that the marginal utility foregone, in not consuming a unit of y, exceeds the marginal disutility which can be avoided through use of that unit for abatement. Hence, prior to time point $\tilde{t}$, abatement is zero ($J = 0$); and since production increases over time, the level of pollution increases with time ($\dot{R} > 0$). Further since at any time point in this early stage of development, production declines with distance ($\overset{x}{Y} < 0$), the level of pollution does likewise ($\overset{x}{R} < 0$). However, at $\tilde{t}$ development of $\tilde{x}$ does

[8] Since from equations (50) and (51)

$$-\overset{x}{W_R} \equiv \overset{x}{g_R} = -\overset{x\cdot}{W_C} = -\sigma \dot{W_C} > 0 ,$$

then it follows that

$$\overset{x}{g_R} = g_{RR}\overset{x}{R} > 0 ;$$

and since $g_{RR} > 0$, by assumption $\overset{x}{R} > 0$.
[9] We also are not able to establish that $\overset{x}{K} < 0$. However, if $\overset{x}{L} < 0$, then $\overset{x}{K} < 0$.

reach a level where it does become desirable to effect abatement; and then development enters a second stage for $\tilde{x}$.

In an attempt to portray the pollution characteristics of a two-stage development process, we may reformulate the model (into which labor does not enter) to be:

$$W = f(C) - \theta[t - \bar{t}(x)]g(R) , \tag{53}$$

where $\bar{t}(x)$ is some increasing function of x such that $\bar{t}(0) > 0$ and $\bar{t}(B) < t_1$. We take $\theta(t - \bar{t})$ to be a usual step function for which

$$\theta(t - \bar{t}) = \begin{cases} 1 \text{ for } t \geqslant \bar{t} \\ 0 \text{ for } t < \bar{t} \end{cases} . \tag{54}$$

Consequently, for $t < \bar{t}$, the disutility from pollution is ignored in welfare evaluation[10]. The level of pollution is given by

$$R = \alpha Y - \theta(t - \bar{t})J . \tag{55}$$

Hence when $t < \bar{t}$, $\theta(t - \bar{t}) = 0$, and no abatement of pollution takes place. The level of consumption, given by

$$C = Y - (1 + n)\dot{K} - \sigma U - \dot{U}^{\tilde{x}} - \theta(t - \bar{t})J , \tag{56}$$

is also unaffected by abatement for $t < \bar{t}$.

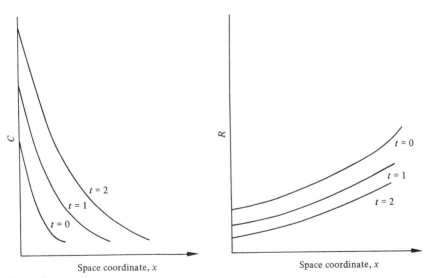

Figure 2.

[10] Observe that, from a social welfare standpoint, it is rather inappropriate to use a welfare function which entirely ignores pollution up to the time when abatement does occur. The pollution can rise to levels which lead to disutility (negative welfare), yet not sufficiently great to justify the release of goods from consumption for abatement. Using the welfare function of equation (53) entirely ignores this disutility.

While the nature of the θ function leads to expectations of discontinuities, one seeks solutions for which $K(x, t)$, $U(x, t)$, and $J(x, t)$ are continuous and individually continuously differentiable. It then becomes necessary to show that such solutions do exist.

Formally the Lagrange equations for the optimization of welfare $\overline{W}$ are:

$$f_C \frac{dF}{dK} - \theta(t-\overline{t})g_R \alpha \frac{dF}{dK} = -(1+n)\dot{f}_C , \qquad (57)$$

$$\alpha f_C = \overset{x}{f_C} , \qquad (58)$$

$$-\theta(t-\overline{t})f_C + \theta^2(t-\overline{t})g_R = 0 . \qquad (59)$$

But by equation (54),

$$\theta^2(t-\overline{t}) = \theta(t-\overline{t}) .$$

Hence equation (59) becomes

$$(f_C - g_R)\theta(t-\overline{t}) = 0 . \qquad (60)$$

Thus the space-time region becomes divided into two subareas, to each of which pertains a different set of Lagrange equations. The field must join continuously at the boundary curve described by the equation $t = \overline{t}(x)$.

Unfortunately we have not been able to advance the analysis of this model to obtain satisfactory results. Nor have we been able to do so for a model wherein R is a stock, and for which we replace equation (55) by

$$\dot{R} = \alpha Y - \theta(t-\overline{t})J . \qquad (61)$$

All we can currently do satisfactorily is model two separate stages of development:
(1) the stage during which no space point effects abatement [for which $\theta(t-\overline{t}) = 0$ for all x], and to which the model of section 2 pertains, and
(2) the stage during which all space points effect abatement [for which $\theta(t-\overline{t}) = 1$ for all x], and to which the models of section 5 pertain.

6 Pollution, diffusion, decay, and rent
At this point we wish to introduce both diffusion and decay (depreciation) effects into the pollution stock model for which $\theta(t-\overline{t}) = 1$ for all x. The diffusion relates to the spread of the stock of pollution from one space point to another in the social system. The decay (depreciation) relates to the decrease in the stock of pollution at a given space point with the passage of time, such decrease being automatically removed from the social system.

There are of course many ways to embody a diffusion effect in our model. For our purposes, which are strictly pedagogical, it is useful to view diffusion as direction independent, and to involve simply flows of pollutants from points of greater stock to points of smaller stock. Hence we have for U_R, the flow of pollution per unit of time through a point x

at time t,

$$U_R = -\gamma \dot{\overset{x}{R}} \tag{62}$$

when γ is a positive constant.

With regard to the decay, D_R, of the stock of pollution per unit time, again many types of processes may be envisaged. We choose to use a simple proportionate relation,

$$D_R = -\beta R , \tag{63}$$

where β is a positive constant. Accordingly equation (46) must be restated as

$$\dot{R} = \alpha Y - J - \overset{x}{U}_R - \beta R ,^{(11)} \tag{64}$$

or

$$J = \alpha Y + \gamma \overset{xx}{R} - \beta R - \dot{R} . \tag{64a}$$

Also, since from equation (64) we obtain a different equation for the variable J to substitute into the consumption relation of (35), we must replace the consumption equation (47) by

$$C = (1 - \alpha)Y - (1 + n)\dot{K} - \overset{x}{\dot{U}} - \sigma U + \dot{R} + \overset{x}{U}_R + \beta R , \tag{65}$$

or, since $\overset{x}{U}_R = -\gamma \overset{xx}{R}$, we have

$$C = (1 - \alpha)Y - (1 + n)\dot{K} - \overset{x}{\dot{U}} - \sigma U + \dot{R} - \gamma \overset{xx}{R} + \beta R . \tag{66}$$

We now obtain a new set of Lagrange equations (Euler conditions) for optimal space-time development. Equations (48), (49), and (50) remain

[11] Note that we must use $\overset{x}{U}_R$ in equation (64), rather than U_R, in order to capture the essence of a flow. This point is best seen if we consider a general length Δx. Then we know that the change in stock of pollution over Δx (that is, $\dot{R}\Delta x$) must equal the addition to pollution because of production (that is, $\alpha Y \Delta x$), plus the decrease due to abatement $(-J\Delta x)$, plus the decrease due to depreciation (that is, $-\beta R\Delta x$), plus the increase due to flow in at x {which is U_R at $x[\equiv U_R(x)]$}, plus the decrease due to the flow out at $x + \Delta x$ {which is U_R at $x + \Delta x[\equiv U_R(x + \Delta x)]$}. So we have

$$\dot{R}\Delta x = \alpha Y \Delta x - J\Delta x - \beta R \Delta x + U_R(x) - U_R(x + \Delta x) .$$

Dividing through by Δx, we obtain

$$\dot{R} = \alpha Y - J - \beta R + \frac{U_R(x) - U_R(x + \Delta x)}{\Delta x} ,$$

which, as $\Delta x \to 0$, becomes equation (64).

Note that if the flow is constant over space, as would be the case when the stock of pollution over space were a linear function of x, then the flow into a small interval at point x, namely $U_R(x) = -\gamma \dot{\overset{x}{R}}$ [from equation (62)], would be equal to the flow out of the interval, $U_R(x + \Delta x) = -\gamma \dot{\overset{x}{R}}$, since $\dot{\overset{x}{R}}$ is a constant. Hence $\dot{R}\Delta x$ would be unaffected. Note also that while U_R depends on both x and t, we drop t in the argument of U_R for convenience.

unchanged. Equation (51) must be replaced by

$$W_R + \beta W_C - \gamma \frac{\partial^2 W_C}{\partial x^2} = \dot{W}_C .^{(12)} \tag{67}$$

For the moment imagine that $\partial^2 W_C/\partial x^2 = 0$ so that the third term on the left-hand side can be ignored. Then if we were to multiply both sides of equation (67) by dt and integrate from t to t_1, we would have

$$W_C \bigg|_{\text{at } t} = -\int_t^{t_1} (W_R + \beta W_C) dt + W_C \bigg|_{\text{at } t_1} . \tag{68}$$

That is we obtain the basic investment principle from a pollution standpoint. To understand equation (68), we first must examine the meaning of the expression $-(W_R + \beta W_C)$. This expression suggests that whenever R increases by one unit, so that a gross disutility of $-W_R$ is incurred, at the same time this unit is subject to depreciation by the fractional amount β, so that β less of the good y must be taken out of consumption (as J) to combat the level of R. But the value of a unit of y in consumption is W_C, so that βW_C is saved because of depreciation; hence the gross disutility $-W_R$ must be reduced by βW_C to give the *net disutility* $-(W_R + \beta W_C)$. Another way to see the meaning of $-(W_R + \beta W_C)$ is to consider a reduction of one unit in R. In this case the gross disutility $-W_R$ would be foregone—but also the reduction of one unit would mean that there would not be incurred the β fraction of depreciation, nor the depreciation gain in utility βW_C associated with that fraction. Hence the net disutility foregone would be $-(W_R + \beta W_C)$.

Now we are able to interpret equation (68). It states that the utility foregone at t, because J is increased and hence $\dot{R}$ is decreased by one unit, must equal the cumulative sum of the net disutility avoided (net welfare gained), because the decrease in $\dot{R}$ by one unit means that, at all subsequent points of time, R is one unit smaller than it would otherwise be, and hence at all these points of time there is net disutility which is avoided. Finally, at t_1 we must also allow for a gain, because it is not necessary to take a unit of good out of consumption to achieve that decrease in R at t_1, which is achieved because we have taken a unit of good out of consumption at t.

But $\partial^2 W_C/\partial x^2$ is not zero when $\sigma \neq 0$. Therefore we cannot ignore the third term of the left-hand side of equation (67). This term reflects the influence of the entire space–time development pattern on any given

---

[12] Recall that the general form of the Lagrange equations when second partials exist is

$$\frac{\partial \mathcal{L}}{\partial q} = \frac{\partial}{\partial t}\left(\frac{\partial \mathcal{L}}{\partial \dot{q}}\right) + \frac{\partial}{\partial x}\left(\frac{\partial \mathcal{L}}{\partial \tilde{q}}\right) - \frac{\partial^2}{\partial^2 t}\left(\frac{\partial \mathcal{L}}{\partial \ddot{q}}\right) - \frac{\partial^2}{\partial x^2}\left(\frac{\partial \mathcal{L}}{\partial \tilde{q}^{xx}}\right) .$$

See Hildebrand (1965).

point via the flow of pollution which, in turn, is influenced by the flow of goods. Specifically if we arbitrarily change the $R(x, t)$ function by a small amount, $\delta R(x, t)$, we know that, in addition to the direct change in welfare at our space-time point via the W_R and βW_C factors, plus the indirect change in welfare via the $\partial W_C/\partial t$ factor because $\dot{R}(x, t)$ must change, there is another indirect change in welfare through the $\gamma \partial^2 W_C/\partial x^2$ factor because $\overset{xx}{R}(x, t)$, and thus $\overset{x}{U}_R(x, t)$, must change as well[13]. Now when $R(x, t)$ arbitrarily increases everywhere, and so $\overset{xx}{R}$ changes at every point (x, t), we know that per unit increase (decrease) in $\overset{xx}{R}$ at (x, t) there will be released (or additionally required) γ units of the abatement good J to combat pollution [see equation (64a)]. Hence γ units of the good are available for (or shifted from) consumption. The welfare value of γ units is, of course, γW_C. Now if σ, the transport rate, approaches zero, the welfare maximization objective tends to (1) diffuse the γ units of any released J throughout the system very rapidly, leaving little welfare gain at (x, t), or (2) obtain the required γ units of J from all over the system and only little from (x, t) itself. These effects are reflected in the relationship obtained from equation (50), namely

$$\gamma \frac{\partial^2 W_C}{\partial x^2} = \sigma^2 \gamma W_C . \tag{69}$$

This means that the curvature of the W_C curve, $\partial^2 W_C/\partial x^2$, is very low when σ approaches zero, so that the curve approaches a horizontal straight line. On the other hand if σ is large, the spatial flow effect tends to be small, and a large part of the γ units may be viewed as remaining for (or obtained at the expense of) consumption at (x, t). Thus if we rewrite equation (67) as

$$-(W_R + \beta W_C) + \sigma^2 \gamma W_C = -\frac{\partial W_C}{\partial t} , \tag{70}$$

we see that the net disutility incurred (equivalent to the utility lost), when the stock of pollution is increased by one unit of R, is further increased. This increase is the disutility arising (utility lost) by virtue of the fraction σ^2 of the γ amount of abatement good J that must be taken out of consumption at (x, t) to combat the additional pollution flowing there from the rest of the system. Thus the left-hand side of equation (70) may be viewed as a doubly-adjusted W_R, reflecting the two variations, δR and $\delta \overset{xx}{R}$. The right-hand side of equation (70) reflects a third force,

---

[13] The change in total welfare associated with the $\delta R(x, t)$ is

$$\delta W = \int_0^B \int_0^{t_1} \left(W_R + \beta W_C - \dot{W}_C - \gamma \frac{\partial^2 W_C}{\partial x^2} \right) \delta R \, dx \, dt ,$$

which must be zero for arbitrary δR.

associated with the arbitrary variation δR, namely the force associated with $\delta \dot{R}$. For maximization, these three independent forces must have a net value of zero. We can now see that the equation (70) reflects what may be viewed as a 'doubly-adjusted' investment principle, which we obtain when we multiply both sides by dt and integrate from t to t_1.

It is instructive if we also consider equation (70) when the arbitrary variation of δR is associated with a decrease in the stock of pollution at $R(x, t)$. Then the equation reads: *the net disutility avoided* $-(W_R + \beta W_C)$ (equivalent to the utility gained), must be increased by the disutility avoided, $\sigma^2 \gamma W_C$ (equivalent to the utility gained), because $\sigma^2 \gamma$ of abatement good J for consumption at (x, t) is now released [because of decreased flow of pollution to (x, t)] to equate with $-\partial W_C / \partial t$, and this is a positive quantity.

Equation (70) may be usefully viewed graphically as a set of forces operative on a small length Δx. By using equation (69), equation (70) may be restated as:

$$(W_R + \beta W_C)\Delta x + \gamma \frac{\partial W_C}{\partial x}\bigg|_{\text{at } x} - \gamma \frac{\partial W_C}{\partial x}\bigg|_{\text{at } x + \Delta x} = \frac{\partial W_C}{\partial t}\Delta x \, ,$$

or

$$(W_R + \beta W_C)\Delta x + \gamma \sigma W_C\bigg|_{\text{at } x} - \gamma \sigma W_C\bigg|_{\text{at } x + \Delta x} = \frac{\partial W_C}{\partial t}\Delta x \, .$$

These terms can then be depicted as shown in figure 3. The two forces at the center are caused locally within the interval, and are associated with production, consumption, investment, and pollution within the interval. The forces at the end of the interval are generated by the flow of pollution from and to the rest of the system. The flow of pollution must certainly be related to the flow of goods, and this is apparent since

$$\frac{\partial W_C}{\partial x} = \sigma W_C \, .$$

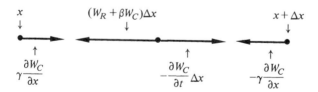

Figure 3.

Having now completed our interpretation of the Lagrange equations (Euler conditions), we examine the implications of the model. From equations (49) and (50) we obtain the solution for W_C (Isard and Liossatos, 1973) as:

$$W_C(x, t) = W_C(0, 0)\exp\left(\sigma x - \frac{1-\alpha}{1+n}\int_0^t \frac{\partial F}{\partial K}\mathrm{d}t\right) \, . \tag{71}$$

This solution gives $W_C(x, t)$ as a wave propagating to the right (positive x-axis) with a speed,

$$\frac{dx}{dt} = \frac{1-\alpha}{\sigma(1+n)} \frac{\partial F}{\partial K} . \tag{72}$$

Further, for any time point, W_C increases with x; and for any space point, W_C decreases with t. [See Isard and Liossatos (1973) for a graphic representation of W_C.]

From equations (49), (50), and (67), we obtain:

$$W_R = \left(\gamma\sigma^2 - \frac{1-\alpha}{1+n} \frac{\partial F}{\partial K} - \beta \right) W_C . \tag{73}$$

We can easily show that, as with equation (15),

$$\frac{\partial}{\partial x} \left(\frac{1}{1+n} \frac{\partial F}{\partial K} \right) = 0 . \tag{74}$$

Further, since γ, σ, α, and β are constants independent of x, it follows from equation (73) that W_R behaves like W_C, namely like a wave, but in more complicated fashion than W_C. However, we can see that since $W_R < 0$ and $W_C > 0$, the coefficient multiplying W_C in equation (73) must be negative. Accordingly

$$\gamma\sigma^2 < \frac{1}{1+n} \frac{\partial F}{\partial K} + \beta .$$

Further, if we differentiate (73) with respect to x, and take into account equation (74), we obtain:

$$\overset{x}{W}_R = \left[\gamma\sigma^2 - \frac{1-\alpha}{1+n} \frac{\partial F}{\partial K} - \beta \right] \overset{x}{W}_C . \tag{75}$$

Since $\overset{x}{W}_C > 0$, $\overset{x}{W}_R < 0$, or $-\overset{x}{W}_R > 0$. That is, the marginal disutility occasioned by pollution, $-W_R$, increases with x. Consequently, since

$$-\overset{x}{W}_R = \overset{x}{g}_R = g_{RR} \overset{x}{R} > 0 ,$$

and since $g_{RR} > 0$, it follows that $\overset{x}{R} > 0$. From equation (62) $U_R < 0$, and thus the flow of pollution is from $x = B$ to $x = 0$—that is, towards the center.

As before, $\dot{W}_C < 0$ implies $\dot{C} > 0$; $\overset{x}{W}_C > 0$ implies $\overset{x}{C} < 0$; equation (74) implies that $\overset{x}{K} < 0$ and $\overset{x}{Y} < 0$; and if $\dot{K} > 0$, we know that $\dot{R} < 0$ and $\dot{Y} > 0$.

For this model we see, from equation (72), that the relevant definition of mass is:

$$\rho = \frac{\sigma(1+n)}{1-\alpha} , \tag{76}$$

and that again the momentum is $\partial F/\partial K$. Force is $\partial(\partial F/\partial K)/\partial t$. We can see that the introduction of pollution into the model adds another inertial element $(1-\alpha)^{-1}$ to it, and consequently increases mass density. Accordingly the process of wave propagation of W_C is slowed down.

In this section we wish to make a few remarks about consumer surplus or rent. To do so, we must take some reference level of consumption against which to make welfare comparisons. The most useful reference level is that level which corresponds to the minimum of consumption of good y necessary to sustain life (assuming the consumption of no other 'free' goods). We may designate this level C min, and it may be said to correspond to the level of consumption at the frontier of the *'agricultural'* society, where we take the frontier to correspond to a zero rent, zero consumer surplus, space–time point with a welfare of M. Formally we must assume that the frontier (a wave front) always lies within the interval $[O, B]$. That is, we assume that $C(0,0) > C\min > C(B, t_1)$.

We now are able to define consumer surplus at any space–time point as

$$S(x, t) = \int_{C\min}^{C(x, t)} W_C(C)\,\mathrm{d}C = W(C(x, t)) - W(C\min) = W(C(x, t)) - M .$$

Note that

$$\frac{\mathrm{d}S}{\mathrm{d}x} < 0 \qquad \text{since } \overset{x}{W}(C(x, t)) < 0 ,$$

and that

$$\frac{\mathrm{d}S}{\mathrm{d}t} > 0 \qquad \text{since } \dot{W}(C(x, t)) > 0 .$$

So for any time point, consumer surplus falls with distance from the center, becoming zero at the frontier (the wave front); and for any space point, consumer surplus increases over time. Equally important is the fact that the frontier propagates as a wave front over time—that is, the agriculturally developed society increases its spatial extent with time.

Further if we allow one, and only one, consumer to be located at each point in space, and if there is pure competition among consumers for location in space while at the same time there is one, and only one, landlord (say society, or a leader), then the spatial pattern of consumer surplus may be viewed as the spatial pattern of rent which accrues to the landlord from competitive bidding at a market.

7 Concluding remarks
We now wish to bring this paper to a close. In the context of an optimal space–time development model, we introduced in section 2 labor as a production factor. Its incorporation, however, suggests that in a later manuscript population should be introduced. In section 3 we examined the implications of allowing the transport rate to change over time and

also to be a function of volume of trade. In section 4 we examined the implications of differential fertility.

In section 5 we introduced pollution as a basic variable, and in section 6 we introduced diffusion and decay (depreciation) of the stock of pollution. In section 5, however, we were not able to make as much progress as we would have hoped. We were not able to develop a single integrated model to cover a society which passes from a no-abatement phase to a full-abatement phase, where the transition time (from no abatement to abatement) for any space point is given as a function of space. However, some useful results were derived for separate substages. Further, an integrated model for initial exploration is proposed.

However, there are still many points at which the analysis for an integrated model would need improvement. First we should allow pollution to be related to both consumption and transportation as well as to production. Doing so leads to still more complicated models. For example we might have

$$\dot{R} = \dot{R}(C, U, Y, J) .$$ \hfill (77)

Further, we might recognize that abatement goods are produced via capital and labor, such that we have a new function

$$J = J(K_J, L_J) .$$ \hfill (78)

Additionally we may introduce into the welfare function variables such as $\overset{x}{R}$ and $\overset{x}{J}$ to reflect sensitivity of consumers to pollution levels, and abatement not only at x but also in the neighboring area. For example, we might have a general welfare function

$$W = W(C, L, R, \overset{x}{R}) .$$ \hfill (79)

References

Hildebrand, F. B., 1965, *Methods in Applied Mathematics* (Prentice-Hall, Englewood Cliffs, NJ).

Isard, W., Liossatos, P., 1973, "On optimal development over space and time", *Regional Science Perspectives, 3,*

Space Through Time: A Case Study with New Zealand Airlines †

P.C.FORER
University of Bristol

1 Introduction

This paper represents some of the findings from research on time-space convergence in the New Zealand Airline network. Basically the paper accepts that space, measured by travel time or cost, is not constant, and it seeks to investigate the nature and manner of change in space through time. Janelle (1968a, 1968b) has advanced two conceptual models which introduce the notion of time-space convergence and relate it to the processes of centralization and specialization in urban activities through time. Time-space convergence results from transport innovations which cause travel time between places to decrease and distance to decline in significance. This paper focuses on the problems of definition and measurement of the concepts which arise from Janelle's work, and is particularly concerned with the empirical verification of hypothesized measures of time-space convergence on a suitable data set.

1.1 The data base

The New Zealand internal airline system provided an isolated well-documented, dynamic, and contrasting network of reasonable size. The study period used was the postwar period, from 1947 to 1970. Within this period five dates were taken for complete network coverage: 1947, 1953, 1958, 1965, and 1970. In addition, complete data for the last week in March for every year were assembled for many directly linked towns to provide a detailed statement of convergence between city pairs with the annual cyclic fluctuations removed. Finally the size of the network varied from 18 airports in 1947 to 36 in 1965. As most of the network measures available are sensitive to size and, more acutely, sensitive to the spatial distribution of nodes, a 17 node network of 'ever present' airports was extracted and represented by the relevant elements from the full networks' minimum path matrices. These matrices were derived from airline timetables and by using Kissling's (1969) shortest path program. They represent shortest paths between all airport pairs and define distance in four ways:

1 Euclidean distance;
2 Network-restrained distance; here units of measurement are still statute miles but paths are dictated by network structure.
3 Cost distance; defined from airline fare tables transformed into the equivalent 1965 prices.

† A fuller version of this paper, which expands certain lines of arguments, is available (see Forer, 1972).

4 Time distance; due to the scheduled nature of air travel, it has been
necessary to incorporate a frequency weighting into the time measure.
Times are airport-to-airport. Full data is not available on town–airport
times but these appear to have remained fairly constant.

In all cases the graphs are nonplanar and each node is defined as a
terminus, not a junction.

1.2 A working definition of space

The selected minimum path matrix represents distances between all
common nodes for the given year and space. In a situation where all
traffic is channelled via the network between given nodes, this clearly
represents the transport space if not the actual placement of nodes in two-
dimensional euclidean space. If one characteristic such as cost or time
were predominant in determining movements, the relevant matrix would
prove more germane than the standard map.

If, however, one relaxes the assumptions on channelling and traffic
generation, which in the normal multi-transport-media situation with
population dispersal is a necessity, this definition of 'space' becomes more
questionable. In the present context, however, the term is retained and
space is seen as manifested by the minimum path matrices.

Space so defined is the summation of distances between a selected
group of points. It loses its absolute and continuous qualities to some
degree and becomes highly relative and formalized, but it presents a
manipulable extract from the total entity. It is on these spaces and the
distances that compose them that we shall focus attention.

There are three principal sections of the paper: section 2 covers general
trends in the networks and nodal access; section 3 outlines an initial
attempt at describing the spaces; and section 4 deals with a function of
distance through time which is termed the convergence curve.

2 Shrinking space and the network

2.1 Dispersion in the network

The best description of the extent of a network is the dispersion

$$\sum_{i=1}^{n} \sum_{j=1}^{n} d_{ij} \, ,$$

where d_{ij} is the internode distance in the network under consideration.
This was obtained for the three alternative spaces of network distance,
time, and cost. (The data for the last of these yielded only three points.)
By taking 1947 as 100, dispersion at other dates was represented as a
percentage. The networks for the 17 common nodes in 1947 and 1970
are illustrated as figure 1 and the values for the three spaces are given in
figure 2.

Time and cost reveal monotonic decreases in dispersion, while network
distance only wavers from this in 1970 when the collapse of many

speculative cross-country services after 1965 led to some areas of poorer access. The figures speak for themselves, with time and cost space shrinking over and above the simple gains due to improved connectivity. If we take into account the effect of traffic volume by weighting each path by the amount of traffic on it, the changes are even more dramatic. The time dispersion is down by 65%.

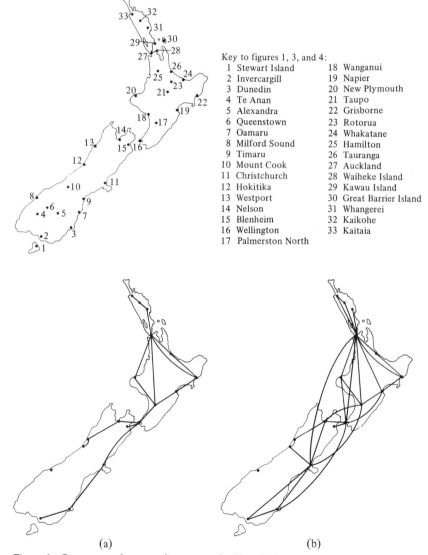

Key to figures 1, 3, and 4:

1	Stewart Island	18	Wanganui
2	Invercargill	19	Napier
3	Dunedin	20	New Plymouth
4	Te Anan	21	Taupo
5	Alexandra	22	Grisborne
6	Queenstown	23	Rotorua
7	Oamaru	24	Whakatane
8	Milford Sound	25	Hamilton
9	Timaru	26	Tauranga
10	Mount Cook	27	Auckland
11	Christchurch	28	Waiheke Island
12	Hokitika	29	Kawau Island
13	Westport	30	Great Barrier Island
14	Nelson	31	Whangerei
15	Blenheim	32	Kaikohe
16	Wellington	33	Kaitaia
17	Palmerston North		

(a)   (b)

Figure 1. Common node network structure for New Zealand airlines. (a) 1947; (b) 1970.

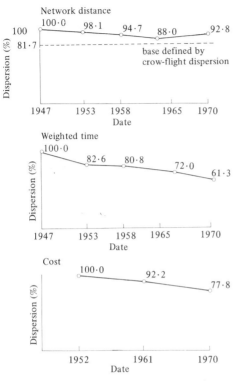

Figure 2. Dispersion in a standard network.

Of more interest is what is happening to the individual nodes within this contracting system. The access surfaces shown in figures 3 and 4 serve to illustrate this. One would expect in an area with the spatial configuration of New Zealand that access in euclidean terms would be represented as a bowl with its lowest point in the area of Cook Strait; in our terms the precise shape depends on the nodes considered. If we consider network distances for the year 1939, a similar pattern to that for euclidean space emerges, as it does for time space in that year. The main differences centre on the comparative status of the west and east coast corridors in South Island. If we look at network distance in 1970, a similar surface exists, augmented by more points but still largely a long thin bowl. The significant departure from this pattern emerges with the surface for time space in 1970 which exhibits a variety of convolutions, most notably a series of depressions around the main centres. It should be stated that the data cover for the two years differs, but that this does not preclude comparison between the two 1970 maps[1]. Nor should it

---

[1] The maps were also drawn for a common data set and they follow the results above, although less strikingly. The maps, being based on weighted graphs, are more germane than the simple connectivity surfaces of Hebert and Murphy (1971).

be forgotten that the surfaces are fitted to a selected group of points
between which simple interpolation is not viable. Indeed the complete
access surface would reveal each airport as a depression in its own right.
Nevertheless something is clearly afoot in time space which warrants
investigation.

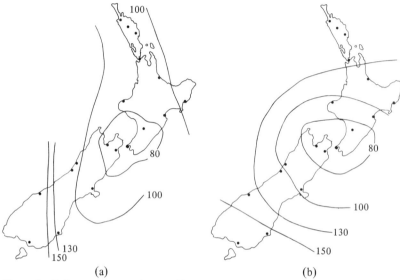

(a)   (b)

Figure 3. Relative access surfaces: (a) time—1939; (b) network distance—1939.

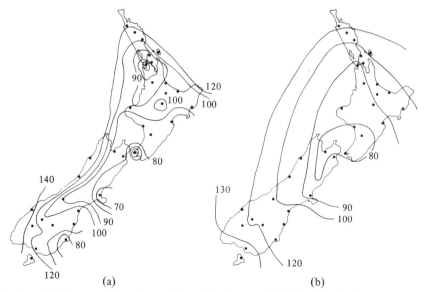

(a)   (b)

Figure 4. Relative access surfaces: (a) weighted time—1970; (b) network distance—1970.

2.2 Convergence indices

In tables 1 and 2, results from the application of three measures of time-space convergence for New Zealand airline and other data are illustrated. Column 2 in table 1 (minutes saved per mile per annum) is based on Janelle's index, redefined as equal to

$$\sum_{j} \left[\frac{T_{ij}(t) - T_{ij}(t+1)}{A d_{ij}} \right] ,$$

for nodal figures, where
$T_{ij}(t)$ is a measure of the separation of nodes i and j in travel time (minutes), at time t;
$t, t+1$ are the beginning and end of a time period;
A is the number of years between t and $t+1$;
d_{ij} is the distance in crow-flight miles between nodes i and j.

In the case of table 2, column 2 (mean network convergence), the index of convergence is constructed in a manner similar to that above, except that the measures of spatial separation, T_{ij} and d_{ij}, are in this case summed over i as well as j. These latter results thus measure convergence over the whole network, rather than at each node. Both results therefore measure convergence in terms of minutes saved per mile per annum. This absolute index has the disadvantage that it relies on euclidean distance as a

Table 1. Mean convergence rates for time space calculated from New Zealand airline data, 1947-1970.

Town	Minutes saved per mile per annum	Change from average time (%)	Average population ranks[b]
Invercargill	0·0291	3·04	5·8
Dunedin[a]	0·0247	2·79	4·0
Christchurch[a]	0·0261	2·59	3·0
Hokitika	0·0238	1·33	15·4
Westport	0·0230	1·44	14·0
Nelson	0·0212	1·94	10·6
Blenheim	0·0171	1·63	13·0
Wellington[a]	0·0180	2·16	2·0
Palmerston N.	0·0063	0·66	5·2
New Plymouth	0·0276	2·00	7·4
Napier	0·0279	2·36	7·6
Gisborne	0·0181	1·75	10·0
Tauranga	0·0319	2·37	10·6
Auckland[a]	0·0214	2·38	1·0
Whangerei	0·0161	2·21	10·8
Kaikohe	0·0136	1·56	16·4
Kaitaia	0·0151	1·45	16·2

[a] Metropolitan status.
[b] Average rankings in five postwar censuses.

measure of trip length; only if we assume map and time distances to be perfectly linearly related will this index show the proportional time reductions achieved

However, since there is strong evidence against such an assumption, an alternative, relative index is proposed, which can be expressed, for nodal values, as

$$\sum_{j} \left[\frac{[T_{ij}(t) - T_{ij}(t+1)]}{A[T_{ij}(t) + T_{ij}(t+1)]} 200 \right].$$

This measures the percentage change from the average of the travel times at t and $t+1$, and allows a definition of convergence independent of the length of route (see column 3, table 1). In all cases, the higher the value of the index the greater is the time-space convergence over the period of time considered.

Table 2 compares results for the New Zealand airlines with Janelle's results for Michigan roads and also with a selection of transoceanic routes for the period 1899–1970. On the whole the New Zealand airlines exhibit faster convergence than Michigan's roads, although this change has fluctuated with time. The standard deviation of mean convergence rates can be used as a measure of differentiation between nodes by time-space convergence. Again the New Zealand network leads. The data set of the transoceanic routes is a small sample of routes out of London to various ports. Clearly in this case intermedia convergence has exceeded our intramedia examples. [The results are very sparse and although data are readily available for many media the disparity in time and place of these three examples stresses the dearth of research in this topic. It appears that no substantive comparable results exist, although the concept is implicit in many works (see Moline, 1971).]

The results from both indices used in the New Zealand case (table 1) are not immediately encouraging to a model of time-space convergence. One might predict that the three or four metropolitan nodes of Auckland,

Table 2. Mean network convergences and standard deviation of mean convergence rates using an absolute index.

Data set	Mean	Standard deviation
Michigan roads 1940–1965	0·01631	0·001917
Transoceanic 1899–1970	0·07779	0·032050
N.Z. air network 1947–1970	0·0212	0·006561
N.Z. air network 1947–1953	0·0298	0·01702
N.Z. air network 1953–1958	0·0027	0·03326
N.Z. air network 1958–1965	0·0171	0·01439
N.Z. air network 1965–1970	0·0357	0·03590

Wellington, Christchurch, and arguably Dunedin would exhibit greatest convergence, both between themselves on a pair basis and when the average convergences from one town to all others is computed (the mean convergence rate). In fact this does not clearly emerge due largely to three effects.

(1) The 1947 network represented the effective return of civilian flights after global hostilities and has a better claim as a datum than prewar dates due to intervening dislocation. Nevertheless the 1947 network embodies much that was learnt from the earliest services. In consequence the major centres already have some degree of preference in linkage and services. There is thus less room to improve and this reflects in their index figures.

(2) The structure of the network is a dominant feature. The effect of a branch situation for a node is that all paths to other nodes pass through the joining link, and therefore, if this link contracts (or stretches) greatly, this effect is embodied in all paths to other nodes. This magnifying effect of change can best be seen in the South Island figures where the trunk-route convergence has exaggerated the effects of convergence for Invercargill and Dunedin. The effect also pertains to other nodes as diminishing trunk-route times channel minimum paths onto the main links. An increasing number of provincial town paths proceed via a metropolitan centre to most other destinations and thus much of their mean convergence is associated with the main centres. However, these immediate links to the trunk routes are initially low frequency, and so have potential for convergence in excess of the main centres, whose mean convergence rates they thus exceed. This effect is inherent in a network approach, but, on an interurban scale, for the present a field approach in the manner of Angel and Hyman (1972) is impractical.

(3) As previously mentioned there exist network changes on two scales. First there is the making and breaking of links, the structural change, which tends to be spatially local but creates a high order of convergence. Second there is frequency and flight-time adjustment, the isomorphic change, which is more universal but of lesser magnitude. A model of spatial convergence over a long period thus needs to be also a model of linkages. Again the relatively high connectivity of the large centres at the datum gives more scope for small-town convergence in later years.

Attempts to deal with these problems and the general convergence problem are still under way. It is proposed here to deal with only one more characteristic of the changes. This is the apparent fluctuation in rates of convergence through time. There is clearly no progression of change, but rather periods of high and low convergence. These may be due to regional changes, or the result of technology, the economy, or politics. Unfortunately very little appropriate information is available about these kinds of changes and we are unable to clarify them at present.

2.3 Relative access

The 17-node standard network allows us to express the access of any node as a percentage of average access (access being the dispersion accounted for by paths from any node to all others). Here 100 equals average access and lower figures improving access. This is a measure of relative access independent of overall convergence. We can hypothesize that through time the larger centres should not only improve their absolute access but also their relative access. Smaller centres, while having reduced distances to other towns, nevertheless comparatively lose out. Testing this for time space, we have four intervals of time and can classify nodes as to whether they improve or deteriorate with regards to relative access. A score of 4 denotes a monotonically improving situation, a score of 0 the reverse. Table 3 gives the results with average population ranking in parentheses. At this admittedly rough level of measurement we again see the emergence of the twin themes of network position and town size.

A short note on the case of Palmerston North; in prewar years this was the articulation point for all services, there being little in the way of direct intermetropolitan links. Although this situation altered postwar it still retained vestiges of its enhanced status, the gradual devolution of which accounts for its low ratings.

The results of these simple indices suggest that the linking of properties of space to the settlement pattern is justified, but that a measure of network structure is involved, and that the nature of the convergences involved raises some conceptual problems.

Table 3. Changes in relative access (score) and population (ranking in parentheses).

Score	Town	Score	Town
4	Invercargill (5·8) Dunedin (4·0) Auckland (1·0)	1	Hokitika (15·4) Westport (14·0) Blenheim (13·0)
3	Christchurch (3) Wellington (2·0) Napier (7·6) Whangerei (10·8)		New Plymouth (7·4) Kaikohe (16·5) Kaitaia (16·4)
		0	Palmerston North (5·2)
2	Nelson (10·6) Gisborne (10·0) Tauranga (10·6)		

3 Dynamic distance: a few snapshots

The finer mesh of spatial changes thus presents us with certain problems in any attempt to fit a model of space warping to urban structures. There seem to exist two avenues of approach. The first is to use a cause-effect model based on urban changes. The second is based on alternative geometries. The latter will be further discussed in section 4. Here we will concern ourselves only with a very simple descriptor of the geometry involved by looking at the notion of distance profiles.

3.1 Distance profiles

From any town one can take a random transect and plot crow-flight distance against a surrogate such as network distance from the chosen origin. This can be extended to plotting for all points from the origin without employing a transect. On an isotropic plane, 'network' distance and crow-flight distance would give a line of the form $Y = X$, a straight line passing through the origin at $45°$. For cost we might expect a similar curve but with a positive intersection on the Y axis equivalent to a minimum fare or terminal cost. Time on a private mode of transport would be linear with a zero constant and a slope proportional to speed. With public transport there might well be terminal waiting time.

In reality we have three main influences which modify these profiles through time:
1 an evolving transport media;
2 the cost in time or fares of interconnections;
3 the channelling and distorting effect of network structure.
These can be illustrated by two hypothesized relationships that exist in the airline industry, and New Zealand in particular, but bear extension to the general case:
(1) Figure 5 shows the first of these; the likelihood of direct connection between two nodes is proportional to the size of the nodes and inversely proportional to the distance between them. In the case of airlines this is subject at the long-range end to flight capability, and at the shorter end to minimum length constraints often dictated by competing media. The effect of this relationship, which is explicit or implicit in almost every transport geography, is to make network-distance space approximate euclidean space for shortish journeys or between large centres. As connectivity increases this resemblance becomes more marked. If the trips

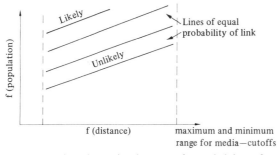

Figure 5. The relationship between the probability of a direct link between two nodes, the population of the nodes, and the distance between the nodes.

are lengthy and between small towns then shortest paths will tend to pass via other modes and be distended. In terms of our distance profile, with network distance on the X axis we can try to represent this by a simple power curve of the form $Y = aX^b$, where a and b are constants. We thus expect b to be less than 1.

(2) The cost in time or money for connections is clearly connected with network structure and should lead to similar results for fares, or costs, and time. The nonappearance of this relationship is due to the effects of transport technology. These effects may themselves extend range and thus allow better long-distance connections where they are merited. More to the point, aeroplane manufacturers have slowly evolved a whole tree of specialist aeroplanes. As Davies (1964) shows, these aeroplanes tend to become progressively faster, longer-range, heavier, able to fly farther per unit cost, and larger through time. Usually the minimum values for each of these variables improve, but not in proportion to the maximum figures. The result is a greater scatter of points as time passes, reflecting increasing options. Figure 6 shows this for cruising speed through time.

The main point of relevance to us is that it has become impossible to equate speed and cost with a linear distance profile. Long time distances have shrunk compared to shorter ones; also economies of scale have made middle-distance flights more economic to operate (and the concept of middle-distance lengthens as full-payload range grows). Also demand acts via the urban distribution to increase frequencies of mid-range flights, thus reducing waiting times most in this case. Theoretically then our time and cost profiles should increase in slope, which denotes lower expenditures per unit statute distance, and become curved with $b > 1$. This is in direct conflict to the tendencies found for network distance.

For empiric confirmation, the minimum path matrix was taken for the standard network nodes for the five dates and the four different space matrices, as enumerated in section 1, regressed on each other [2]. Some of the results appear in table 4.

The crow-flight matrix represents our traditional space and is fitted to three relative spaces. Also these spaces are regressed one on the other. This in effect examines the changes and warping of space within network distance since network distance defines the channelling options within which time and cost operate. Thus the travel-time curve assumes its expected form at a far earlier date in the distance profile when the euclidean distance axis is replaced by network distance.

Linear and exponential fits were also tried but found to be less capable of the description required. The results could generally be improved by fitting a constant into the power equation. Finally it should be said that

[2] Each matrix is taken as a variable and each shortest path as an observation, and thus by regressing each space one on the other a 4×4 correlation matrix is achieved.

a similar exercise was performed on the full 1970 network of 33 nodes. Although differentiation between the nodes was increased, the power curve still explained almost 90% of the variance. The parameters obtained were similar to those for the common-node subset. Table 4 then confirms our expectations.

The spotlight really belongs to the distance profile of free (euclidean) distance against time. The waning effect of network distance meets an increasingly strong counter-current in time distance until finally the effects

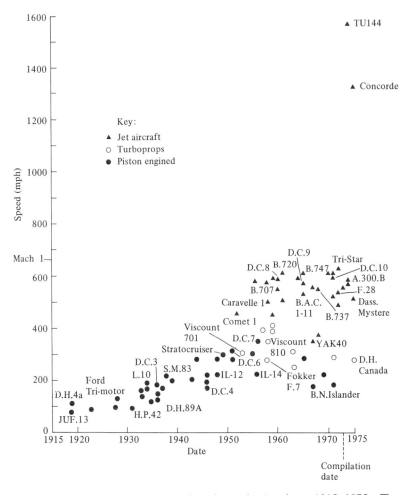

Figure 6. Civil aircraft cruising speeds and introduction dates, 1915–1975. The major types of airliner are included, and outstanding marques labelled on the graph. There are many small planes used for short routes with speeds around and below the B.N.Islander but these are not represented. Point density would be greatly increased in that area of the graph if they were.

of transport technology win the day, and reverse the nature of the distance profile. The result is not interesting for this alone. The power curve covers over twice the variance of a linear model in 1970 (91% to 44%).

This is symptomatic of our problems in mapping alternative spaces into the two euclidean dimensions of a conventional map, but it also suggests that we may be able to achieve some progress in other realms. It suggests that if deviations from the relative space profiles are studied, either by individual profiles or towns' residuals, a simple but efficient model of time separation could be produced, operating from standard terrestrial coordinates. Such a model would be dependent on a suitable scale being chosen and certainly needs further fieldwork before it can be firmly put forward, but results here are encouraging. The results through time are apparently stable and might also provide some clues for a temporally changing model. They almost cry out for comparison with data sets in other areas and other media of transport. Plentiful data are available for such studies.

However, the success here should not suggest that time space can be easily mapped, at least not in traditional terms. While it is possible to extract a fairly powerful one-dimensional expression of relative spaces, there is no guarantee that this can be transferred into a coordinate system in two or three dimensions. Zenithal mapping has been tried in representing time space from one point, and even this ran into some difficulties.

The next section discusses the change in relative distance through time as described by convergence curves, and searches for order in these functions.

Table 4. Parameters for the fitting of distance profiles by a power curve of the form $Y = aX^b$. (% described refers to the % variance explained.)

Case 1: X = network distance; Y = euclidean distance.

	1947	1953	1958	1965	1970
a	0·99	0·97	0·96	0·95	0·95
b	0·97	0·97	0·98	0·99	0·98
% described	98·3	97·6	97·9	98·7	98·1

Case 2: X = weighted time; Y = euclidean distance.

	1947	1953	1958	1965	1970
a	0·90	0·96	1·01	1·08	1·10
b	0·96	0·98	0·97	0·98	1·01
% described	95·6	98·6	93·4	91·5	91·4

Case 3: X = weighted time; Y = network distance.

	1947	1953	1958	1965	1970
a	0·91	0·97	1·01	1·08	1·12
b	0·99	1·01	1·01	1·00	1·03
% described	97·1	96·8	96·0	94·5	94·5

4 Convergence curves

Time-space convergence between any pair of places can be measured by changes in time, cost, or mileage between two dates. As a measure of change over a certain travel-time period this has much to commend it. Unfortunately it implies linearity throughout the interval, which can be an oversimplification. It is possible to extend data and represent surrogate distance through time as a graph which we shall henceforth term a convergence curve. Examples of these curves occur spasmodically in the transport literature (Stratford, 1967; Janelle, 1968b; Davies, 1964; Watkins, 1970; Ward and Hoffman, 1960) although their spatial significance is seldom acknowledged and their nature never investigated to any depth. The curves, with surrogate distance on the Y axis and chronological time on the X axis, are generally characterized by being downwardly concave. This might imply a negative power or exponential model, or some similar, more complex, function. These curves represent the chronological equivalent of Tobler's (1961) transformation graphs of map distance against actual distance. The short discussion that follows is aimed at exploring the possible forms the convergence curve can take.

4.1 The simple case

If the chosen points are, say, airfields then the time curve can be plotted with reference to lapsed stage time between the points with respect to one transport medium. The simple case is thus separation between two points in one medium. If we allow also that frequency of service fluctuates and affects the passenger, the time convergence curve will result from two functions: technology and frequency, the latter directly allied to demand.

4.2 Technological change

Within a single transport medium the pattern is for a downwardly concave curve representing the diminishing speed returns from technology once an original breakthrough has been exploited. Although 'rejuvenations' occur, the overall pattern asserts itself for most media (Ajo, 1969). When it comes to a longer time span, in which media replace each other, the new pattern usually mimics the old. Figure 7 represents a hypothetical example. As the stagecoach gives way to railways and railways to aeroplanes, we see that the scale of each curve is such as to give an overall envelope which is generally concave when the curves are plotted on the same axes. Also in both inter- and intra-media convergence curves the absolute time savings diminish greatly but the percentage savings over short periods tend to remain more constant. The continuity of the curves is somewhat of an illusion. Change is tied to specific innovations, and these may be introduced and retained for some time because of lack of alternatives or more likely because of operating economies. Thus the curve can in many cases be seen as a step function.

4.3 Frequency change

Frequency change tends to be related to demand, although other factors bear upon it. One pleasant aspect of its inclusion in a formulation of time separation is that travel time becomes a more continuous variable. Although there is a tendency for some periodicity in scheduling, for instance around the 6–7 and 12–14 flights a week frequencies, its inclusion provides scope for a more fluent curve. Most models of waiting time based on frequency, excepting those which are drastically transforming ones, will tend to approximate a downwardly-concave form, and quite likely a negative power function.

4.4 The general case

The simple case can be extended to include changing media through time. However, it should still be recognized that if a competing-media situation arises, if a time of decay or stagnation sets in, if demand fluctuates wildly, or even if war intervenes, then in such cases the simplified case ceases to exist and may be replaced by discontinuous or fluctuating functions.

Equally, a similar effect occurs when we move to the case where a whole range of media can form part of a segmented journey. Transport media do not evolve in isolation. A given route may find itself suited by only one technology, be it bicycle or Boeing. In the general case, however, trips involve several changes and each medium may have individual and characteristic convergence curves. On their own these may be interpretable, but the composite curve for the full journey may turn

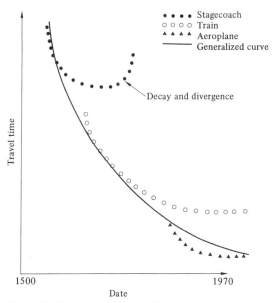

Figure 7. Convergence curves for the multi-media situation.

out hard to describe. Although the general convergence curves would be interesting to model and compare, it must be said that usually the number of points available will restrict the use of suitably sophisticated techniques.

Finally we should say that if the curves can be suitably described it should be possible to relate them to urban settlements and use them in the study of the same. We can hypothesize that an ideal curve exists which represents the immediate adoption of any suitable innovation.

However, the distribution of demand, capital, and other resources means that real-world routes will adopt innovations or retain old techniques in differing degree. Some poorer routes will be unable to finance new equipment, some may attract the best, and others may even revert to older methods. The spatial diffusion of new technology will itself affect differing curves differently. So it is reasonable to expect deviations from the ideal curve of convergence, and many of these, at one scale or another, can be related to the urban system and must also be an input into it. The empirical results presented later in this paper attempt to investigate these deviations further. The choice of region, time, and routes provides a situation as near the simple case as possible, and visual inspection reveals the general agreement of actual and predicted behaviour.

4.5 Empirical findings

The method used in examining convergence curves was basically to reduce data sets of cost and travel-time curves to a standard form. For this the maximum separation of two points (places) was taken as 100 and all other values expressed as percentages of this. Scale thus being removed, the starting date was set to zero for the year prior to initial services. Thus a service started in 1947 had its origin moved to (0, 1946).

To these transformed figures three basic curves were fitted. The linear curve $Y = aX + b$ was minimal in parameters but questionable for most flights due to its implications of 'negative time'. The other two models were asymptotic fits of power and exponential curves: $Y = aX^b + c$ and $Y = a \exp(bX) + c$. The asymptote provided the expression of the base level to which the system was tending, although in certain cases this appeared extremely low. Of the three models the theoretically preferable and generally best-fitting one was the power curve. Further sophistication of the model was ruled out due to the number of data points available. This basic power curve model will be the only one covered here. However, the other models were tested and yielded similar though not identical results.

Figure 8 gives four examples of power curves fitted to data. Two are for intercity flights, Christchurch–Auckland, using weighted time and cost; the third covers the situation on one of the poorest links, Wellington–Hokitika; and the final one shows just flight time for Christchurch–Auckland. The step-function effect of equipment is plainly displayed.

Given these results, five parameters could be used to describe each route. Three of these, *a*, *b*, and *c*, are parameters of the power curve fitted, and can be roughly interpreted as follows:

a is the general slope coefficient, and is closely related to the Janelle (absolute) convergence coefficient;

b indicates the tendency to curvature and thus towards stabilization; it is usually negative;

c is the asymptotic tendency.

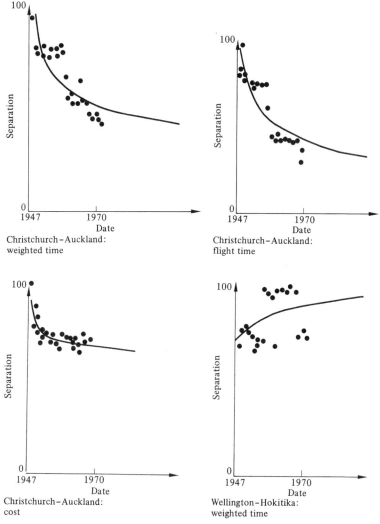

Figure 8. Convergence curves: four examples of power curves fitted to data.

The other two parameters which describe convergence are r and d:

r is the correlation coefficient, and can either be interpreted as indicating erratic change or an unsuitable function. The former interpretation is taken here, that is, a high value of r denotes strong stable evolution. Where r indicates a poor fit of data to the proposed curve, it can be shown that routes tend to be underdeveloped, decaying, or subject to wide variations in traffic generation;

d is the date when the service started, expressed as its dual, the length of operation. This parameter was retained as arguably the date of linkage is significant in itself, or equally it may affect the curve's form. The relevance of d is not firmly establishable, and in some tests only links between ever-present nodes were examined, thus effectively removing d from consideration.

4.6 Clustering
A typology of routes was established using a nonhierarchic clustering programme developed by Hitchin (see Jones, 1970). Data for routes on weighted time and standardized cost were collected, both for all routes and long-standing routes only. The results covered here are those using z scores for the raw parameters, equal weighting being accorded to each [3].

4.7 Expectations
Our expectations for convergence curve types have to be made against the background of technological change discussed earlier, and of the emergence of a distinct but diverse hierarchy of routes over the period 1947–1970.

The values of each of the parameters can be dichotomized as being above or below the mean or median value for this parameter. Such a dichotomy would hopefully help to distinguish between larger city pairs and short distances as opposed to smaller towns and longer distances.

The rationale is that we expect times on high-order links to converge most, because of a higher level of demand and higher frequency of service, as well as better technology. As a result of economies of scale in operation, these two factors should reinforce each other. Consequently international and trunk-route operators and possibly direct feeder routes will have a values less than the mean, as will tourist routes which came into operation late and tend to converge at a rate to compensate for this. On the other hand poorer-quality links and the positively decaying will have a values greater than the mean denoting low convergence.

As to b, this parameter will tend to reflect the state of the curve. If the curve is stable then a lower-than-average negative value will be expected. If on the other hand a route still exhibits strong change and no

[3] Principal components analysis was investigated with regards to obtaining orthogonal axes for grouping. In practice some assumptions were questionable, but in any case results resembled the 'straight' grouping.

stabilization, a higher than average, possibly positive, value of b will result. Partly linked to this we might expect the low energy routes to have high terminal separations and thus higher c values.

The preceding considerations apply to travel time. Cost is a separate concern and depends a great deal on pricing policies which may well mask any variation in routes.

4.8 Results

As stated, attention will be focused on power curves alone. Cost curves lose least by this restriction since they invariably provide the best fit to the power model. The results obtained are, however, rather disappointing due to the nature of the data. Fares were only generally available on routes between or out of the main centres. The result is a fairly homogeneous sample in which parameters are not as diverse as for travel time. When taking all suitable cost convergence curves between any extant nodes, a grouping by parameters placed privately operated services and tourist routes together. Meanwhile the international routes are clustered with a batch of provincial routes. The main conclusion that emerges from these groupings is that competition, fare structure, and low variation between available options probably militate against clear distinctions emerging. When examining individual curves, it is interesting that, while many time curves are still evolving, most cost curves seem to have reached their minima, and since 1967 there are signs of actual cost divergence.

4.9 Time curves

The results for time curves are more encouraging. They appear in table 5 which includes a statement of the most typical parameter values. Dealing first of all with the full data set, we can characterize the following grouping. Group 4 includes the tourist nodes, group 5 the high-energy links, group 6 the largely social service routes of Northland and Westland, and group 2 includes just one route. Of the remaining groups, group 1 represents the body of services while group 3 seems somewhat of a 'dustbin' category. On the whole they fit in more or less with expectations. The international routes are not brought out as a group, mainly because the two routes that are included were started immediately after the war and are major links to New Zealand.

Examples of the oddities within the groups can be identified with reference to group 1. We can ask why the Kaikohe–Auckland and Wellington–Christchurch routes are in the same group. Firstly we note that the former leans heavily towards group 6 and the latter towards group 5; also the Kaikohe–Auckland route has been affected by network changes which rather adulterate its form.

When only common nodes are considered, a three group clustering is adopted, losing about 13% of the total variance (see table 6). Group 3 (of table 5) now becomes the new group 2 while the remaining routes split either side of it, the new group 3 representing the more convergent routes.

Table 5. Groupings by curve parameter—all routes.

Group 1.	Exemplar: Auckland-Dunedin, $Y = 105 \cdot 3\, X^{-0 \cdot 152} + 3 \cdot 24$, $R = -0 \cdot 799$.
Also:	Kaikohe-Auckland, Tauranga-Auckland, New Plymouth-Auckland, New Plymouth-Wellington, Invercargill-Dunedin, New Plymouth-Palmerston North, Auckland-Rotorua, Auckland-Gisborne, Palmerston North-Christchurch, Wellington-Nelson, Wellington-Christchurch.
Group 2:	Exemplar: Christchurch-Mount Cook, $Y = 77 \cdot 05\, X^{-0 \cdot 777} + 22 \cdot 6$, $R = -0 \cdot 984$.
Group 3:	Exemplar: Gisborne-Napier, $Y = 64 \cdot 4\, X^{-0 \cdot 425} + 34 \cdot 7$, $R = -0 \cdot 715$.
Also:	Whangerei-Auckland, Westport-Nelson, Westport-Wellington, Auckland-Napier, Gisborne-Wellington.
Group 4:	Exemplar: Invercargill-Stewart Island, $Y = 99 \cdot 7\, X^{-0 \cdot 080} + 4 \cdot 7$, $R = -0 \cdot 596$.
Also:	Fox Glacier-Hokitika, Kawau Island-Auckland, Taupo-Auckland, Timaru-Christchurch, Blenheim-Christchurch, Nelson-Christchurch, Alexandra-Dunedin.
Group 5:	Exemplar: Christchurch-Auckland, $Y = 125 \cdot 03\, X^{-0 \cdot 330} + 2 \cdot 1$, $R = -0 \cdot 857$.
Also:	Auckland-Nandi, Auckland-Sydney, Auckland-Christchurch, Auckland-Wellington, Christchurch-Dunedin, Napier-Wellington, Christchurch-Wellington, Wellington-Dunedin.
Group 6:	Exemplar: Nelson-Hokitika, $Y = 63 \cdot 3\, X^{0 \cdot 083} + 3 \cdot 7$, $R = 0 \cdot 397$.
Also:	Wellington-Blenheim, Kaikohe-Kaitaia, Kaitaia-Auckland, Westport-Hokitika, Auckland-Palmerston North, Palmerston North-Wellington, Wellington-Hokitika, Napier-Palmerston North, Gisborne-Palmerston North.

Table 6. Groupings by curve parameters—common node set.

Group 1:	Exemplar: Wellington-Blenheim, $Y = 111 \cdot 4\, X^{-0 \cdot 223} + 3 \cdot 03$, $R = -0 \cdot 163$.
Also:	Kaikohe-Kaitaia, Kaitaia-Auckland, Kaikohe-Auckland, Auckland-Gisborne, New Plymouth-Wellington, Westport-Hokitika, New Plymouth-Palmerston North, Auckland-Palmerston North, Nelson-Hokitika, Palmerston North-Wellington, Wellington-Hokitika, Napier-Palmerston North, Gisborne-Palmerston North.
Group 2:	Exemplar: Gisborne-Napier, $Y = 64 \cdot 04\, X^{-0 \cdot 425} + 34 \cdot 7$, $R = -0 \cdot 715$.
Also:	Whangerei-Auckland, Westport-Wellington, Westport-Nelson, Auckland-Napier, Gisborne-Wellington.
Group 3:	Exemplar: New Plymouth-Auckland, $Y = 111 \cdot 4\, X^{-0 \cdot 223} + 3 \cdot 60$, $R = -0 \cdot 849$.
Also:	Christchurch-Wellington, Christchurch-Auckland, Auckland-Christchurch, Tauranga-Auckland, Auckland-Dunedin, Auckland-Wellington, Christchurch-Dunedin, Napier-Wellington, Palmerston North-Christchurch, Wellington-Christchurch, Wellington-Dunedin, Wellington-Nelson.

4.10 Hierarchy or continuum?
The results described suggest that certain characteristics of standardized convergence curves relate to the urban structure. Knowledge of settlement distribution, operating hierarchies, and operational options (Morlok, 1967) suggests discrete changes which might reflect in discrete types of curves. Given the spatial distribution and tetra-primate nature of New Zealand settlements, this might be held to be especially true. Equally there is some room for gradation between ideal types and chance oddities in parameters.

The weight of evidence supports the probability of a group of ideal curves. However, lengthy discussion of this is out of place for two reasons. In the first place we have dealt here with the simplest possible case of convergence, that of direct links or stopping links between two cities. Most normal journeys will involve movements on several stages of the network. The convergence curves for this wider data set will be not only complex, but, by being an amalgam, will almost certainly blur any existing hierarchy from the city-pair level.

Secondly whether the clusters exist or not the evidence supports the hypothesis that convergence curves relate to the process of urban development. If the curves are taken as indicators of the shrinking of space, then a uniformly shrinking space would be characterized by a collection of similar parameters and similar curves. Differentials in the curves denote differential warping of the spaces. If the 1947 separations are taken as a datum, then some links will have left space virtually unaltered. Others, typified by high-energy trunk routes, have warped it to their advantage. While the situation will be confused by changes in network morphology and composite journeys, these will not alter the access improvements accruing to nodes associated with such links. It is significant that travel cost, which showed little divergence in curve type, also revealed little pattern in relative access evolution, while with travel time the opposite applies.

With further work it might prove possible to verify the existence of a hierarchy. A great deal of work could be done on 'cleaning up' the groups that emerge. Certainly it would be useful to have a classifiable set of parameters rather than a multivariate continuum. The taxonomy thus available would facilitate both theoretical consideration of spatial evolution, and also regional, temporal, and intermedia comparisons. Meanwhile work is in progress on possible continuous relationships.

5 Conclusion
Janelle (1968b) has pointed out some implications of time-space convergence for central place theory. The converse relationship also holds; that is, time space which evolves is partly a function of the central place pattern, or any other urban settlement pattern. It is implicit in the original models that cyclic causality exists, that places define spaces

and react spatially within these realms to modify themselves and thence the spaces. The current study is simplistic in that it takes one highly specialized set of spaces. Interaction via trade offs between time and cost are not considered. Clearly in everyday occurrences questions of trade off, perception, and restricted knowledge are brought to bear, and the relevant spaces for one problem may be irrelevant or misleading for another. For example, the impact of airline evolution in New Zealand can be limited to a small sector of the populace, albeit an important elite (Tornquist, 1970). No extension of the subject to these less simple fields is attempted here, although there is no *a priori* reason for supposing that the conclusions reached in this paper would be reversed if this extension was carried out. Physical travel is also only part of communication, and other developing communications media are further areas for study.

While there seems ample grounds for endorsing the hypothesis of a relative space, certain problems have been uncovered. One problem is the effect of primal advantage: the early dominance of some centres which reduces their later ability to converge; or their mercurial early convergence which can have the same effect. Basically this is a problem of defining a generally acceptable datum date. Another problem is the recurrent one that any simple model has strong positive feedback built into it while for much of the time the returns in convergence are in fact diminishing. A third is the different manifestations of structural as opposed to isomorphic change.

But the most fascinating problem is how to cope with the overall notion of relative space. There seem to be two alternative approaches. The more pedestrian of these is to work in a basically nonspatial manner, or at least in the dimensions of network space. Certainly the space, as defined by the matrix, can be a relative one. Nevertheless the calculations work, by way of the structure of the defined paths, on a largely one-dimensional basis.

The alternative approach is the attempted mapping of the spaces, or at least the points we have to typify them. Angel and Hyman (1970) investigate the possibilities of departing from plane euclidean geometry to describe velocity fields, although the assumptions and current limitations of the approach make it unsuitable for interurban relative spaces. Quite possibly and most attractively the urban system could be related to the space it helps define via a surrogate field of demographic force. This would be analogous to gravity and could be utilized with the aid of post-Gaussian geometry and possibly tensor analysis. There are similarities between the behaviour of geodesics in strong gravitational fields and the minimum time paths in a developing network. Equally there are strong dissimilarities, most particularly the tendency for transport media to link points in isolation of intervening areas. A network's geometry would almost certainly be restricted in its area of concern, and would be concerned with points rather than continua.

The most seductive path of all lies in the direction of tensor geometry—
in physics the notions of Riemann on curved space were used in conjunction
with relativity to produce a description of relative space related to the
gravitational field. With network evolution and settlement changes one
might look for relationships between alternative spaces and some form of
demographic field. One of several parallels lies in that much as the effect
of gravity is to curve geodesics, so, in time space especially, geodesics are
attracted towards large centres.

If we pursue the analogy too far it can prove troublesome, quite
naturally; the notion of curvature for instance usually distends distances
near large masses while in our case the reverse applies. But it is quite
common to speak of euclidean mappings being transformed by a sort of
differential stretching and loosening into time maps; that is, our elastic
sheet is subjected to a variety of stresses and strains [see Bickley and
Gibson (1962) for a strong analogy]. A key problem is the efficacy of
multidimensional mapping and the evolution of a theory oriented towards
the effect of transport innovation.

Regional scientists may agree that the notion of a dynamic and relative
space can be of use in certain empirically founded studies, as well as of
central importance to many theoretical models of the spatial paradigm.
The main body of the paper shows some problems in describing time space
in general, and in substantiating proposed models in particular. The final
paragraphs are a tentative suggestion that if geometry is the language of
space (Harvey, 1969) then perhaps the geometry of relativity should be
the language of relative space.

References

Ajo, R., 1969, "Response of a system to repeated psychological shock", *Geografiska Annaller,* **51**, 8-15.

Angel, S., Hyman, G. M., 1970, "Urban velocity fields", *Environment and Planning,* **2**, 211-224.

Angel, S., Hyman, G. M., 1972, "Urban spatial interaction", *Environment and Planning,* **4**, 99-118.

Bickley, W. G., Gibson, M., 1962, *Via Vector to Tensor* (English University Press, London).

Davies, R. E. G., 1964, *History of the World's Airlines* (Oxford University Press, London).

Forer, P. C., 1972, "Space through time: a case study with New Zealand airlines", Seminar paper A, number 23, Department of Geography, University of Bristol.

Harvey, D., 1969, *Explanation in Geography* (Edward Arnold, London).

Hebert, B., Murphy, E., 1971, "Evolution of an accessibility surface", *Proceedings of the Association of American Geographers,* **3**, 75-80.

Janelle, D. G., 1968a, "Spatial reorganisation: a model and concept", *Annals of the Association of American Geographers,* **58**, 348-364.

Janelle, D. G., 1968b, "Central place development in a time-space framework", *Professional Geographer,* **20**, 5-10.

Jones, S., 1970, "Two cluster programmes", Dissertation for Degree of B. Soc. Sci., Department of Geography, University of Bristol.

Kissling, C., 1969, "Linkage importance in a regional highway network", *Canadian Geographer,* **13**, 113-127.

Moline, N. T., 1971, "Mobility and the small town", University of Chicago, Department of Geography Research, Paper Number 132.

Morlok, E. K., 1967, *An Analysis of Transport Technology and Network Structure* (Northwestern University Press, Evanston, Ill.).

Stratford, J., 1967, *Air Transport Economics in the Supersonic Age* (Macmillan, London).

Tobler, W., 1961, *Map Transformations of Geographic Space*, Ph. D. Thesis, University of Washington, Seattle, Washington.

Tornquist, G., 1970, "Contact systems and regional development", *Lund Studies in Geography,* Ser.B, *Human Geography,* Number 25, The Royal University of Lund, Department of Geography.

Ward, R. J., Hoffman, L. A., 1960, *Readings in Economic Geography* (Holt, Rinehart and Winston, New York), pp.105-111.

Watkins, J. D., 1970, "Development needs of the domestic air network", *Flight International,* 26th February, 297-299.

Two Disequilibrium Models of Regional Growth

H.W.RICHARDSON
University of Kent at Canterbury

Economists have not made much of an individual contribution to the theory of regional growth. Their only major achievement has been to adapt the neoclassical models used to explain aggregate growth to the regional level (Borts, 1960; Borts and Stein, 1964; Romans, 1965; Siebert, 1969)[1]. 'Achievement' is perhaps an inappropriate word, since the emphasis on neoclassical models has in my view retarded economists' understanding of the regional growth process. Indeed, if the world really were a neoclassical world there would be no such field as regional economics. The reasons for this view scarcely need much explanation to regional scientists. For instance, perfect competition cannot be assumed in regional economic analysis since space itself and the existence of transport costs limit competition; oligopoly, pure monopoly, or monopolistic competition are much more appropriate market structures. Similarly the related assumptions that investors and location decisionmakers are profit maximisers and that would-be migrants are income maximisers induce the neoclassicist to adopt a simplistic approach to the analysis of interregional factor flows, and to ignore or underplay the valuable research on spatial mobility of factors carried out by other social scientists. Furthermore, in view of the finding at the national level that the 'residual' tends to make a larger contribution to the growth rate than growth in factor inputs, it is surprising, if understandable, that the neoclassicists have given so little attention to the spatial diffusion of innovations and technical progress. Finally, key phenomena in regional analysis—such as agglomeration economies in location and urbanisation, transport costs, interdependence of location decisions, metropolitan– regional relationships—have no place in the neoclassical system.

In view of these deficiencies, one wonders why neoclassical models have attracted so much attention from regional economists. Upon reflection it is not too difficult to explain. One reason must be the domination of the economics profession and the evolution of economic thought by neoclassicism[2], and also the relative ease with which ideas in aggregate growth theory can be borrowed for regional economic analysis; second, the neoclassical model has the attraction of being holistic, embracing a

[1] I ignore export base theory on the grounds of its obvious inadequacies. Unfortunately, export base models have enjoyed something of a revival in recent years in regional econometric models, primarily because they offer a useful way of linking regional growth performance to gross national product. For a particularly blatant example see Bell (1967).

[2] Readers of Leijonhüfvud (1968) know, of course, that even Keynes was a neoclassicist in thin disguise.

theory of factor mobility as well as a theory of growth; third, the 'pure' model yields neat precise predictions which happen to fit, insofar as they can be tested [3], a certain number of important historical cases [4]. In particular, if we assume full employment, perfect competition, one homogeneous commodity, zero transport costs, regionally identical production functions exhibiting constant returns to scale, a fixed supply of labour, and no technical progress, it can be shown that the wage (marginal product of labour) is a direct function and the return to capital (marginal product of capital) an inverse function of the capital–labour ratio (K/L). Labour will flow from low- to high-wage regions and capital will flow in the opposite direction (since low returns to capital imply high wages, and high returns are obtained in low wage regions). These flows continue until factor returns are equalised in each region. According to this view the process of regional growth will be associated with a convergence in regional *per capita* incomes.

I do not need to comment on the value of such a model. Quotations from two fellow economists make the point very well. "Life of the conventional economist is easy. But is it worth living?" (Olsen, 1971, p.216). Kaldor (1966, pp.309–310) expands on the same theme when he speaks about "the intellectual sterility engendered by the methods of neoclassical economics ... There is no room here for increasing returns, learning by doing, oligopolistic competition, uncertainty, obsolescence, and other troublesome things which mar the world as we know it". In any event, removal of any one of several key assumptions "is sufficient to cause the whole structure to collapse like a pack of cards".

Despite the sketchiness of the evidence, the most unsatisfactory prediction of the neoclassical model is that capital will flow from rich to poor regions. Empirical observation (however crude and impressionistic) and *a priori* reasoning suggest that the flow is much more likely to be in the opposite direction. If this is the case, the interregional growth process will be disequilibrating rather than equilibrating. My modest objective here is to present two alternative disequilibrium regional growth models which are consistent with the hypothesis that capital flows tend to polarise towards the more developed regions. Model I is merely an updated cumulative causation model; model II integrates a probabilistic framework for simulating interregional savings–investment flows conceived as a Markov process into a simple fixed capital–output ratio, fixed savings–income ratio growth model.

---

[3] Some of the critical tests, such as whether interregional capital flows are determined by regional differences in rates of return to capital, have been impossible to carry out because of the absence of satisfactory capital yield and capital flow data.

[4] Particularly the United States for most—but not all—of its post-industrial historical development. Many countries exhibit divergence tendencies, but these are often ignored or treated as 'aberrations'.

I would not pretend that either model goes far enough in satisfying the conditions required for an acceptable regional growth theory. In my view such conditions include:
1 the explicit inclusion of space and distance, both interregionally and intraregionally;
2 the recognition of the importance of agglomeration economies and locational preferences as determinants of concentration and dispersion of both population and economic activity;
3 the integration of the urban dimension in regional growth analysis.
The models discussed in this paper fall short of these standards. Nevertheless space is implicitly treated in both, since spatial agglomeration economies are an important component of increasing returns in cumulative causation theory, while the polarisation of savings flows assumed in the Markov chain model reflects spatial elements. Also it would be possible to construct the savings flow matrix in model II either in terms of a set of metropolitan regions or as an interregional–subregional model. These may be small concessions, but they are much better than the spacelessness assumptions of neoclassical theory [5].

Model I: a revised cumulative causation model
Myrdal (1957) deserves the credit, of course, for being the first to develop a disequilibrium regional growth model. His cumulative causation theory can be summed up in a few sentences. Market forces lead to the clustering of increasing returns activities in certain areas of the economy. Regardless of the initial location advantage (for example, natural resource endowment), this buildup becomes selfsustaining because of increasing internal and external economies at these centres of agglomeration. The limited advantages of backward regions (such as cheap labour) are insufficient to offset these agglomeration tendencies. The main influence on the rate of growth of lagging regions is the induced effects of growth in the prosperous areas. These are of two kinds: spread (favourable) and backwash (unfavourable) effects. The former include markets for the (typically primary) products of the lagging regions and diffusion of innovation. Normally, however, these are outweighed by backwash effects —particularly by disequilibrating flows of labour, capital, goods, and services from poor to rich regions. Thus the free trade of an interregional system operates to the disadvantage of poor regions by inhibiting industrialisation and distorting their pattern of production. Hence, regional growth is a disequilibrating process: "the play of forces in the market normally tends to increase, rather than to decrease, the inequalities between regions" (Myrdal, 1957, p.26).
Myrdal's theory was loosely defined and expressed in rather emotive language. Kaldor (1970) has recently suggested a variant of the

[5] To the neoclassicist a 'region' is equivalent to a 'sector'; space is irrelevant.

cumulative causation hypothesis which is more capable of being modelled. I claim no originality for the model which follows. Its sole objective is to formalise Kaldor's extension of the cumulative causation theory into a testable model.

The theory rests on two props:

1 The principle of cumulative causation is merely the existence of increasing returns to scale (including external and agglomeration economies) in manufacturing (Verdoorn law). Increasing returns favour the rich regions and inhibit development in the poor; because of scale effects the rich regions gain a virtual monopoly of industrial production. Moreover, because competition in industry is imperfect while near perfect competition prevails in agriculture, movements in terms of trade favour the rich regions.

2 The behaviour of a region's production and exports depends upon:
(i) an exogenous variable, the rate of growth of world demand for the region's products;
(ii) an endogenous variable, the movement of 'efficiency wages' in the region relative to other regions in the system.

Relative efficiency wages are the key element in the model. They determine whether the region's share in overall markets is rising or falling. The lower relative efficiency wages are, the higher the growth rate in output. The movement in efficiency wages is determined by the change in money wages relative to the change in productivity; that is, it is equal to W/T where W is the money wage index and T is an index of productivity. But money wages, and their rate of increase, will be similar in *all* regions, because of institutional factors, the effects of interregional labour mobility on the narrowing of wage differentials, and nationwide collective bargaining[6]. On the other hand, because of increasing returns, higher growth rates in productivity will be experienced in regions with the faster growth rates in output. These regions will thus have the lower efficiency wages (relatively falling W/T). Hence the relatively fast-growing regions tend to acquire cumulative advantages over the slower growing ones[7].

The model may be expressed in formal terms as follows:

$$t_i = f_i^{(1)}(y_i) \tag{1}$$

[6] Regional money wages still move in parallel even if regional growth rates in employment vary widely.

[7] Regional growth differentials may be held in check by spread effects: (a) diffusion of growth and stimulation of the demand for 'complementary' products from poor regions; (b) the possibility of diseconomies associated with high rates of industrial growth (for example, environmental problems); (c) the impact of interregional labour mobility in keeping divergences in real earnings per head in check; and (d) built-in fiscal stabilisers. Also wage subsidies (such as the Regional Employment Premium) may be given to backward regions as a protective device, since a wage subsidy may be treated as equivalent to a cut in efficiency wages.

$$\frac{W_i}{T_i} = f_i^{(2)}(t_i), \tag{2}$$

$$y_i = f_i^{(3)}\left(\frac{W_i}{T_i}\right), \tag{3}$$

and

$$W_i = \overline{W}, \tag{4}$$

where t is the rate of productivity growth, y is the growth rate in output, $\overline{W}$ is the national money wage, and i is the ith region, $f^{(1)}$, $f^{(2)}$, and $f^{(3)}$ being different functions ($f^{(1)} > 0$: $f^{(2)}$, $f^{(3)} < 0$).

The diagrammatical representation in figure 1 illustrates clearly the circular cumulative nature of the regional growth process according to this model. Rising growth rates in output induce higher productivity which reduces efficiency wages, and in turn the fall in efficiency wages leads to a higher growth rate in output, and so on.

This version of the cumulative causation model yields readily testable hypotheses. These are (a) that a region's rate of productivity growth is an increasing function of its rate of growth of output; (b) the rate of increase in money wages is approximately the same in all regions; and (c) if (b) does not hold, a weaker hypothesis, though still sufficient to make the model work, is that the regional dispersion in productivity increases is substantially wider than the regional dispersion in money wage increases.

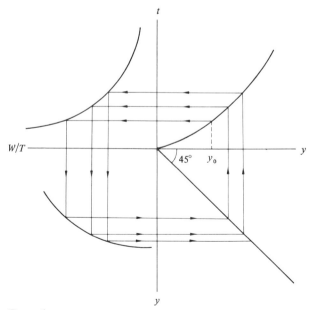

Figure 1.

As figure 1 clearly shows, and as Myrdal's reference to '*circular* and cumulative causation' suggests, the model is circular. To this extent it is unsatisfactory. In particular it needs a trigger to set the spiral in motion. It does not really explain why some regions enjoy high growth rates, but rather, given that they have high growth rates, why these growth rates persist. Hence Myrdal stressed initial locational advantages such as natural resource endowment to act as the missing trigger. Kaldor's solution is no better since he subscribes to crude export base theory.

Another defect is that reliance on a simple Verdoorn law relationship is too aggregative for the regional economist since it says very little about the complex role played by agglomeration economies, external scale economies, and indivisibilities in the spatial concentration ('polarisation') of economic activity.

In addition the concept of efficiency wages as a mechanism for explaining how productivity performance induces faster growth raises unsettled questions. First, it is possible for money wages in very prosperous fast-growing regions to rise much faster than elsewhere and for this tendency not to be offset by higher productivity growth. The failure of efficiency wages to fall does not necessarily imply that growth in these regions will slacken. The results may be higher prices (which may have negligible effects on the growth rate) rather than slower growth. This is consistent with the argument sometimes advanced that the rich regions in the economy are the prime generators of economy-wide inflation. Second, the assumption that regional growth rates depend upon relative efficiency wages implies that regions are in direct competition with each other. But the sectoral composition of output may differ so widely between regions that this assumption is false. This is particularly the case when the national economy is an open economy and the prosperous regions specialise in foreign export industries. In this example (which may conform to the UK pattern) efficiency wages relative to foreigners may be much more critical than efficiency wages relative to other regions. The model might explain international growth differentials better than interregional.

Model II: an absorbing Markov chain model

An absorbing Markov chain may be used to simulate the interregional savings–investment process if we assume that
1 the transient state matrix Q can be interpreted as an interregional savings flow matrix;
2 investment is the absorting state;
3 the initial destinations of savings as reflected in the savings flow coefficients are probabilistic rather than deterministic;
4 the first destinations of savings are not necessarily the ultimate destinations. This merely involves accepting the existence of financial institutions that act as intermediaries between savings and investment.

Thus, the cells of the transitional probability matrix may be interpreted as expressing the probabilities of savings being placed in local (diagonal entries) and extraregional (off-diagonal entries) financial institutions, or directly into local investment. The equilibrium solution of the Markov process is achieved when all generated savings end up in the absorbing state as investment.

As is well-known, the transitional probability matrix P can be partitioned in an absorbing Markov process into four submatrices:

$$P = \left(\begin{array}{c|c} Q & R \\ \hline 0 & I \end{array} \right) , \tag{5}$$

where Q is the matrix for transient states and R is the absorption matrix. There is a matrix T with the same dimensions as R such that

$$T = (I - Q)^{-1} R . \tag{6}$$

This matrix [8] T contains the probabilities of inputs to the system getting from each transient state to each absorbing state after circulating through the transient states as indicated by the matrix Q.

If we assume an aggregate capital stock, then the diagonal matrix $\hat{R}$ can represent intraregional absorption (investment) coefficients while Q is the interregional savings flow matrix. If s^0 is an initial vector of savings where the element s_i^0 represents the savings generated in region i, and Δk^e is the equilibrium distribution vector of regional capital stock increments, we may write

$$\Delta k^e = s^0 (I - Q)^{-1} \hat{R} , \tag{7}$$

where $\sum \Delta k_i^e = \sum \Delta s_i^0$.

This interregional savings–investment process may be combined with a standard regional growth model, thereby making the savings vector endogenous. Let us assume the simplest possible model based on a savings–income and an output–capital stock relation. If we abstract from constant terms, assume no savings–income and output–capital stock lags, and treat the functions as linear, then we may write

$$s = \hat{A}y , \tag{8}$$

and

$$y = \hat{V}^{-1}k , \tag{9}$$

where $\hat{A}$ is the diagonal matrix of regional propensities to save, $\hat{V}^{-1}$ is the inverse of the diagonal matrix $\hat{V}$ of regional capital–output ratios, y is the vector of regional incomes, and k is the vector of regional capital stocks.

---

[8] At the limit the P matrix can be written as

$$\lim_{n \to \infty} P^n = \left(\begin{array}{c|c} 0 & T \\ \hline 0 & I \end{array} \right) .$$

Substituting equation (9) into equation (8) we obtain

$$s = \hat{A}\hat{V}^{-1}k \ . \tag{10}$$

Substituting $\hat{A}\hat{V}^{-1}k^0$ for s^0 and Δk^1 for Δk^e in equation (7), we obtain

$$\Delta k^1 = \hat{A}\hat{V}^{-1}k^0(I-Q)^{-1}\hat{R} \ . \tag{11}$$

This framework allows regional capital stock growth to be expressed as a function of the initial interregional capital stock distribution. It also permits the comparative static conditions of interregional capital market equilibrium to be satisfied (that is, total investment at the end of each period equals the sum of regional savings generated during the period). We may write

$$k^1 = k^0 + \Delta k^1 \ , \tag{12}$$

$$= k^0 + \hat{A}\hat{V}^{-1}k^0(I-Q)^{-1}\hat{R} \ . \tag{13}$$

Via matrix multiplication, let $\ Z = \hat{A}\hat{V}^{-1}(I-Q)^{-1}\hat{R}$, then $\tag{14}$

$$k^1 = k^0 + k^0 Z \ . \tag{15}$$

Thus

$$k^1 = k^0(I+Z) \ . \tag{16}$$

This equation may be expanded to extend the growth process into the future, that is,

$$k^n = k^0(I+Z)^n \ . \tag{17}$$

The time periods of the model (and in particular the synchronisation between the Markov process and the growth sequence) are implicit in the way in which the model has been constructed. We assumed no lags in equations (8) and (9), but the $\hat{V}^{-1}$ matrix requires that the output flow–capital stock ratio should be measured over a defined time period. If this time period is assumed to be one year, then the model as constructed implies that a savings–investment equilibrium is also brought about one year after the initial flow of savings was generated. This means that the rounds of each Markov process add up to one year. The model also implies that the expanding capital stock does not create income continuously as savings are absorbed but only at the end of each year.

This model is not necessarily a disequilibrium model. It all depends on the structure of the Q matrix. If, however, we build polarisation tendencies into the matrix—for instance, by assuming that the regions of the system are hierarchically structured and that for any region j its savings flow coefficient to a higher order region i is always greater than the corresponding coefficient to a lower order region m, while the intraregional absorption coefficients are also hierarchical (that is, $\hat{r}_i > \hat{r}_j > \hat{r}_m$)—then the regional growth paths will move in favour of the higher order regions regardless of the initial state or the closed-economy growth paths. If either the closed-economy growth paths are the same for all regions ($\hat{A}\hat{V}^{-1}$ collapsed into a scalar) or the higher order regions grow faster than the lower order regions, then this system exhibits cumulative divergence with regional income differentials widening over time. On the other hand, if in the closed-economy case the lower order regions were to grow faster than the higher order regions, the effect of opening up the system to interregional capital flows would be a convergence in regional growth rates. In all cases, however, steady growth in an open interregional system is most unlikely [9].

The economic interpretation of polarisation forces in the Q matrix can be based on either one or both of two arguments. First, regional investment may be a function of agglomeration economies, and agglomeration economies may be assumed to be a function of regional size. This hypothesis can be squared with an 'interregional capital flows are a function of relative rates of return' hypothesis if agglomeration economies are reflected in higher rates of return. Second, savers and investors may have subjective preferences for investing in large (high-order) regions because of risk aversion behaviour and attempts to minimise uncertainty [10].

Conclusions

I am not concerned in this paper with the question of whether either of the regional growth models I have described is realistic or not. Both are potentially capable of empirical testing, though such a test lies outside the scope of this paper. My motivation was rather different. So many of the regional growth models in current use by economists are equilibrium models. In my view this fact has tended to bias how economists have looked at the regional growth process, and induced them to close their eyes to historical examples which do not easily fit these models. Presentation of two potential disequilibrium models is worthwhile, if only to redress the balance. Moreover it is a common tendency in regional economics to extrapolate from a short-run to a long-run equilibrium. The Markov chain model, in particular, has the pedagogic virtue that it illustrates the possible compatibility between a comparative-statics equilibrium in interregional capital markets and the dynamics of an interregional system in which regional incomes diverge over time.

---

[9] The improbable condition for steady state growth is that regional variations in $\hat{A}\hat{V}^{-1}$ should be exactly offset by regional variations within the $(I-Q)^{-1}R$ matrix.
[10] The preference for investing at the centre rather than the periphery has been stressed by Hirschman (1958, pp.184-186), Friedmann (1966, p.15) and Alonso (1968, pp.25, 39).

References

Alonso, W., 1968, "Industrial location and regional policy in economic development", WP number 74, Institute of Urban and Regional Development, University of California, Berkeley, California.

Bell, F. W., 1967, "An econometric forecasting model for a region", *Journal of Regional Science,* **7**, 109-127.

Borts, G. H., 1960, "The equalisation of returns and regional economic growth", *American Economic Review,* **50**, 319-347.

Borts, G. H., Stein, J. L., 1964, *Economic Growth in a Free Market* (Columbia University Press, New York).

Friedmann, J., 1966, *Regional Development Policy: A Case Study of Venezuela* (MIT Press, Cambridge, Mass.).

Hirschman, A. O., 1958, *The Strategy of Economic Development* (Yale University Press, New Haven, Conn.).

Kaldor, N., 1966, "Marginal productivity and the macroeconomic theories of distribution", *Review of Economic Studies,* **33**, 309-319.

Kaldor, N., 1970, "The case for regional policies", *Scottish Journal of Political Economy,* **17**, 337-347.

Leijonhüfvud, A., 1968, *On Keynesian Economics and the Economics of Keynes* (Oxford University Press, New York).

Myrdal, G., 1957, *Economic Theory and Underdeveloped Regions* (Duckworth, London).

Olsen, E., 1971, *International Trade Theory and Regional Income Differences: United States, 1880-1950* (North-Holland, Amsterdam).

Romans, J. T., 1965, *Capital Exports and Growth Among US Regions* (Wesleyan University Press, Middletown, Conn.).

Siebert, H., 1969, *Regional Economic Growth: Theory and Policy* (International Textbook Company, Scranton, Penn.).

A Gravity Flows Approach to an Interregional Input-Output Model for the UK

I.R.GORDON
University of Kent at Canterbury

1 Introduction

Variations in levels of regional economic activity may be represented in large part as the outcome of three sets of interregional flows—involving transactions in goods and services, migration of population, and movement of industry (that is, movement of combinations of capital and managerial capacity)—and of the interactions between these three subsystems. A single model of each subsystem would distinguish flows between each pair of regions and between relevant groups, such as industrial sectors, in each region, thus permitting explicit account to be taken of appropriate spatial relations.

Choice of the particular aspects to be treated as exogenously determined in a given context would largely determine the structure of an integrated model. It may be suggested that interregional-flow-based models are best suited to applications involving medium-term time horizons of around 5–10 years. Over this sort of period relevant exogenous changes may most readily be specified with respect to developments in the national economy such as shifts in the composition of final demand or in underlying rates of productivity growth. To handle these it would seem most appropriate to treat the flows of goods and services as forming the central element of the three subsystems defined here, and to represent this subsystem in the form of an interregional input–output model. This type of model is essentially demand-driven in character, but for the other two subsystems a more general form of interaction model might be employed in this context, reflecting on a more equal footing developments in both the region of origin and of destination for a particular flow. Savings and investment flows would not be separately distinguished, being treated as the result of, on the one hand, the movement of industry, and, on the other, the changes in capacity levels and in savings levels entailed by the input–output model.

Some of the more important types of interaction between the three subsystems may be readily identified: movement of industry would directly affect regional trading patterns by changing the spatial distribution of supply sources; the varying efficiency of migration in matching shifts in the demand for labour would be reflected in the growth of the final demand sectors in each region; movement of industry in its turn would reflect *inter alia* the required capacity growth in regions of origin, and the relationship between output and migration changes in all regions.

The remainder of this paper will consider only the first of these three subsystems, but in discussing the structure and implementation of the input–output model, it is useful to relate it to this wider context. This may help, in particular, to distinguish those limitations on the model arising primarily from its artificial separation from the other two subsystems, and possible limitations of a more basic nature, arising from the concentration on regional interdependencies and neglect of any independent shifts in the performance of single regions.

In the context we have cited, this subsystem may be of central importance but in the UK, and probably elsewhere, it is also distinguished as that about which least direct information is currently available. The 1961 and 1966 population censuses have made available quite detailed migration flow data, and since Howard's study (Board of Trade, 1968) the basic facts about at least the longer distance moves of manufacturing industry are fairly well established. By contrast, virtually no information is available from official sources about regional technical relationships, or about the absorption by individual regions of goods or services produced by themselves or by other regions. Even such data as is directly collected on interregional flows from various transport surveys is of little use in tracing producer–purchaser relationships, particularly because, in a geographically small country such as the UK, an unduly large proportion of the sampled flows are likely to relate to local movements by the distributive trades and high-weight–low-value commodities such as building materials. Thus any attempt at simulating the effects of interregional input–output relationships on regional activity levels in this country must start by simulating the base-year relationships themselves. For the interregional model currently being implemented at the University of Kent this preliminary step is being attempted on the basis of a trading model of the gravity type. In the sections that follow we consider in turn the relationships between this trading model and assumptions about the form of interregional competition, the interregional input–output framework in which it is embodied, and finally our current approaches to the implementation of this model for the regions of the UK.

2 A gravity approach to interregional trade

A particular, though by no means unique, difficulty in modelling interregional trade flows is that of bridging the gap between micro and macroeconomic relationships—an undertaking which cannot be achieved by purely deductive methods. The conditions of aggregation are such that only under stringent assumptions about the homogeneity of the products of different regions, and the identity of individual utility functions and budget restraints, or about the precise form of their variation, can interregional trade functions be deduced directly from

microeconomic hypotheses[1]. Equally, economic theory suggests no
satisfactory approach to the disaggregation of macroeconomic
relationships. We have therefore to resort to more probabilistic
approaches, while checking that the models generated can be interpreted
in a manner consistent with economic assumptions about the character
of spatial competition. In a more general context, Wilson (1971) has
shown that the gravity model, historically derived as an empirical
generalisation of phenomena involving flows over a distance, represents in
its exponential form that description of a system at an intermediate level,
the meso-state, which is consistent with the largest number of
combinations of events at a lower level in the system, the micro-states,
within constraints imposed on the aggregate performance of the system.
As such, the family of models may have applications for all sorts of
trading relations between subgroups of a population, particularly when
the groups are separated spatially or otherwise.

We may consider as an example an economy involving transactions
between a set of producer groups i $(1, 2, ..., m)$ and a set of consumer
groups j $(1, 2, ..., n)$. Macroeconomic relationships indicate the total level
of sales (in some appropriate quantity measure) for each producer group,
S_i, and of purchases by each consumer group, D_j, together with the
average price level, $\bar{P}$, but say nothing about the relationships between
individual producer and consumer groups. If the sets of prices for
individual consumer groups (or producer groups) are identical, the most
probable set of trading flows, T_{ij}, consistent with the available information,
is given by

$$T_{ij} = \frac{S_i D_j}{\sum_i S_i} .$$ (1)

This set of flows is more probable than the various other sets consistent
with our basic assumptions in the sense that it will be the most frequently
generated if individual purchases are selected randomly. However, the
sets of prices, P_{ij}, may vary for *both* consumer and producer groups as a
result of discriminatory pricing policies, tariffs, or, in an interregional
context, because of costs involved in overcoming the distance between
individual pairs of producer and consumer groups. In this case the most
probable set of trading flows satisfying the known constraints is given by

---

[1] Niedercorn and Bechdolt (1969) have attempted to derive the 'gravity law' of
spatial interaction from assumptions about the form of the individual's utility function,
but their derivation required each individual to make trips to all possible destinations,
equivalent in our context to purchasing goods and services in some quantity from all
possible sources. A modified version (Niedercorn and Bechdolt, 1970) using Lancaster's
(1966) goods-characteristics approach involved the same implausible result, although a
simplifying assumption that the same mix of characteristics was available at all
destinations should have restricted all trips to the nearest destination.

the more general model

$$T_{ij} = A_i B_j S_i D_j \exp(-\beta P_{ij}) , \tag{2}$$

where

$$A_i = \left[\sum_j B_j D_j \exp(-\beta P_{ij}) \right]^{-1} , \tag{3}$$

$$B_j = \left[\sum_i A_i S_i \exp(-\beta P_{ij}) \right]^{-1} . \tag{4}$$

The A_i and B_j terms represent the Lagrange multipliers associated with the prior assumptions about sales and purchases by individual groups, while the β parameter represents the Lagrange multiplier associated with the assumption about average price (or total expenditure). With a given set of constraints the equilibrium flow pattern is unaffected by the addition or subtraction of a constant from the price measure P_{ij}, and the latter may appropriately be expressed in terms of deviations from some base-cost level.

If we attempt to relate the model generated by this essentially statistical approach to the economic assumptions involved in its application to interregional trade flows, it is clear that the parameter β attached to the price variable is of particular significance, and is associated with the type and degree of competition in the market under consideration. Increases in the β value, with a fixed set of assumptions about prices, sales, and purchases by a group, reflect a tightening of the constraint on total expenditure (that is, a reduction in average price paid), with an increasing proportion of purchases being made from the cheapest source. Thus, as the β value tends towards infinity, one would expect the pattern of flows generated by the gravity model to approximate to that expected under assumptions of perfect competition, including the assumption of a completely homogeneous product and perfect information.

Under these conditions, the expected flow pattern is that given by the solution of a linear programming transportation problem. The form of this problem is closely related to the assumptions involved in the derivation of the doubly-constrained gravity model [equations (1) to (3)]. In both cases, total sales and purchases by a group together with the set of prices are assumed as given; for the linear programming (LP) problem the objective is to identify the unique set of flows minimising total expenditure in the system while the gravity model seeks to select the most probable of a number of sets of flows consistent with an assumed level of total expenditure. We cannot, however, induce the latter to yield the LP solution simply by reducing the assumed level of total expenditure to an absolute minimum, since the model will always generate mn nonzero flows, whereas the LP solution involves a basic set of no more than $m+n-1$ positive flows. Below some particular expenditure level, the gravity model can only satisfy all the aggregate constraints by adopting negative values for some of both the A_i and B_j factors, and generating some (relatively small) negative flows. Nevertheless simulation in a number of trading situations shows that the minimum expenditure level consistent with nonnegative flows in the doubly-constrained gravity model can be within a half per cent of the absolute minimum indicated by the LP solution[2].

Given homogeneous commodities and perfect information, the LP approach is relevant in monopolistic as well as perfectly competitive environments. Neither assumption, however, is applicable to the great majority of goods and services involved in interregional trade, in which monopolistic competition represents the norm. At a practical level the heterogeneity of commodity classifications is widely recognised, but it is sometimes suggested that this is essentially a result of technical inadequacies in the classifications employed. In a few sectors, such as agriculture, mining, or the power industries, further disaggregation may offer effectively homogeneous commodity groupings. More typically, however, commodities have to be recognised as simply more or less appropriate groupings of innumerable individual products distinguished from each other by their intrinsic characteristics (including spatial and temporal characteristics) and by more subjective forms of product differentiation (Chamberlin, 1957). Ideally, a model of regional trade should treat these individual products, rather than any type of establishment or commodity grouping, as its basic unit. A suitable framework for such a model exists in Lancaster's (1966) goods-characteristics approach, involving a consumer preference ordering of sets of characteristics of goods (rather than of the goods themselves) complemented by a series of technical relationships between individual products and the (smaller number of) defined characteristics. But the potentially vast number of products and the absence of a unique basis for their identification prevent any direct practical implementations.

In a world of fundamentally heterogeneous commodities, involving subjectively as well as objectively differentiated products, the transmission of relevant product information cannot be regarded as a costless process. Rather, the costs of acquiring and distributing product information, together with related aspects of the marketing and servicing functions, form an essential element in the determination of interregional trade, comparable in importance with direct transportation costs (although less readily measurable) as a component of total 'costs of overcoming distance'. In different circumstances the greater part of these costs may fall on either producer or purchaser, but these differences of practice may be of little consequence for the analysis since in either case the parties involved have to make similar trade-offs between these costs and price factors. Typically, the producer may seek to enlarge his market either

[2] Similar results have been obtained in relation to maximum expenditure, with negative β values, that is, for the upper asymptote of the typical S curve relating expenditure totals and β values.

by a policy of price reduction (or price stability) or by intensified selling effort in new or unsaturated market areas, while the user may choose between incurring extra administrative, service, or transport costs, seeking cheaper sources of supply, and making use of the most readily accessible source. In either case the efficient choices represent points on a series of demand curves relating sales of the products in question, as a proportion of requirements for the commodity in each area, to a measure of 'price' incorporating production costs and total distance costs whether incurred by producer or purchaser.

If this product demand function is assumed to take the form of an exponential function with a single parameter value β' applicable to all purchasing regions, we may represent sales of a particular product k, part of commodity group r, produced in region i, to each purchasing region j $(1, 2, ..., n)$ as

$$T_{ij}^k = \alpha_k D_j^r [\exp(-\beta' P_{ij}^k)] , \tag{5}$$

where D_j^r is the total demand in j for commodity group r, P_{ij}^k is the price in j of the particular product k from the commodity group r, and α_k is a constant. An aggregate demand function for the particular commodity and area of origin would then take the form of a similar demand function for a representative (average) product multiplied by the total number of products (within the group) produced in region i. The number of products produced in an area is not a readily measurable quantity, however, and for practical purposes would have to be represented by some proxy indicator. With a typically heterogeneous commodity we may choose the regional output of the commodity for this role, at least for cross-sectional comparisons. With this particular approximation we obtain a function for the flow of commodity r from region i to region j similar to that suggested on probabilistic grounds by the gravity model:

$$T_{ij}^r = \alpha_r S_i^r D_j^r [\exp(-\beta' P_{ij}^{\bar{k}})] , \tag{6}$$

where $\bar{k}$ is a representative product from the commodity group r, and α_r is a constant.

The doubly constrained gravity model of equation (2) may be rewritten as

$$T_{ij} = S_i D_j [\exp(-\beta P_{ij}^*)] , \tag{7}$$

where

$$P_{ij}^* = P_{ij} + P_{Si}^* + P_{Dj}^* , \tag{8}$$

$$P_{Si}^* = -\beta^{-1} \ln A_i , \tag{9}$$

and

$$P_{Dj}^* - -\beta^{-1} \ln B_j . \tag{10}$$

That is to say, the attraction and generation factors can be replaced by adjustments to the sets of prices attributed to each selling and purchasing region. If the initial set of P_{ij} values reflects only the distance-cost variations, as would be appropriate with a homogeneous commodity, the P_{Si}^* and P_{Dj}^* values represent imputed price variations specific to the supply or demand in the particular regions of the average product in the commodity group concerned. The existence of these price elements is a direct reflection of the heterogeneity of the commodity.

These imputed prices, like the shadow prices derivable from the dual to a programming problem, represent marginal values associated with the relaxation of a particular constraint. They are not, however, directly comparable with the supply and demand shadow prices which would be obtained from the dual of the transportation problem. In the latter case, the demand shadow prices represent the delivered price of the commodity irrespective of source, while the supply shadow prices represent the F.O.B. price of the commodity irrespective of destination. In the gravity model, however, the delivered price is given by equation (8), and the F.O.B. price (assuming P_{ij} includes only distance costs) by

$$U_{ij} = P_{Si}^* + P_{Dj}^* . \qquad (11)$$

Thus, with the gravity model, both F.O.B. and delivered prices are specific to individual combinations of selling and purchasing regions, a possibility which is eliminated from the linear programming model by the assumption of a homogeneous commodity requiring a single price level in each spatially separated market.

Comparison of actual sets of imputed prices obtained by the two approaches for a range of commodities traded between the regions of the UK shows a marked contrast in the distribution of values. By solving the dual to a series of transportation problems, formulated in terms of actual regional outputs and deliveries, and proxy measures of distance costs, O'Sullivan (1972) has shown that there is a consistent tendency for above average shadow demand and supply prices to be concentrated in the more remote regions with the lowest shadow prices being found in the most accessible regions. However, applying gravity models, incorporating realistic estimates of β values for the commodity in question, to similar problems yields a very different pattern, with the lowest P_{Si}^* and P_{Dj}^* values (corresponding to the highest A_i and B_j factors) tending to occur in the least accessible regions and vice versa. In terms of the prices imputed to trade flows between pairs of regions of similar accessibility, the contrast between the two models is extreme. It is, however, greatly reduced if comparisons are made in terms of the *average* price which a particular region pays or receives for a commodity, because of the much more diverse set of interregional flows assumed by the gravity model.

Applications of either model for forecasting purposes, whether directly or as sources of shadow prices for more behavioural location models

(Harris, 1970), require some understanding of the reasons for the
divergence of these two sets of prices. Two aspects deserve comment here,
relating to the respective assumptions on commodity homogeneity and to
the interpretations of the assumed output constraints. The programming
approach's assumption of a homogeneous commodity rules out not only
the general possibility of diversity but the more specific possibility of
quality differences (in terms of the preferences of the average purchaser).
In the case of the gravity model, however, the imputation of a below
average price to a particular source of supply may reflect either the
ability to produce a fixed quality good for a lower price than competing
regions, or the fact that at a given price its products are regarded as of
a higher quality than competing regions. Thus the high A_i factors and low
P_{Si}^* values for industries in peripheral regions may reflect one expected
adaptation to such a situation, in a concentration on the production of
relatively small quantities of specialised and high quality goods.

More fundamentally this type of interpretation of the gravity model
implies that the assumed levels of sales of each region approximate to
equilibrium levels of output, reflecting the degree of competitiveness of
the region as a producer of the commodity in question, of which the
imputed prices afford a measure. By contrast the programming approach
emphasises the role of the assumed levels of capacity as constraints on
output levels, even where they have been derived directly, or indirectly,
from existing levels of output, while the shadow prices represent
indicators of the degree and direction of disequilibrium in the existing
situation. In part the differences may be in the implicit time horizon,
since capacity levels related to equilibrium output levels in a previous
period can represent (short-term) constraints on output in the current period
—but they may also reflect more fundamental presumptions about the
degree of complexity or irrationality embodied in existing trading patterns.

Thus O'Sullivan (1972) follows Stevens (1961) in emphasising the
direct relationship obtaining between LP shadow prices and location rent
when production costs (including normal profits) are assumed to be the
same at all locations. In an input-output context this assumption appears
altogether too strong since it ignores variations between locations in the
delivered price of intermediate inputs. We may prefer to analyse the
imputed F.O.B. price of commodity r in region i in terms of the imputed
delivered prices of the inputs and an imputed value added,

$$U_i^r = \sum_q (a_{qr}^i V_i^q) + Y_i^r ,\qquad(12)$$

where
   U_i^r is the imputed F.O.B. price of r in region i;
   V_i^q is the imputed delivered price of q in region i;
   Y_i^r is the imputed value added in commodity r in region i;
   a_{qr}^i is the input coefficient (in quantity terms) for commodity q used in
      production of commodity r.

Or, in the heterogeneous commodity case,

$$U_{ij}^r = \sum_q \sum_j (a_{qr}^i c_{ji}^q V_{ji}^q) + Y_{ij}^r \,, \tag{13}$$

where

c_{ji}^q is the proportion of commodity q used in region i obtained from
    region j;

U_{ij}^r, V_{ij}^r, Y_{ij}^r are the imputed average values of r sold from region i to
    region j in terms of F.O.B. prices, delivered prices, and value added
    respectively.

However, the imputed value added (Y_i^r or Y_{ij}^r) remains an ambiguous
quantity, including both production costs and location rent so that a high
value may reflect either inefficiency or unexploited locational advantage,
high marginal costs or high marginal revenue, according to how we interpret
the form and conditions of competition in the commodity concerned.

3 The interregional input–output model

At the national level, the basic Leontief (1941) input–output model
embodies a set of linear equations relating the output of each of the m
sectors of the economy to the inputs required from each sector. The 'ideal'
interregional input–output model (Isard, 1951) represents an elaboration of
this national model by treating each of the m sectors in each of n regions as
constituting a sector in its own right, thus requiring the identification of
mn equations involving a possible $(mn)^2$ intersectoral relationships. This
model represents an 'ideal' in terms of the amount of information
incorporated for any given set of regions and sectors. In practical
implementations, where there are economic limitations on the size of the
model which can be estimated or manipulated, this generality has to be
traded-off against the number of sectors and regions that can be
distinguished. Thus the loss of informational content involved in the
choice of a more restricted form may be more than compensated for by
the finer degree of disaggregation that can be achieved with given
resources.

A major simplification of the 'ideal' interregional model can be
achieved by treating all flows of a particular commodity as being routed
via a supply pool in the region of production and a demand pool in the
region of absorption (Moses, 1955; Chenery, 1953). A particular
region's purchases of a commodity are assumed to be drawn from the
various supplying regions in fixed proportions which are independent of
the purchasing sector. With this approach, the 'ideal' model's full
($mn \times mn$) matrix of input coefficients relating inputs and outputs of
each sector in each region is treated as the product of two sparse matrices:
the first, $\hat{\mathbf{A}}$, showing for each region the technical relationships between
sectors; the second, $\mathbf{F}$, showing the interregional purchasing pattern for
the product of each sector. Both of these matrices are also ($mn \times mn$) in
dimension but the $\hat{\mathbf{A}}$ matrix comprises n block-diagonal matrices (one for

each region) each of dimension ($m \times m$), while the $\mathbf{F}$ matrix comprises n^2 diagonal matrices of similar dimensions. The number of individual coefficients to be estimated in any practical application is therefore considerably fewer than with the 'ideal' model, while the separation of the two sparse matrices [involving together a possible $nm^2 + mn^2$ positive elements compared with the $(mn)^2$ positive elements of the full matrix, $\mathbf{F\hat{A}}$] enables a very considerable reduction in the computing resources required for operation of the model (Polenske, 1970).

This supply and demand pool approach differs from the 'ideal' model in recognising that the products of the same sector from different regions are likely to be more readily substitutable for each other than are products of different sectors. It has even been argued that "the regional origin of the particular batch of a given kind of good absorbed by its users in one particular region is as irrelevant to them as the ultimate regional destination of his output is to a producer" (Leontief and Strout, 1963). However, the inherent heterogeneity of commodity groupings necessarily involves some preferences for individual products which happen to be produced in particular regions. The supply-demand pool approach has to be justified more pragmatically as a simplification of the 'ideal' model which enables its practical implementation and the elaboration of a finer sectoral classification without introducing any systematic distortion into the model.

In the 'ideal' model the assumption that each sector in each region represents an independent sector implies that trading coefficients be defined similarly to technical coefficients as proportions of the requirements of the absorbing sector. Thus each column of both the matrices $\mathbf{\hat{A}}$ and $\mathbf{F}$ would sum to unity (if value added is included as a row in the former and international imports in the latter). The Chenery (1953) and Moses (1955) models employed similar matrices of column coefficients, $\mathbf{C}$, for the interregional trading relations (that is, $\mathbf{F} = \mathbf{C}$). When the assumption of complete independence for a sector *in* a region is dropped and the possibility of interregional (if not intersectoral) substitution is acknowledged, other possible forms for the trade coefficient matrix $\mathbf{F}$ have to be considered. In particular, Leontief and Strout (1963) have proposed that the flows of a particular commodity should be treated as proportional to not only the size of the demand pools but also to the relative sizes of the regional supply pools for the commodity concerned. Polenske has also considered the case where flows are proportional only to the size of the supply pools [with a row-coefficient matrix $\mathbf{R}$, and $\mathbf{F} = (\mathbf{R}')^{-1}$], and compared the efficiency of the three forms in forecasting situations (Polenske, 1966, 1970).

The more comprehensive of these comparisons, involving data on Japanese interregional trade, showed the row-coefficient model to be extremely inaccurate but revealed no discernible difference in the overall predictive ability over a three year period of the other two models.

Mathematically, both the row-coefficient and the Leontief–Strout models can exhibit unfortunate properties in particular circumstances: Polenske (1970) found that the Leontief–Strout method could yield singular matrices, while the row-coefficient method may easily predict negative flows. A more fundamental basis for comparison, however, is in terms of the economic rationale for these alternative models. Polenske (1966) has suggested that the row-coefficient model reflects the indifference of consumers towards the regional origin of purchases, and a form of rationing practised by producers[3] interested in retaining their market links. Essentially therefore it is a model of response to supply changes, which yields theoretically implausible results when applied to varying levels of demand[4]. It is thus incompatible with the basic Walrasian assumption of input–output models that output changes are generated only by shifts in demand and price changes by shifts in supply.

The Leontief–Strout approach represents a form of gravity model in so far as it expresses trade flows as proportional to the distribution of both supply and demand for the commodity, although in this context it does not explicitly relate flow levels to distance costs[5]. In the previous section it was suggested that for a heterogeneous commodity the term relating to the size of the supply pool [that is, S_i in equations (2)–(5)] appeared in the gravity function as a proxy for the number of products within the commodity group produced in that area.

Extension of this interpretation from a cross-sectional context to the comparative statics of the Leontief–Strout model requires rather more heroic assumptions. We would have to presuppose that an increase in the sales of existing products induced an immediately proportionate increase in the number of products, to which consumers also adapted instantaneously. Induced product diversification of this type offers a plausible interpretation of the proportionality of the S_i term in the Leontief–Strout model—unlike explanations in terms of direct economies of scale—but it is clearly not a short-term phenomenon, since new products require time for development and promotion. Further lags of several years are to be expected before purchasing patterns are fully

---

[3] Of fruit and vegetable products in this particular case.

[4] In order to maintain fixed row-coefficients, an increase in demand in a single region s would increase sales, to that region and elsewhere, of those regions selling the largest proportion of their output in s, while reducing the sales in all regions of producing regions to which s was of less importance as a market.

[5] Although distance costs are not an essential part of the 'point-estimate gravity model' developed by Leontief and Strout, they are, as is noted in the next section, suggested by the authors as a starting point for the estimation of base-year flows where these are unknown.

adapted to the new range of supply sources[6]. Thus it is more appropriate to represent the process of cumulative causation via induced product diversification recursively than by an instantaneous form of the Leontief-Strout model. The interregional input-output model can then be formulated as a column coefficient model with an initial **C** matrix being revised at intervals of five years or so to reflect output changes in the previous period. At the close of each period therefore the pattern of trade flows would involve an element of disequilibrium which would fall to be resolved in the next period.

The basic interregional input-output model outlined here may be represented by the matrix equation

$$\Delta X = C\hat{A}\Delta X + C\Delta Y , \tag{14a}$$

where

ΔX is the column vector of gross output changes by sector,

ΔY is the column vector of exogenous demand changes by sector,

giving

$$\Delta X = (I - C\hat{A})^{-1}C\Delta Y , \tag{14b}$$

or, in order to avoid the inversion of a full ($mn \times mn$) matrix (Polenske, 1970),

$$\Delta X = (C^{-1} - \hat{A})^{-1}\Delta Y . \tag{14c}$$

Normally in input-output models the ΔY vector represents changes in the level of final demand, but in an interregional model it is desirable to treat a large part of final demand as endogenous through the inclusion within the matrices **C** and **Â** of a household sector. Row entries for this sector represent sales of labor to the other productive sectors while column entries show the absorption of output from these sectors in the form of personal consumption and some categories of public current expenditure. Entries for the sector in the **C** matrix reflect interregional commuting and any other temporary labour movements.

The specification of the vectors in equations (14) in the form of increments to demand or output permits the use of linear nonhomogeneous technical and trade relationships involving marginal rather than average coefficients in the **Â** or **C** matrices. In practice, lack of data (even at the national level) rules out this possibility except for consumer expenditure. Consumption functions for individual consuming units (for example, households) are suitably approximated by linear nonhomogeneous functions with significant constant terms, positive or negative, for most commodities and for total expenditure. An aggregate

[6] This expectation is supported by the evidence of substantial lags before changes in communications patterns, such as the Severn Bridge, yield their full effects on purchasing patterns.

consumption function for a commodity may therefore be specified as

$$E_i = h(e_i \bar{y} + c_i) \,, \tag{15}$$

where

E_i is the aggregate expenditure by consumers on commodity i;
h is the number of households;
$\bar{y}$ is the average household income;
e_i and c_i are to be specified.

In order to reduce this function to an equation involving only aggregate consumption and aggregate income we have to specify the elasticity of h with respect to total incomes[7]. In Tiebout's (1969) terms growth is extensive if the elasticity is unitary, and intensive if the elasticity is zero. In the former case the appropriate consumption coefficients for the $\hat{A}$ matrix are

$$a_{iH} = e_i + c_i \bar{y}^{-1} \,, \tag{16a}$$

that is, the average coefficients, while in the latter the appropriate coefficients are the marginal coefficients

$$a_{iH} = e_i \,. \tag{16b}$$

At the national level this household elasticity must (except for the effect of Irish migration) be close to zero. For the majority of individual regions, however, it appears to be much closer to unity, except in the very short term[8]. Appropriate values can only be determined in terms of the functioning of particular labour markets and of the migration process, which cannot be fully considered within the current model. In the meantime the most suitable approach is probably to adopt average coefficients [that is, equation (16a)] and to concentrate, where possible, on self-balancing changes in the final demand vector, involving no net change in national income.

4 Implementing an interregional input–output model for the UK

The interregional input–output model for the UK currently being implemented at the University of Kent follows the form outlined in the previous section, and is founded on a regional disaggregation of the published national tables for 1963 (Central Statistical Office, 1970) and gravity model estimates of base-year interregional flows of each commodity. The final model will distinguish some forty sectors in each of the eleven standard regions but the basic flow matrices are being estimated for seventy five commodity groups and some sixty subregions for subsequent aggregation.

[7] Or perhaps total incomes from a particular source, for example, employment.
[8] That is, over one to two years before migration has fully responded.

The detailed structure of the model, in areas such as the treatment of overseas trade, is being evolved heuristically from experiments with cruder and more aggregated models. The basic approach can, however, be indicated in terms of four steps:

(1) the estimation of regional gross outputs and of the components of final demand by commodity;

(2) application of technical coefficients (that is, matrix $\hat{A}$) and foreign trade coefficients to derive estimates of domestic demands and supplies by region for each commodity;

(3) the matching of regional supplies and demands using gravity models for each commodity to generate trade flow estimates and the matrix of interregional trade coefficients C;

(4) operations on the resultant interregional matrices to derive specific or general solutions of the model.

The derivation of detailed regional and subregional estimates of expenditure and output represents a substantial and time-consuming aspect of the implementation of the model but presents no fundamental problems. A substantial part of the data is being derived directly or indirectly from the results of the 1963 Census of Production (Board of Trade, 1970). The remainder is drawn from a wide range of sources, following the approach of Woodward (1970), and ensuring consistency at all stages with prior national or regional totals for particular aggregates. The definitions and conventions used follow closely those of the national input–output tables except that re-exports are excluded from interregional trade and that an attempt has been made to distinguish intermediate inputs into the public sector [9] so as to allocate demands more accurately to the region of absorption.

Insufficient data, even in the form of possible proxy measures or indicators, is available to build up estimates of regional technical relationships or of interregional flows in similar fashion. In the first case, the general assumption made has been that input coefficients for a sector are identical in all regions, corresponding to the published national estimates. The degree of inaccuracy involved in this assumption is unknown at present, although a number of possible factors leading to variation in regional technical coefficients are readily identifiable. In particular, differences in the size and age of plants, the product-mix, time lags in the diffusion of techniques, and relative price differences between substitutable inputs may be expected to be relevant. In most cases, however, the incidence of the non-price factors may be expected to be fairly random, limiting the cumulative effect on estimates of total intermediate demand for a particular commodity. The price factor clearly has particular importance as a possible source of more systematic errors. Without detailed production function data the scope and form of possible

[9] Rather than including these directly in the final demand vector.

substitutions is not readily determined. Particular attention may be given, however, to possible substitutions between the energy inputs and between labour and capital, since in both cases immobility or high transport costs produce significant regional variations in price relatives which may affect most industries in a similar fashion. Independent regional coefficients for energy inputs may be estimated from existing aggregate data and from an adaptation of Wigley's work on the Cambridge fuel submodel (Department of Applied Economics, 1968) for use with regional price differences. Independent coefficients may also be estimated for labour and capital inputs, although it should be noted that the significance of assuming identical regional coefficients for these two inputs is somewhat different than for the intermediate inputs. In principle, although usually presented in monetary terms, input–output coefficients relate to quantity relationships between sectors. Thus, if the household sector is made endogenous, consumer expenditure should be treated as a linear function of the physical output of the sector, that is, the volume of labour supplied. However, in reality these coefficients do not reflect technical relationships, but rather the dependence of consumption on the *value* of income from employment (cf.Leontief *et al.*, 1965), so that the labour and capital input coefficients would thus represent not an absence of substitution but a unitary elasticity of substitution (that is, an aggregate Cobb–Douglas production function).

The influence of non-price factors can only be taken into account in so far as their effects are also concentrated on capital and labour inputs [as may be the case with the size of plant factor (Ozaki, 1970)] or the energy sectors. Product-mix differences, the most fundamental source of error in technical coefficients, can be allowed for only by making use of the full detail available from the current national input–output table (involving some seventy five commodity groups in 1963). Despite these evident sources of error, it is clear that the development of more refined regional technical coefficients is of lower priority in the context of the interregional model as a whole than the derivation of adequate trade coefficients. In particular we may note the conclusion of a careful American investigation (Walderhaug, 1972) which suggested that technical coefficients of acceptable quality for local input–output tables can be developed from national data.

In the present implementation the C matrix is based on a simulation of base-year trade flows for each commodity using a doubly-constrained gravity model of the type discussed in section 2. Leontief and Strout (1963) first suggested the use of an inverse distance cost function for the simulation of base-year flows. The present application varies from their proposal in employing a more general exponential function [that is, equation (2)] with a single parameter (β) specific to individual commodities in place of a common inversely proportional relation with transport costs (or distance) for all commodities, and in making use of the gravity model for the estimation of intraregional as well as interregional flows. Since neither total distance costs involved in trade in a particular commodity nor unit distance costs for trade between specific pairs of regions can be estimated with any degree of accuracy, the models are calibrated from survey data on flows for specific origins or destinations and from measures of physical distance. Unit distance costs are implicitly assumed to be some monotonic function of distance itself.

If we could equate distance costs simply with transport costs, there would be strong grounds for regarding the former as directly proportional to physical distance. A number of studies (notably Chisholm, 1971) have produced evidence that unit freight costs in both Britain and the US can be closely approximated by a linear function of distance. The positive constant term in the function represents terminal costs which may be treated as a part of the production costs. However, we have little evidence as to the importance or the relationship with physical distance of other elements of distance cost, and the appropriate function can only be selected empirically. The principal data sources available for calibration of the models consist of a number of sample surveys of consignments to and from industrial establishments in particular subregions in the South West, South Wales, and West Cumberland (see for example, Edwards, 1971). Calibration of doubly constrained gravity models with data relating to flows to or from a single zone (or a limited number of zones) is liable to yield biased estimates and spurious variations in the β value from zone to zone because the set of attraction and generation factors cannot be fully specified. To avoid this source of bias it is necessary to carry out the calibration within the context of the full origin and destination matrix, although actual flow data is only available for a few rows or columns. The procedure is essentially iterative, involving the selection of an initial β value (or the equivalent parameter in an alternative form), the derivation of a corresponding set of A_i and B_j values satisfying the constraints on total flows to and from each zone, and the estimation of a new β value from the actual flow data standardised by the appropriate attraction or generation factors. Our experiments to date indicate that for commodity flows this procedure converges quite rapidly, since the A_i and B_j factors are not too sensitive to small changes in the β value.

Estimation of the base-year flows in terms of a fairly detailed geographical and sectoral classification is directed principally at improving the accuracy of the gravity model results, particularly for intraregional flows and for flows between neighbouring areas of separate regions. Hopefully the approach may also permit retrospective checks on the accuracy of trading coefficients against actual survey estimates for some subregions and alternative aggregation for particular applications of the model. In addition it should facilitate simulation of possible effects of communications improvements. Substantial aggregation is necessary, however, in order to reduce the computational demands of operations on the final matrices to reasonable proportions. It is proposed to carry out a general solution for the forty sector eleven region model [using equation (14c)] but, with matrices of this order, specific solutions for particular vectors are so much more economical that for most applications it is planned to use iterative solution methods [on equation (14a)].

5 Conclusion

Input–output models, and interregional input–output models in particular, are by their nature large and demanding in terms of data but essentially simple in structure. In the UK model outlined here, the introduction of a gravity model framework for the simulation of interregional trade flows results in a moderation of both of these characteristics enabling implementation of the model with existing data sources. It is expected that the model will be directly applicable on a practical level to consideration of interregional impacts of a wide range of possible national and local developments as well as illuminating some of the patterns of regional interdependence in the UK. The usefulness of the model for more general regional forecasts, on its own or in conjunction with models of migration and industrial movement, can only be determined by experiment. The model brings together in detailed form a number of the factors which we know to be of basic importance in determining regional activity levels but clearly ignores possible sources of variation in regional competitiveness. The importance of the latter for the regions of the UK will only become apparent, however, when we are able to compare actual regional trends over some past period with those projected by the input–output model. Operationally effective regional forecasting models may well prove to be less detailed but structurally richer than the interregional input–output model outlined here. But the firm discipline of accounting identities, on which the latter is founded at the regional and interregional level, provides a sound point of departure for the development of such models, whatever their ultimate form.

Acknowledgement. Work on the implementation of an interregional input–output model in the Centre for Research in Social Sciences, University of Kent at Canterbury, is financed by the Social Science Research Council and directed by H. W. Richardson and Professor D. A. Lury.

References

Board of Trade, 1968, *The Movement of Manufacturing Industry 1945-1965* (HMSO, London).
Board of Trade, 1970, *Report on the Census of Production 1963* (HMSO, London).
Central Statistical Office, 1970, *Input-Output Tables for the United Kingdom 1963, Studies in Official Statistics Number 16* (HMSO, London).
Chamberlin, E. H., 1957, *Towards a More General Theory of Value* (Oxford University Press, New York).

Chenery, H. B., 1953, "Regional analysis", in *The Structure and Growth of the Italian Economy,* by H. B. Chenery, P. G. Clark, V. Cao-Pinna (US Mutual Security Agency, Rome).

Chisholm, M., 1971, "Freight transport costs, industrial location and regional development", in *Spatial Policy Problems of the British Economy*, Eds. M. Chisholm, G. Manners (Cambridge University Press, Cambridge).

Department of Applied Economics, University of Cambridge, 1968, *A Programme for Growth. Part VIII: The Demand for Fuel 1948-1975,* Ed. R. Stone (Chapman and Hall, London).

Edwards, S. L., 1971, Severnside Industrial Survey, South West Economic Planning Board, Bristol.

Harris, C. C., 1970, "A multi-regional, multi-industry forecasting model", *Papers of the Regional Science Association,* **25**, 169-180.

Isard, W., 1951, "Inter-regional and regional input-output analysis: a model of a space economy", *Review of Economics and Statistics,* **33**, 318-328.

Lancaster, K. J., 1966, "A new approach to consumer theory", *Journal of Political Economy,* **74**, 132-157.

Leontief, W. W., 1941, *The Structure of the American Economy 1919-1929* (Oxford University Press, New York).

Leontief, W. W., Strout, A., 1963, "Multi-regional input-output analysis", in *Structural Inter-dependence and Economic Development,* Ed. T. Barna (Macmillan, London).

Leontief, W. W., Morgan, A., Polenske, K., Simpson, D., Tower, E., 1965, "The economic impact—industrial and regional of an arms cut", *Review of Economics and Statistics,* **47**, 217-241.

Moses, L., 1955, "The stability of interregional trading patterns and input-output analysis", *American Economic Review,* **45**, 803-832.

Niedercorn, J. A., Bechdolt, B. V., 1969, "An economic derivation of the 'gravity law' of spatial interaction", *Journal of Regional Science,* **9**, 273-282.

Niedercorn, J. A., Bechdolt, B. V., 1970, "An economic derivation of the 'gravity law' of spatial interaction: reply", *Journal of Regional Science,* **10**, 407-410.

O'Sullivan, P., 1972, "Linear programming as a forecasting device for inter-regional freight flows in Great Britain", *Regional and Urban Economics—Operational Methods,* **1**, 383-396.

Ozaki, I., 1970, "Economies of scale and input-output coefficients", in *Applications of Input-Output Analysis,* Eds. A. P. Carter, A. Brody (North-Holland, Amsterdam).

Polenske, K. R., 1966, *A Case Study of Transportation Models Used in Multi-regional Analysis,* Ph. D. Thesis, Harvard.

Polenske, K. R., 1970, "A multi-regional input-output model for the United States", Harvard Economic Research Project Report number 21.

Stevens, B. H., 1961, "Linear programming and location rent", *Journal of Regional Science,* **3**, 15-26.

Tiebout, C. M., 1969, "An empirical regional input-output projection model: the State of Washington 1980", *Review of Economics and Statistics,* **51**, 334-340.

Walderhaug, A. J., 1972, "State input-output tables derived from national data", *Proceedings of the Business and Economic Statistics Section, American Statistical Association 1971,* pp.77-85.

Wilson, A. G., 1971, "A family of spatial interaction models, and associated developments", *Environment and Planning,* **3**, 1-32.

Woodward, V. H., 1970, "Regional social accounts for the United Kingdom", in National Institute for Economic and Social Research Regional Papers 1 (Cambridge University Press, Cambridge).

An Area-stratified Regional Econometric Model

N.J.GLICKMAN
University of Pennsylvania

1 Introduction

This paper presents the structure of a macroeconomic econometric forecasting model for the Philadelphia region [1] which has been estimated with annual data for a 1947–1970 sample period. The model is an outgrowth of previous work by Glickman (1971a, 1971b, 1972) and others such as Bell (1967), Crow (1969), and L'Esperence *et al.* (1969). It presents an outline of the structure of the model (section 2) and a preliminary test of its forecasting ability (section 3).

It is useful to note some of the major elements of the model at this juncture:

(1) The research strategy entailed modelling the region's leading industrial sectors. Since the local economy is highly diversified (see Stevens *et al.*, 1967), a rather large model resulted. For a less-diversified economy such as Detroit or Seattle, fewer industrial classes would be necessary. The disaggregation scheme consists of nineteen industrial sectors and a total of one hundred and forty-two equations, of which eighty-seven are stochastic. To the knowledge of the author it is the largest small-area econometric model constructed in the United States.

(2) The model contains thirteen blocks of equations:

    block 1: manufacturing output;
    block 2: nonmanufacturing output;
    block 3: manufacturing employment;
    block 4: nonmanufacturing employment;
    block 5: wages, price, and income;
    block 6: demographic;
    block 7: federal and local government;
    block 8: manufacturing investment;
    block 9: retail sales;
    block 10: the City of Philadelphia;
    block 11: the suburban subregion;
    block 12: banking;
    block 13: consumption.

(3) A separate block is estimated for the City of Philadelphia, the region's nodal point (see block 10). Given the variables determined there and those for the region as a whole (blocks 1–9, 12, and 13), a residual block

---

[1] The region is defined as the Philadelphia Standard Metropolitan Statistical Area (SMSA) which consists of the City of Philadelphia and seven suburban counties (Bucks, Chester, Delaware, and Montgomery Counties in Pennsylvania; and Burlington, Camden, and Gloucester Counties in New Jersey).

for the 'suburban'[2] portion of the region is calculated in block 11. Thus the model contains variables for three separate areal units: the entire region, the City of Philadelphia, and the suburbs. Although the areal disaggregation is not of great magnitude, it goes beyond the 'region-as-a-point-in-space' approach of most econometricians.

(4) The blocks, as well as the equations within the blocks, are primarily simultaneous rather than recursive in their relationship. Most US regional econometric models have been highly recursive. [For a discussion of the structure of regional econometric models, see Glickman (1971b).]

(5) A priori information from the Philadelphia input–output table (see Isard et al., 1967) was employed, with import and export columns of the table determining the delineation of local- from export-oriented industries. In addition the transactions matrix was scrutinized to note important interindustry relations and such linkages were introduced within the structure of this time-series model. This allowed for a more accurate specification of many equations, especially those in the manufacturing output block.

(6) There is a rather large federal and local government sector (block 7). In addition to determining federal personal income tax accruals from the Philadelphia region, the model estimates tax and intergovernmental revenues for both municipalities and school districts; several expenditure variables are also forecasted. Furthermore a large number of policy instruments on the national level are contained in the model. These include intergovernmental revenues, the federal personal income tax rate and defense spending. When simulation experiments are undertaken, these policy variables (as well as local government instruments) will be altered to examine the impact of government policy changes on the region. Also, from the standpoint of local public policy, several important endogenous 'target' variables such as gross regional output, total employment, personal income, unemployment, population, and labor force are determined.

(7) In addition to time-series data, cross-section information is employed in the construction of the model. First, eleven components of household consumption expenditures are estimated from a 1960–1961 Bureau of Labor Statistics sample survey (see block 13). Second, an analysis of income distribution using six Internal Revenue Service tabulations has been undertaken. (This analysis is not presented here.) These data will be useful in making policy simulations involving changes in federal tax policy.

(8) The model is designed to be 'plugged in' to the Wharton Econometric Forecasting Associates' models[3] of the United States, taking as exogenous

[2] The suburban area contains two fairly large cities—Camden, New Jersey and Chester, Pennsylvania. Data limitations precluded separate consideration of these units.

[3] There are two Wharton models currently in operation: McCarthy (1972) presents a quarterly short-term model, while Preston's (1972) annual model is for long-term projections. An earlier version of the quarterly model is presented in Evans and Klein (1968).

many of the variables forecasted by the Wharton models. Thus national forecasts will be translated into forecasts for the region.

2 The structure of the model

The ordinary least squares (OLS) and two-stage least squares-6 principal components (TSLS-6PC) estimates of the regression coefficients for the 1947–1970 sample period are presented in table 1 (p.90). Also included in table 1 are the coefficient of multiple correlation ($\bar{R}^2$), the Durbin–Watson d statistic (DW), and the standard error of the estimate (SEE). The causal relationships among the blocks of the model[4] are shown in figures 1–7. The blocks will be discussed in sections 2.1 through 2.12. In each case, the important elements in the block will be outlined, including the structure of the block, crucial equations, and links to other blocks.

2.1 Block 1: manufacturing output [equations (1)-(13)]

Manufacturing output has been disaggregated into twelve leading manufacturing industries in an effort to explain the activity which was of greatest importance to the growth and development of the region in the postwar period. The following sectors were defined (SIC—Standard Industrial Classification):

Food and kindred products (SIC 20);
Textile mill products (SIC 22);
Apparel and related products (SIC 23);
Printing and publishing (SIC 27);
Chemicals and allied products (SIC 28);
Petroleum and coal products (SIC 29);
Primary metal industries (SIC 33);
Fabricated metal products (SIC 34);
Machinery, except electrical (SIC 35);
Electrical machinery (SIC 36);
Transportation equipment (SIC 37);
Other manufacturing (SIC 19, 21, 24, 25, 26, 30, 31, 32, 38, and 39).

An equation of the following general form was estimated for each variable:

$$QM_i = f(GNP^*, PY, QM_j, QM_i^*, QM_j^*) ,$$

[4] The well-known general form of the model is:

$$By_t + Cz_t = u_t ,$$

where

B is a nonsingular $G \times G$ matrix of coefficients of the endogenous variables;
y_t is a vector of G endogenous variables in period t;
C is a $G \times K$ matrix of coefficients of the exogenous variables;
z_t is a vector of K exogenous variables in period t;
u_t is a vector of G random errors in period t, assumed to have zero means and a constant covariance matrix Σ; also assumed to be nonautocorrelated.

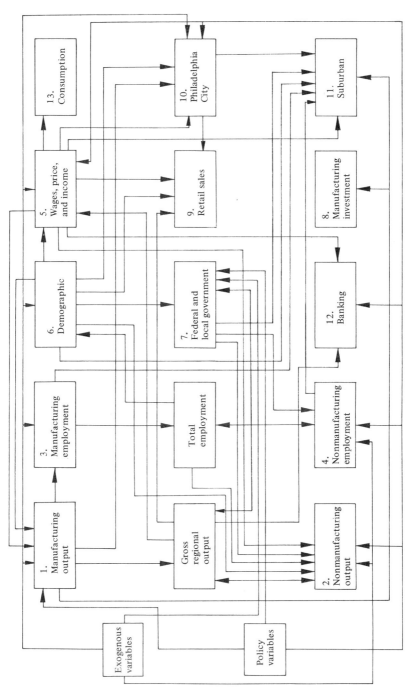

Figure 1. Causal relationships within the model.

where

QM$_i$ is the output of the ith manufacturing industry in the region;

GNP* is the US gross national product;

PY is the personal income in the region;

QM$_j$ is the output of the jth manufacturing industry in the region;

QM$_i^*$, QM$_j^*$ are the national outputs of the ith and jth industries respectively.

Total manufacturing output (QM) is the sum of its components [equation (13)].

Essentially, an economic-base philosophy is adopted: export-oriented industries (determined on *a priori* information from the input–output study) are related to national variables [see equations (2), (3), and (5)–(11)]. On the other hand, local-oriented output is linked to regional variables such as personal income and population [see equations (1)–(4)]. Other variables in this block are related to both local and national variables [see equations (2), (3), and (6)–(12)][5].

Of additional interest is the 'industrial complex' defined by equations (7)–(12). Here the trade relationships among the primary metals, fabricated metals, electrical machinery, nonelectrical machinery, and transportation equipment industries are made explicit.

The principal links between block 1 and other blocks are to the manufacturing employment and manufacturing investment sectors (see

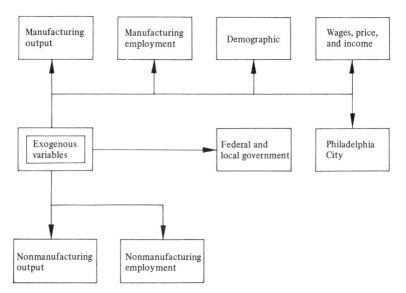

Figure 2. Relationship of exogenous variables to other blocks in the model.

[5] In equation (10), for example, output in electrical machinery (QELM) is a function of local output in nonelectrical machinery (QNEM), national output in electrical machinery (QELM*), and national defense spending (DEF*).

figure 3). It should be noted that there were problems in estimating some of the equations in this block such as those for output in the petroleum and chemical industries; the former is clearly the weakest equation in the block [6].

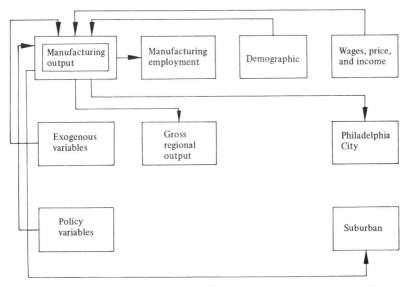

Figure 3. Relationship between the manufacturing output block and the other blocks in the model.

2.2 Block 2: nonmanufacturing output [equations (14)-(21)]

Nonmanufacturing output is divided into six categories:
Contract construction (SIC 15-17);
Transportation and public utilities (SIC 41-49);
Wholesale and retail trade (SIC 50, 52-59);
Finance, insurance, real estate (SIC 60-67);
Services (SIC 70-89);
Government (SIC 91-93).
The general form of the equations in this block is:

$$QNM_i = f(PY, GRO, POP, QNM_j) ,$$

where
QNM_i is the output of the ith nonmanufacturing industry in the region;
PY is the personal income in the region;
GRO is the gross regional output in the region;
POP is the population in the region;
QNM_j is the output of the jth nonmanufacturing industry in the region.

[6] The petroleum industry in Philadelphia consists mainly of refining facilities. The relevant market is much larger than the SMSA, but is clearly not national in character either. Therefore it was difficult to obtain a good fit here.

Thus the major thrust in this block is to link the components of non-manufacturing output with local variables such as personal income (PY), population (POP), and gross regional output (GRO). Government output is divided into two components, federal and local (determined in block 7), and summed in equation (19) to all government. Finally, total non-manufacturing output (QNM) is the sum of its components [equation (20)], and gross regional output is the totality of output in all nineteen sectors [equation (21)].

The principal links to other blocks in the model are with the demographic block (block 6), the wage, price, and income block (block 5), and to the federal and local government block (block 7). In addition, QNM helps determine GRO [through equation (21)] and, in part, is determined by GRO as in equation (15).

2.3 Block 3: manufacturing employment [equations (22)-(36)]
The manufacturing employment block is sectored in the same manner as the manufacturing output block. The generalized form of the manufacturing employment equation is a labor demand function:

$$EM_i = f(QM_i, EM_{i, -1})$$

where
  EM_i is the employment in the ith manufacturing industry;
  $EM_{i, -1}$ is the employment in the ith manufacturing industry in the
      previous year.
In some cases, as in equations (28), (29), and (30), equations reflecting interindustry relations are formulated. The weak equations in this block are those for food [equation (22)], fabricated metals [equation (29)], and transportation equipment [equation (32)]. In equation (22), for instance, the second argument (RFD_{-1}) is a productivity variable lagged one period, and, given its construction [see equation (36)], some upward bias is built into $\bar{R}^2$.

Manufacturing employment (EM), other manufacturing employment (EOM), and total employment (ET) are determined in equations (33) and (34) respectively; equations (34)-(36) are identities [7].

2.4 Block 4: nonmanufacturing employment [equations (37)-(43)]
This block is sectored parallel to block 2 (with the addition of local government employment), and consists of five stochastic equations [equations (37)-(41)] and an equation for total nonmanufacturing employment (ENM) which is the sum of its component parts (including government employment and other employment determined elsewhere in

[7] 'Other employment' [equation (35)] consists of workers in mining, proprietors, the self-employed, unpaid family workers, farm workers, and domestic workers in households. 'Other employment' is a rather small and stable portion of total employment and is determined exogenously.

the model).   In equation (43) there is a derived demand formulation relating gross regional output and government output with total employment.

The generalized form of the equations in block 4, as in block 3, is a labor demand function:

$$ENM_i = f(QNM_i, ENM_{i,-1})$$

where
  ENM_i is the employment in the ith nonmanufacturing industry in the region;
  $ENM_{i,-1}$ is the employment in the ith nonmanufacturing industry in the region in the previous year.

There is little interaction among the variables in this block, with most of the independent variables taken from other blocks (principally blocks 5 and 7).

2.5 Block 5: wages, price, and income [equations (44)-(57)]

There are eight stochastic equations and six identities in this block. Personal income consists of two types of earnings [8] (manufacturing and nonmanufacturing) plus other labor income, proprietors' income, property income, transfer payments, and personal contributions to social insurance.

Average money earnings in the region are related to those in the nation (since earnings in the region must be competitive with those elsewhere to hold the labor force), the number of unemployed in the region (a proxy for general labor market conditions—the higher the level of unemployment [9], the lower the increases in average earnings), and lagged earnings.   Other labor income (OLY) [10] is related to the average real wage and the level of employment in the region.   In equation (50) proprietors' income (PRY) is related to personal income (PY) and to the corporate bond rate (CBR*) which represents the return on capital. Property income (PTY) varies directly with the market value of property and GRO.   Transfer payments (TP), which includes both private and public transfers, is determined by a proxy for business transfer payments (the corporate bond rate) and by total US transfer payments representing public transfers.   Personal contributions for social insurance (PSI) is related to the number of unemployed, the level of personal income, and the labor force.   The consumer price index (P) is a markup over unit labor costs; the unemployment rate (UNR) is included since the rate of price increase will be less when the condition of the economy is weak, that is, when unemployment is high.

[8] Earnings, according to the US Commerce Department definition, include wages plus other labor income and proprietors' income.
[9] The unemployment variable was not statistically significant in the nonmanufacturing sector.
[10] OLY includes employer contributions under private pension plans, compensation for injuries, and other miscellaneous fringe benefits.

This block is pivotal in the model since variables in it, such as personal income, help determine variables in many other blocks. The flow of causality runs from block 5 to manufacturing and nonmanufacturing output, manufacturing employment, federal and local government, Philadelphia City, suburban, retail sales, consumption and banking (see figure 4).

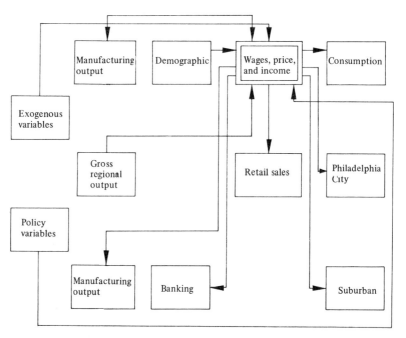

Figure 4. Relationship between the wages, price, and income block and the other blocks in the model.

2.6 Block 6: demographic [equations (58)-(61)]

Here, stochastic equations were estimated for population and the unemployment rate. Population [equation (58)] is related to gross regional output, average earnings, and the natural rate of growth (the number born minus the number who died in the region in a given year). It is hypothesized that higher levels of output and earnings (and thus, higher living standards) will draw more people into the region through migration. The unemployment rate is linked to its national counterpart (UNR*), the change in total employment, and lagged values of itself. Finally, the labor force and the number of unemployed (UNNO) are determined, in conjunction with total employment [equation (43)], in identity equations (60) and (61). Figure 5 indicates the place of the demographic block in the model.

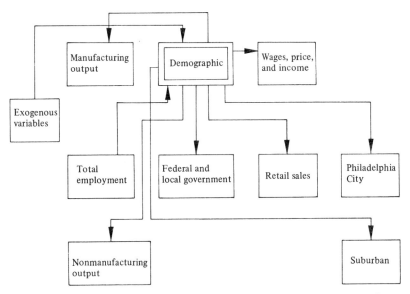

Figure 5. Relationship of demographic variables to other blocks in the model.

2.7 Block 7: federal and local government [equations (62)-(80)]

Another of the important blocks in the model is federal and local government. In addition to federal personal income taxes, and federal government output and employment, the model estimates equations for total expenditures, total revenues, tax and intergovernmental revenues, and tax rates for both local municipal and school districts. In addition, the level of school enrollment (SE) and the market value of property (MVP) are specified.

In equations (67) and (68), total municipal expenditures (MTE) and school expenditures (STE) are respectively determined. Both equations contain common elements: 'demand side' variables (population and school enrollment respectively), and variables which reflect revenue levels, and thus the ability to make expenditures. Intergovernmental revenues [equations (71) and (72)] are related to federal grants-in-aid to state and local governments. Tax revenues, in equations (73) and (74), are defined in an analogous manner, with total employment, gross regional output, and the market value of property appearing on the right hand side. Equations determining the level of school enrollment and the market value of property complete the stochastic portions of this block[11]. Figure 6

[11] Several policy simulations will be undertaken at a later stage which may prove interesting to local policy planners. For instance, the impact of a revenue-sharing scheme, such as the one proposed by the Nixon Administration, and other alternative proposals can be tested using this model. Particularly, the inclusion in equations (71) and (72) of intergovernmental revenues will allow such tests to be made. By calculating total expenditures and total revenues, it will be possible to forecast deficits or surpluses for local governments. Other government-related simulations will be undertaken.

shows the relationship between block 7 and the other portions of the model.

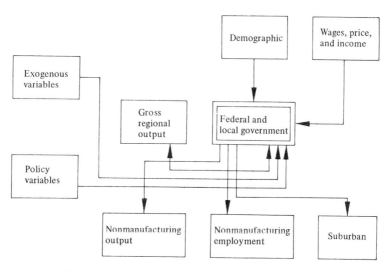

Figure 6. The relationship between the federal and local government block and the other blocks in the model.

2.8 Block 8: manufacturing investment [equations (81)-(83)]

In equation (81) total manufacturing investment (IM) is a function of manufacturing output (QM), lagged capital stock (KM_{-1}), and lagged investment (IM_{-1}), constituting a stock adjustment equation with a distributed lag adjustment process. Equations (82) and (83) are identities which define new levels of the capital stock and the amount of depreciation; the latter is calculated as a fixed proportion of capital stock, with the assumption that the useful life of capital is fifteen years.

2.9 Block 9: retail sales [equations (84)-(90)]

This is a simple block in which total retail sales and its components (automobile, food, drug, gasoline, general merchandise, and 'other' sales) are related to personal income, population, and gross regional output.

The general form of the equation is:

$$R_i = f(PY, PPY, GRO, POP) \, ,$$

where

R_i is component i of retail sales;
PY is the personal income in the region;
PPY is the personal income in the City of Philadelphia;
GRO is the gross regional output;
POP is the population.

2.10 Block 10: City of Philadelphia [equations (91)-(112)]

The model is stratified into two subregions: the City of Philadelphia and the suburbs. For the City of Philadelphia, equations were estimated for major private sector variables such as personal income, employment, and output for a 1951–1970 sample period. In some cases these variables are taken as functions of regional aggregates; see, for instance, equations (92) and (94). In addition there are fifteen equations for the municipal government and the school district. These follow the same general specification as their regional counterparts in block 7.

2.11 Block 11: suburban [equations (113)-(127)]

Given equations for certain variables for both the region and the City of Philadelphia, a block of equations for the subregion was calculated. Each equation is an identity:

suburban variable = regional variable − City of Philadelphia variable .

2.12 Block 12: banking [equations (128)-(131)]

The banking submodel consists of three stochastic and one identity equation[12]. In equations (128) and (129) demand deposits (DD) and time deposits (TD) are respectively determined. In both cases the corporate bond rate (CBR*), representing the price of loanable funds, in conjunction with variables showing the ability to generate such funds (PY, GRO) determine the dependent variables. Equation (130) is an identity which relates total deposits (TOTD) to its components, time deposits and demand deposits. Finally, total loans and investments in the reserve district (LIN) is taken as a function of total deposits.

2.13 Block 13: consumption [equations (132)-(142)]

No time series measuring household consumption expenditures are available for US regions. However, a US Department of Labor survey provides a cross-section view of this activity for 1960–1961 (see US Department of Labor, 1964). This allowed for simple Engel-type relationships to be estimated for total consumption and ten components. These equations will be used for forecasting purposes.

3 A test of the model

Given the structure of the model, as described in section 2, the next step in the research was to 'solve' the model for all of the endogenous variables in terms of all of the exogenous variables and to conduct a series of tests. The first set of simulations with the model was directed towards gauging its effectiveness in forecasting the turns in the business cycle during the sample period. Given (a) the regression coefficients, (b) the starting

---

[12] The equations in this block are for the entire Philadelphia Federal Reserve District, which includes part of southern New Jersey, eastern Pennsylvania, and all of Delaware, in addition to the Philadelphia SMSA. It was not possible to obtain banking data for the SMSA alone.

values for all of the endogenous variables, and (c) the values of all of the exogenous variables for each of the sample period years, the ability of the model to predict the values of the endogenous variables for each year in the sample was tested. That is, each of the endogenous variables in the model was allowed to interact with other endogenous variables and with the exogenous variables in the model (as they do in the real world), and differences between the predicted and actual values of the endogenous variables were calculated. To do so, a computer program (Norman, undated) which solves large-scale models using the Gauss–Seidel iterative technique was employed.

Table 2 presents the results of this simulation experiment. Shown are the mean absolute percent error (MAPE)[13] statistics for key endogenous variables in the model, calculated using the OLS and TSLS-6PC regression coefficients. The errors are reasonably small (averaging $1 \cdot 65\%$ per year for the OLS coefficients if one omits the unemployment variable) and the model accurately forecasts changes in the business cycle. (It is interesting to note that the OLS regressions yield results superior to TSLS-6PC in eleven of fourteen cases.)

Table 2. Difference between actual values and simulation calculations—the mean absolute percent error (1951–1970).

Variable	OLS (%)	TSLS-6PC (%)
QM	1·54	1·83
QNM	1·10	3·92
GRO	0·97	2·87
EM	2·54	2·77
ENM	1·83	1·57
ET	1·21	1·48
PY	1·50	2·79
P	1·38	2·02
LF	1·27	1·17
POP	1·49	2·05
UNR	14·85	14·78
MVP	1·97	2·52
PPY	2·73	3·26
PET	1·91	2·47

[13]
$$\text{MAPE} = \sum_{i=1}^{t} \left| \frac{y_{it} - \hat{y}_{it}}{y_{it}} \right| \times 100 \Bigg/ T \, ,$$

where
y_{it} is the observed value of the ith endogenous variable;
$\hat{y}_{it}$ is the calculated value of the ith endogenous period;
T is the number of observations.

4 Concluding remarks

The success of the *ex post* sample-period simulation experiment indicates that the model is capable of replicating economic development in the region [14]. Thus economic forecasts and policy simulations will be undertaken as further tests of the model's viability.

Several types of policy simulations are envisioned. First the model will be 'linked' to the Wharton forecasting models, employing the latter's forecasts for national economic variables (which are exogenous to this model), and calculating the resulting forecasts for the Philadelphia region. This has been done with the author's earlier model of the Philadelphia economy (Glickman, 1971a). Short-term, medium-term, and long-term forecasts will be made assuming different types of national economic development and public policy. For instance, different assumptions about the nature of national monetary and fiscal policy can be made and applied to the Wharton model; the solutions of the Wharton model for these different assumptions will then be translated into regional forecasts.

Other policy simulations will deal with local government in the region. First, the impact of intergovernmental revenues can be estimated through the government block and the effects of different levels of intergovernmental revenues on the economy can be determined. Thus the

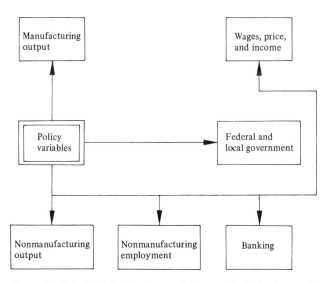

Figure 7. Relationship of policy variables to blocks in the model.

[14] A second type of sample period simulation was carried out by reestimating the model for the period 1947-1968. This resulted in a new set of coefficients, and, given the real values of the exogenous variables for 1969-1970, it was possible to use this second model to predict the values of the endogenous variables for 1970. This second test was also successful in terms of low values of MAPE.

impact of the US Administration's revenue-sharing plan and alternative proposals can be tested. Other kinds of government-oriented simulations are possible. Among these are forecasts of revenue and expenditure patterns as well as the impact of differing tax rates on the local economy.

Finally, simulations involving forecasts of pollution levels in the region will be carried out. Engineering data have been collected on emissions according to type of pollutant (SO_2, NO_2, etc.) and to industrial class under different emission control schema. Thus we have P_{im}, the amount of pollution in the ith industry from the mth pollutant. Given our data for output in industry i (Q_i), a pollution coefficient $G_{im} = P_{im}/Q_i$ can be calculated for each industry in the model. We can then make forecasts of pollution levels under different assumptions of development policy (for example, is industry i to be favored over industry j on the basis of environmental impact?) as well as assumptions concerning pollution control laws.

The process of regional model building has been hampered by poor data and imperfect theory. Research workers in this field are in much the same position as pioneers in national econometric modelling were thirty years ago. These 'facts of life' result in models which often lack perfect theoretical and statistical bases. This model is certainly no exception. The Philadelphia model must undergo further tests and the reestimation of many equations; in that sense it is not 'finished'. As new data sources are developed and additional observations added, the model will continue to evolve as it has over the past few years. It is still an imperfect tool which will be improved as the data and theory related to it are further developed. Hopefully it is a modest advance in a relatively neglected area of econometrics.

Acknowledgements. The author extends thanks for comments on earlier drafts to Professors F. G. Adams, G. R. Green, B. Harris, L. R. Klein, and B. H. Stevens. K. Ballard provided computational aid. Financial assistance from Wharton-EFA Inc. is gratefully acknowledged. All errors are the responsibility of the author.

References
Bell, F. W., 1967, "An econometric model for a region", *Journal of Regional Science,* 7, 109-127.
Crow, R. T., 1969, *An Econometric Model of the Northeast Corridor,* Ph. D. Thesis, University of Pennsylvania, Philadelphia.
Evans, M. K., Klein, L. R., 1968, *The Wharton Economic Forecasting Model* (Economic Research Unit, Department of Economics, University of Pennsylvania, Philadelphia).
Glickman, N. J., 1971a, "An econometric model of the Philadelphia region", *Journal of Regional Science,* 11, 15-32.
Glickman, N. J., 1971b, "Regional econometric models: the American and Japanese experience", *Papers and Proceedings of the Second Pacific Conference of the Regional Science Association* (Japan Section of the Regional Science Association, University of Tokyo).

Glickman, N. J., 1972, "The structure of a large-scale regional econometric model: towards the simulation of regional development", in *Papers and Proceedings of the 1972 Summer Simulation Conference* (Santa Monica, California); also Department of Economics, University of Pennsylvania, Discussion Paper Number 235.

Isard, W., Langford, T. W., Jr., Romanoff, E., 1967, *The Philadelphia Region Input-Output Study* (Regional Science Research Institute, Philadelphia).

L'Esperence, W. L., Nestel, G., Fromm, D., 1969, "Gross state product and an econometric model of a state", *American Statistical Association Journal,* **64,** 787-807.

McCarthy, M. D., 1972, *The Wharton Quarterly Econometric Forecasting Model Mark III, Studies in Quantitative Economics Number 6* (Economic Research Unit, Department of Economics, University of Pennsylvania, Philadelphia).

Norman, M. R., 1967, "The SIM model solution program", Economics Research Unit, Department of Economics, University of Pennsylvania, mimeo.

Preston, R. S., 1972, *The Wharton Annual and Industry Forecasting Model, Studies in Quantitative Economics Number 7* (Economic Research Unit, Department of Economics, University of Pennsylvania, Philadelphia).

Stevens, B. H., Brackett, C. A., Coughlin, R. E., 1967, *An Investigation of Location Factors Influencing the Economy of the Philadelphia Region* (Regional Science Research Institute Discussion Paper Series, Number 12, Philadelphia).

US Department of Labor, 1964, Bureau of Labor Statistics, "Consumer expenditure and income, Philadelphia, Pennsylvania, 1960-1961", in *Survey of Consumer Expenditures 1960-1961* (US Government Printing Office, Washington).

Table 1. Ordinary least squares (OLS) and two-stage least squares-6 principle components (TSLS-6PC) estimates of the Philadelphia model. $\overline{R}^2$ is the coefficient of multiple correlation; DW is the Durban–Watson $\underline{d}$ statistic; SEE is the standard error of the estimate. A variable with a subscript −1 denotes the value of the variable in the previous year. The numbers in parentheses are t-statistics.

Definitions of variables in table 1

Endogenous variables

Block 1: Manufacturing output ($ millions, 1958)
QFD Food and kindred products
QTEX Textile mill products
QAPP Apparel and related products
QPRP Printing and publishing
QCHM Chemicals and allied products
QPET Petroleum and coal products
QPRM Primary metal industries
QFBM Fabricated metal products
QNEM Machinery (except electrical)
QELM Electrical machinery
QTRN Transportation equipment
QOM Other manufacturing
QM Total manufacturing

Block 2: Nonmanufacturing output ($ millions, 1958)
QCC Contract construction
QTPU Transportation and public utilities
QTRD Wholesale and retail trade
QFIR Finance, insurance, real estate
QSRV Services
QGOV All government
QNM Total nonmanufacturing
GRO Gross regional output

Block 3: Manufacturing employment (thousands)
EFD Food and kindred products
ETEX Textile mill products
EAPP Apparel and related products
EPRP Printing and publishing

Block 3 (continued)
ECHM Chemicals and allied products
EPET Petroleum and coal products
EPRM Primary metal industries
EFBM Fabricated metal products
ENEM Machinery (except electrical)
EELM Electrical machinery
ETRN Transportation equipment
EOM Other manufacturing
EM Total manufacturing

Block 4: Nonmanufacturing employment (thousands)
ECC Contract construction
ETPU Transportation and public utilities
ETRD Wholesale and retail trade
EFIR Finance, insurance, real estate
ESRV Services
ENM Total nonmanufacturing
OE Other nonmanufacturing
ET Total employment

Block 5: Wages, price, and income ($ millions, 1958)
AEM Average earnings in manufacturing ($, 1972)
AENM Average earnings in nonmanufacturing ($, 1972)
AVERN Average real earnings ($, 1972)
MTERN Money total earnings ($ millions, 1972)
MTWB Money total wage bill ($ millions, 1972)
RTWB Real total wage bill
OLY Other labor income
PRY Proprietors' income
PTY Property income
TP Transfer payments
PSI Personal contributions to social insurance

Table 1 (continued).

Block 5: (continued)
PY   Total personal income
PRFT   Regional business profits
P   Consumer price index (100 in 1958)

Block 6: Demographic (thousands)
LF   Labor force
POP   Population
UNNO   Number of unemployed
UNR   Unemployment rate (%)

Block 7: Federal and local government ($ millions, 1958)
FIT   Federal income tax paid by residents of region
QFED   Federal government output
EGOV   All government employment (thousands)
ELGOV   Local government employment (thousands)
EFED   Federal government employment (thousands)
MTE   Municipal governments—total expenditure
STE   School districts—total expenditure
MTR   Municipal governments—total revenue
STR   School districts—total revenue
MIR   Municipal governments—intergovernmental revenue
SIR   School districts—intergovernmental revenue
MTXR   Municipal governments—tax revenue
STXR   School districts—tax revenue
METR   Municipal governments—effective tax rate (%)
SETR   School districts—effective tax rate (%)
SE   School enrollment (thousands)
MVP   Market value of property
GTE   Total local government expenditure
GTXR   Total tax revenue

Block 8: Manufacturing investment ($ millions, 1958)
IM   Investment in manufacturing
KM   Capital stock in manufacturing
D   Depreciation

Block 9: Retail trade ($ millions, 1958)
RETS   Retail sales
AUTS   Automobile sales
FOOD   Food store and restaurant sales
DRUG   Drug store sales
GAS   Gasoline sales
GMRCH   General merchandise store sales
ORETS   Other retail sales

Block 10: City of Philadelphia ($ millions, 1958)
PQM   Manufacturing output, City of Philadelphia
PPY   Personal income, City of Philadelphia
PEM   Manufacturing employment, City of Philadelphia (thousands)
PENM   Nonmanufacturing employment, City of Philadelphia (thousands)
PET   Total employment, City of Philadelphia (thousands)
PMWB   Manufacturing wage bill, City of Philadelphia
PMTE   Municipal government—total expenditure, City of Philadelphia
PSTE   School district—total expenditure, City of Philadelphia
PMTR   Municipal government—total revenue, City of Philadelphia
PSTR   School district—total revenue, City of Philadelphia
PMTXR   Municipal government—tax revenue, City of Philadelphia
PSTXR   School district—tax revenue, City of Philadelphia
PMIR   Municipal government—intergovernmental revenue, City of Philadelphia
PSIR   School district—intergovernmental revenue, City of Philadelphia
PMDOE   Municipal government—operating expenditure, City of Philadelphia
PMEGV   Municipal government—employment, City of Philadelphia
PSE   School enrollment, City of Philadelphia (thousands)
PWEN   Welfare enrollment, City of Philadelphia (thousands)
PWE   Welfare expenditure, City of Philadelphia
PUR   Public utilities—revenue, City of Philadelphia
PUE   Public utilities—expenditure, City of Philadelphia
PROD   Productivity variable for manufacturing in region

Table 1 (continued).

Block 11: Suburban ($ millions, 1958)

SQM	Manufacturing output, suburban subregion
SPY	Personal income, suburban subregion
SEM	Manufacturing employment, suburban subregion (thousands)
SENM	Nonmanufacturing employment, suburban subregion (thousands)
SET	Total employment, suburban subregion (thousands)
SMWB	Manufacturing wage bill, suburban subregion
SMTE	Municipal governments—total expenditure, suburban subregion
SSTE	School districts—total expenditure, suburban subregion
SMTR	Municipal governments—total revenue, suburban subregion
SSTR	School districts—total revenue, suburban subregion
SMTXR	Municipal governments—tax revenue, suburban subregion
SSTXR	School districts—tax revenue, suburban subregion
SMIR	Municipal governments—intergovernmental revenue, suburban subregion
SSIR	School districts—intergovernmental revenue, suburban subregion
SSE	School enrollment, suburban subregion (thousands)

Block 12: Banking ($ millions, 1972)

DD	Demand deposits
TD	Time deposits
TOTD	Total deposits
LIN	Loans and investments

Block 13: Consumption ($ millions, 1958)

CTOT	Consumption, total
CFOOD	Consumption, food
CHSE	Consumption, housing
CCLTH	Consumption, clothing
CPC	Consumption, personal care
CMC	Consumption, medical care
CREC	Consumption, recreation
CED	Consumption, education
CTA	Consumption, auto transportation
CTO	Consumption, other transportation
CREAD	Consumption, reading

Exogenous variables ($ billions, 1958)

GNP*	Gross national product
DEF*	US Department of Defense expenditures
UNR*	US rate of unemployment (%)
QTEX*	US output in textiles
QAPP*	US output in apparel
QPRP*	US output in printing and publishing
QCHM*	US output in chemicals
QPET*	US output in petroleum
QPRM*	US output in primary metals
QNEM*	US output in nonelectrical machinery
QELM*	US output in electrical machinery
QFED*	US output in federal government
GIR*	Total intergovernmental revenue originating with the federal government
AEM*	US average earnings in manufacturing ($, 1972)
AENM*	US average earnings in nonmanufacturing ($, 1972)
TP*	US transfer payments
FETR*	Effective tax rate on federal personal income tax (%)
NATG	Natural growth of population in the region (thousands)
TIME	Time (1948 ≡ 1, 1949 ≡ 2, etc.)
LOG TIME	The natural logarithm of TIME
PRMTR	Real property tax rate, City of Philadelphia (%)
CBR*	Corporate bond rate (%)

Table 1 (continued).

Equation	Dependent variable	Regression estimates and identities	$\bar{R}^2$	DW	SEE	Estimation method
Block 1: Manufacturing output						
(1)	QFD	$= 45 \cdot 9693 + 0 \cdot 6107 \text{ QFD}_{-1} + 0 \cdot 0154 \text{ PY}$ $(3 \cdot 4336) \quad (1 \cdot 9692)$	$0 \cdot 9287$	$2 \cdot 2900$	$30 \cdot 4130$	TSLS-6PC
		$= 45 \cdot 7180 + 0 \cdot 6392 \text{ QFD}_{-1} + 0 \cdot 0141 \text{ PY}$ $(3 \cdot 6735) \quad (1 \cdot 8448)$	$0 \cdot 9288$	$2 \cdot 2586$	$30 \cdot 3892$	OLS
(2)	QTEX	$= 35 \cdot 8144 + 0 \cdot 0330 \text{ PY} + 25 \cdot 4676 \text{ QTEX}^* - 19 \cdot 7938 \text{ TIME}$ $(1 \cdot 4336) \quad (3 \cdot 0294) \quad (-2 \cdot 2470)$	$0 \cdot 8656$	$2 \cdot 1469$	$19 \cdot 7042$	TSLS-6PC
		$= -13 \cdot 1199 + 0 \cdot 0438 \text{ PY} + 22 \cdot 9173 \text{ QTEX}^* - 23 \cdot 9269 \text{ TIME}$ $(2 \cdot 6828) \quad (3 \cdot 0862) \quad (-3 \cdot 8181)$	$0 \cdot 8687$	$2 \cdot 0577$	$19 \cdot 4772$	OLS
(3)	QAPP	$= -142 \cdot 9882 + 0 \cdot 0909 \text{ POP} + 14 \cdot 8138 \text{ QAPP}^*$ $(4 \cdot 6977) \quad (1 \cdot 6915)$	$0 \cdot 8808$	$1 \cdot 0502$	$18 \cdot 0524$	TSLS-6PC
		$= -135 \cdot 5528 + 0 \cdot 0889 \text{ POP} + 15 \cdot 5951 \text{ QAPP}^*$ $(4 \cdot 6745) \quad (1 \cdot 8042)$	$0 \cdot 8809$	$1 \cdot 0446$	$18 \cdot 0427$	OLS
(4)	QPRP	$= -99 \cdot 8974 + 0 \cdot 4241 \text{ QPRP}_{-1} + 0 \cdot 0723 \text{ POP}$ $(1 \cdot 7403) \quad (1 \cdot 8454)$	$0 \cdot 7938$	$1 \cdot 6061$	$28 \cdot 5069$	TSLS-6PC
		$= -100 \cdot 9384 + 0 \cdot 4214 \text{ QPRP}_{-1} + 0 \cdot 0728 \text{ POP}$ $(1 \cdot 7703) \quad (1 \cdot 9091)$	$0 \cdot 7939$	$1 \cdot 6029$	$28 \cdot 5043$	OLS
(5)	QCHM	$= -199 \cdot 7284 + 89 \cdot 7330 \text{ QCHM}^*$ $(33 \cdot 7475)$	$0 \cdot 9810$	$1 \cdot 4036$	$30 \cdot 3910$	OLS
(6)	QPET	$= -78 \cdot 4883 + 46 \cdot 8389 \text{ QPET}^* + 0 \cdot 3667 \text{ QPET}_{-1}$ $(3 \cdot 5472) \quad (2 \cdot 3309)$	$0 \cdot 5810$	$1 \cdot 7626$	$24 \cdot 9586$	OLS
(7)	QPRM	$= -34 \cdot 3560 + 0 \cdot 5549 \text{ GNP}^* + 0 \cdot 3752 \text{ QFBM}$ $(4 \cdot 2482) \quad (1 \cdot 4556)$	$0 \cdot 9023$	$1 \cdot 6512$	$30 \cdot 6972$	TSLS-6PC
		$= -38 \cdot 4946 + 0 \cdot 5438 \text{ GNP}^* + 0 \cdot 3990 \text{ QFBM}$ $(4 \cdot 9644) \quad (1 \cdot 9211)$	$0 \cdot 9024$	$1 \cdot 6563$	$30 \cdot 6842$	OLS
(8)	QFBM	$= 114 \cdot 0895 + 15 \cdot 4729 \text{ QPRM}^* + 0 \cdot 2524 \text{ QELM}$ $(3 \cdot 5543) \quad (4 \cdot 3733)$	$0 \cdot 8917$	$2 \cdot 0018$	$22 \cdot 0975$	TSLS-6PC
		$= 109 \cdot 3448 + 17 \cdot 3351 \text{ QPRM}^* + 0 \cdot 2227 \text{ QELM}$ $(4 \cdot 1734) \quad (4 \cdot 1203)$	$0 \cdot 8934$	$2 \cdot 0368$	$21 \cdot 9306$	OLS

Table 1 (continued).

Equation	Dependent variable	Regression estimates and identities	$\bar{R}^2$	DW	SEE	Estimation method
Block 1 (continued)						
(9)	QNEM	$= 18\cdot3336 + 16\cdot0908\ \text{QNEM}^* + 0\cdot2312\ \text{QNEM}_{-1} + 0\cdot2578\ \text{QELM}$ (3·1245)　　　　　(2·1186)　　　　　(1·8000)	0·9646	1·8209	24·0123	TSLS-6PC
		$= 18\cdot8416 + 16\cdot8296\ \text{QNEM}^* + 0\cdot2398\ \text{QNEM}_{-1} + 0\cdot2310\ \text{QELM}$ (3·7016)　　　　　(2·2776)　　　　　(2·0391)	0·9647	1·8437	23·9783	OLS
(10)	QELM	$= 23\cdot1359 + 0\cdot0190\ \text{DEF}^* + 16\cdot9866\ \text{QELM}^* + 0\cdot4873\ \text{QNEM}$ (2·3161)　　　　　(2·3883)　　　　　(2·4228)	0·9542	1·4935	31·9749	TSLS-6PC
		$= 23\cdot8691 + 0\cdot0190\ \text{DEF}^* + 17\cdot2126\ \text{QELM}^* + 0\cdot4802\ \text{QNEM}$ (2·3222)　　　　　(2·6848)　　　　　(2·7274)	0·9542	1·4945	31·9733	OLS
(11)	QTRN	$= -175\cdot9138 + 0\cdot0219\ \text{DEF}^* + 1\cdot1418\ \text{QNEM} - 8\cdot4571\ \text{TIME}$ (1·8124)　　　　(4·9994)　　　　(−1·9731)	0·8544	1·7842	47·1936	TSLS-6PC
		$= -134\cdot7432 + 0\cdot0244\ \text{DEF}^* + 0\cdot9403\ \text{QNEM} - 5\cdot3741\ \text{TIME}$ (2·0770)　　　　(4·5895)　　　　(−1·3568)	0·8614	1·6242	46·0329	OLS
(12)	QOM	$= 1\cdot0233 + 0\cdot0380\ \text{GRO} + 0\cdot3995\ \text{QOM}_{-1}$ (2·7758)　　　　(1·7475)	0·6767	1·5226	105·9781	TSLS-6PC
		$= 4\cdot5971 + 0\cdot0368\ \text{GRO} + 0\cdot4153\ \text{QOM}_{-1}$ (2·7014)　　　　(1·8218)	0·6768	1·5397	105·9555	OLS
(13)	QM	$= \text{QFD} + \text{QTEX} + \text{QAPP} + \text{QPRP} + \text{QCHM} + \text{QPET} + \text{QPRM} + \text{QFBM} + \text{QNEM} + \text{QELM} + \text{QTRN} + \text{QOM}$	....	....	....	....
Block 2: Nonmanufacturing output						
(14)	QCC	$= -491\cdot7632 - 43\cdot3119\ \text{CBR}^*_{-1} + 0\cdot5933\ \text{QCC}_{-1} + 0\cdot5608\ \text{ET}$ (−4·1420)　　　　　(5·8045)　　　　　(5·1113)	0·9166	1·5194	24·0387	TSLS-6PC
		$= -496\cdot2558 - 43\cdot6929\ \text{CBR}^*_{-1} + 0\cdot5906\ \text{QCC}_{-1} + 0\cdot5654\ \text{ET}$ (−4·2865)　　　　　(5·8586)　　　　　(5·3307)	0·9168	1·5172	24·0157	OLS
(15)	QTPU	$= -132\cdot3154 + 0\cdot0676\ \text{GRO} + 0\cdot0792\ \text{POP} - 54\cdot9016\ \text{CBR}^*$ (7·1588)　　　　(1·7222)　　　　(−5·2553)	0·9624	1·4089	28·2226	TSLS-6PC
		$= -138\cdot1608 + 0\cdot0679\ \text{GRO} + 0\cdot0805\ \text{POP} - 55\cdot6812\ \text{CBR}^*$ (7·4774)　　　　(1·8205)　　　　(−5·4003)	0·9624	1·4164	28·2077	OLS

Table 1 (continued)

Block 2 (continued)

No.	Equation				Method
(16) QTRD	$= -80 \cdot 2984 + 0 \cdot 2537\ PY + 0 \cdot 2653\ QTRD_{-1} - 77 \cdot 6016\ TIME$ $\quad\quad\quad\ (2 \cdot 4123)\quad (0 \cdot 9523)\quad\quad\quad (-2 \cdot 2135)$	0·9096	1·7689	61·4239	TSLS-6PC
	$= -150 \cdot 3916 + 0 \cdot 1058\ PY + 0 \cdot 5934\ QTRD_{-1} - 28 \cdot 6684\ TIME$ $\quad\quad\quad\ (2 \cdot 2828)\quad (3 \cdot 7040)\quad\quad\quad (-1 \cdot 8238)$	0·9411	1·6877	49·5819	OLS
(17) QFIR	$= -8 \cdot 5507 + 0 \cdot 1596\ PY + 0 \cdot 6747\ QTPU - 44 \cdot 8714\ TIME$ $\quad\quad\quad\ (4 \cdot 1551)\quad (3 \cdot 8605)\quad\quad\quad (-2 \cdot 9876)$	0·9652	1·8942	40·9004	TSLS-6PC
	$= -35 \cdot 2481 + 0 \cdot 1630\ PY + 0 \cdot 6871\ QTPU - 46 \cdot 4188\ TIME$ $\quad\quad\quad\ (5 \cdot 5124)\quad (4 \cdot 0107)\quad\quad\quad (-4 \cdot 0130)$	0·9652	1·9379	40·8901	OLS
(18) QSRV	$= -609 \cdot 4242 + 0 \cdot 2175\ PY$ $\quad\quad\quad\quad (55 \cdot 6514)$	0·9929	0·9662	48·2492	TSLS-6PC
	$= -601 \cdot 0955 + 0 \cdot 2167\ PY$ $\quad\quad\quad\quad (55 \cdot 6568)$	0·9929	0·9604	48·2018	OLS
(19) QGOV	$= QFED + GTE$	····	····	····	····
(20) QNM	$= QCC + QTPU + QTRD + QFIR + QSRV + QFED + GTE$	····	····	····	····
(21) GRO	$= QM + QNM$	····	····	····	····
Block 3: Manufacturing employment					
(22) EFD	$= 17 \cdot 6380 + 0 \cdot 7008\ EFD_{-1} - 0 \cdot 2423\ RFD_{-1}$ $\quad\quad\quad\ (7 \cdot 1633)\quad\quad\quad (-3 \cdot 3868)$	0·8979	1·5262	0·5993	OLS
(23) ETEX	$= -7 \cdot 2991 + 0 \cdot 0663\ QTEX + 0 \cdot 7227\ ETEX_{-1}$ $\quad\quad\quad\ (3 \cdot 9685)\quad\quad (11 \cdot 7047)$	0·9850	1·2974	1·6154	TSLS-6PC
	$= -7 \cdot 2467 + 0 \cdot 0658\ QTEX + 0 \cdot 7293\ ETEX_{-1}$ $\quad\quad\quad\ (5 \cdot 2216)\quad\quad (14 \cdot 6538)$	0·9850	1·3015	1·6145	OLS
(24) EAPP	$= 0 \cdot 1280 + 0 \cdot 0468\ QAPP + 0 \cdot 2968\ ETEX + 0 \cdot 5411\ EAPP_{-1}$ $\quad\quad\quad (3 \cdot 2069)\quad\quad (5 \cdot 2032)\quad\quad (2 \cdot 9188)$	0·8346	1·3280	1·4763	TSLS-6PC
	$= 1 \cdot 5522 + 0 \cdot 0458\ QAPP + 0 \cdot 2989\ ETEX + 0 \cdot 5206\ EAPP_{-1}$ $\quad\quad\quad (3 \cdot 3561)\quad\quad (5 \cdot 5296)\quad\quad (2 \cdot 8442)$	0·8353	1·3130	1·4730	OLS

Table 1 (continued).

Equation	Dependent variable	Regression estimates and identities	$\overline{R}^2$	DW	SEE	Estimation method
Block 3 (continued)						
(25)	EPRP	$= 9{\cdot}8790 + 0{\cdot}0116\ \text{QPRP} + 0{\cdot}6179\ \text{EPRP}_{-1}$ $\qquad\qquad (2{\cdot}3882) \qquad\qquad (4{\cdot}7480)$	0·8389	1·3563	0·8488	TSLS-6PC
		$= 8{\cdot}8919 + 0{\cdot}0091\ \text{QPRP} + 0{\cdot}6694\ \text{EPRP}_{-1}$ $\qquad\qquad (2{\cdot}1404) \qquad\qquad (5{\cdot}5643)$	0·8417	1·3386	0·8415	OLS
(26)	ECHM	$= 15{\cdot}1701 + 0{\cdot}0070\ \text{QCHM} + 0{\cdot}4959\ \text{ECHM}_{-1}$ $\qquad\qquad\ \ (3{\cdot}7310) \qquad\qquad (3{\cdot}5625)$	0·9267	1·9649	0·8228	TSLS-6PC
		$= 14{\cdot}9888 + 0{\cdot}0069\ \text{QCHM} + 0{\cdot}5023\ \text{ECHM}_{-1}$ $\qquad\qquad\ \ (3{\cdot}7681) \qquad\qquad (3{\cdot}6795)$	0·9271	1·9950	0·8208	OLS
(27)	EPET	$= 1{\cdot}1373 + 0{\cdot}0138\ \text{QPET} + 0{\cdot}8541\ \text{EPET}_{-1} - 0{\cdot}1030\ \text{TIME}$ $\qquad\qquad (3{\cdot}8576) \qquad\quad (10{\cdot}2456) \qquad\quad (-3{\cdot}5389)$	0·9627	2·2407	0·4659	TSLS-6PC
		$= 2{\cdot}4646 + 0{\cdot}0082\ \text{QPET} + 0{\cdot}8406\ \text{EPET}_{-1} - 0{\cdot}0926\ \text{TIME}$ $\qquad\qquad (3{\cdot}1487) \qquad\quad (11{\cdot}2606) \qquad\quad (-3{\cdot}5777)$	0·9700	2·0595	0·4180	OLS
(28)	EPRM	$= -20{\cdot}1514 + 0{\cdot}0138\ \text{QPRM} + 0{\cdot}7387\ \text{EFBM} + 0{\cdot}4839\ \text{EPRM}_{-1}$ $\qquad\qquad\ \ (4{\cdot}5195) \qquad\qquad (6{\cdot}8506) \qquad\qquad (6{\cdot}3955)$	0·8970	1·2136	1·1179	TSLS-6PC
		$= -18{\cdot}6057 + 0{\cdot}0127\ \text{QPRM} + 0{\cdot}7003\ \text{EFBM} + 0{\cdot}5011\ \text{EPRM}_{-1}$ $\qquad\qquad\ \ (4{\cdot}4538) \qquad\qquad (7{\cdot}2999) \qquad\qquad (6{\cdot}8352)$	0·8983	1·3258	1·1106	OLS
(29)	EFBM	$= 23{\cdot}5582 + 0{\cdot}3279\ \text{ETRN} + 0{\cdot}3091\ \text{EPRM}$ $\qquad\qquad\ \ (6{\cdot}1893) \qquad\qquad (3{\cdot}1823)$	0·6757	1·5611	1·4894	TSLS-6PC
		$= 25{\cdot}3221 + 0{\cdot}2520\ \text{ETRN} + 0{\cdot}3258\ \text{EPRM}$ $\qquad\qquad\ \ (5{\cdot}9430) \qquad\qquad (3{\cdot}8003)$	0·7209	1·6242	1·3816	OLS
(30)	ENEM	$= 8{\cdot}6045 + 0{\cdot}0423\ \text{QNEM} + 0{\cdot}2682\ \text{EFBM} + 0{\cdot}1723\ \text{ENEM}_{-1}$ $\qquad\qquad (6{\cdot}7951) \qquad\qquad (1{\cdot}9282) \qquad\qquad (1{\cdot}3917)$	0·9440	1·6605	1·5316	TSLS-6PC
		$= 6{\cdot}1393 + 0{\cdot}0389\ \text{QNEM} + 0{\cdot}2916\ \text{EFBM} + 0{\cdot}2359\ \text{ENEM}_{-1}$ $\qquad\qquad (6{\cdot}6927) \qquad\qquad (2{\cdot}3127) \qquad\qquad (2{\cdot}0253)$	0·9452	1·7016	1·5147	OLS

Table 1 (continued).

Block 3 (continued)

(31)	EELM	$= 32 \cdot 1578 + 0 \cdot 0292 \text{ QELM} + 6 \cdot 5590 \text{ LOG TIME}$ $(2 \cdot 2527)$	$0 \cdot 8214$	$0 \cdot 9519$	$4 \cdot 0109$	TSLS-6PC
		$= 31 \cdot 9711 + 0 \cdot 0327 \text{ QELM} + 5 \cdot 8951 \text{ LOG TIME}$ $(2 \cdot 6265) \qquad (2 \cdot 1863)$	$0 \cdot 8221$	$0 \cdot 9190$	$4 \cdot 0031$	OLS
(32)	ETRN	$= -81 \cdot 1342 + 0 \cdot 1752 \text{ EM} + 0 \cdot 4475 \text{ ETRN}_{-1}$ $(3 \cdot 9607) \qquad (3 \cdot 2064)$	$0 \cdot 7426$	$0 \cdot 7822$	$3 \cdot 5727$	TSLS-6PC
		$= -73 \cdot 8404 + 0 \cdot 1606 \text{ EM} + 0 \cdot 4757 \text{ ETRN}_{-1}$ $(3 \cdot 8857) \qquad (3 \cdot 4979)$	$0 \cdot 7439$	$0 \cdot 7886$	$3 \cdot 5635$	OLS
(33)	EM	$= \text{ET} - \text{ENM}$	$\ldots$	$\ldots$	$\ldots$	$\ldots$
(34)	EOM	$= \text{ET} - \text{ENM} + (\text{EFD} + \text{ETEX} + \text{EAPP} + \text{EPRP} + \text{ECHM} + \text{EPET}$ $+ \text{EPRM} + \text{EFBM} + \text{ENEM} + \text{EELM} + \text{ETRN})$	$\ldots$	$\ldots$	$\ldots$	$\ldots$
(35)	OE	$= \text{exogenously determined}$	$\ldots$	$\ldots$	$\ldots$	$\ldots$
(36)	RFD	$= \text{QFD/EFD}$	$\ldots$	$\ldots$	$\ldots$	$\ldots$

Block 4: Nonmanufacturing employment

(37)	ECC	$= 4 \cdot 0030 + 0 \cdot 0749 \text{ QCC} - 0 \cdot 8755 \text{ CBR*} + 0 \cdot 2473 \text{ ECC}_{-1}$ $(10 \cdot 5160) \quad (-3 \cdot 4316) \quad (3 \cdot 5589)$	$0 \cdot 9659$	$1 \cdot 6552$	$1 \cdot 3202$	TSLS-6PC
		$= 4 \cdot 1648 + 0 \cdot 0736 \text{ QCC} - 0 \cdot 8523 \text{ CBR*} + 0 \cdot 2573 \text{ ECC}_{-1}$ $(10 \cdot 9070) \quad (-3 \cdot 3947) \quad (3 \cdot 8306)$	$0 \cdot 9662$	$1 \cdot 7071$	$1 \cdot 3139$	OLS
(38)	ETPU	$= 5 \cdot 5896 + 0 \cdot 0287 \text{ (QTPU} - \text{QTPU}_{-1}) + 0 \cdot 7536 \text{ ETPU}_{-1}$ $(1 \cdot 9708) \qquad (5 \cdot 9200)$	$0 \cdot 8320$	$1 \cdot 6452$	$2 \cdot 7228$	OLS
(39)	ETRD	$= -21 \cdot 4949 + 0 \cdot 0542 \text{ QTRD} + 0 \cdot 6938 \text{ ETRD}_{-1}$ $(4 \cdot 1625) \qquad (9 \cdot 4963)$	$0 \cdot 9865$	$1 \cdot 2788$	$4 \cdot 1388$	TSLS-6PC
		$= -18 \cdot 4740 + 0 \cdot 0493 \text{ QTRD} + 0 \cdot 7196 \text{ ETRD}_{-1}$ $(4 \cdot 2580) \qquad (10 \cdot 9208)$	$0 \cdot 9867$	$1 \cdot 2696$	$4 \cdot 1085$	OLS
(40)	EFIR	$= -0 \cdot 9595 + 0 \cdot 0103 \text{ QFIR} + 0 \cdot 8114 \text{ EFIR}_{-1}$ $(2 \cdot 7875) \qquad (12 \cdot 4289)$	$0 \cdot 9895$	$0 \cdot 9022$	$1 \cdot 2321$	TSLS-6PC
		$= 0 \cdot 4635 + 0 \cdot 0070 \text{ QFIR} + 0 \cdot 8666 \text{ EFIR}_{-1}$ $(2 \cdot 3012) \qquad (15 \cdot 8207)$	$0 \cdot 9901$	$0 \cdot 9137$	$1 \cdot 1973$	OLS

Table 1 (continued).

Equation	Dependent variable	Regression estimates and identities	$\bar{R}^2$	DW	SEE	Estimation method
Block 4 (continued)						
(41)	ESRV	$= -0\cdot8025 + 0\cdot0099\ \mathrm{QSRV} + 0\cdot9581\ \mathrm{ESRV}_{-1}$ $\quad(1\cdot3934)\qquad(10\cdot5645)$	0·9964	0·8786	2·9135	TSLS-6PC
		$= 1\cdot6925 + 0\cdot0126\ \mathrm{QSRV} + 0\cdot9236\ \mathrm{ESRV}_{-1}$ $\quad(1\cdot8385)\qquad(10\cdot5198)$	0·9965	0·8215	2·8876	OLS
(42)	ENM	$= \mathrm{ECC} + \mathrm{ETPU} + \mathrm{ETRD} + \mathrm{EFIR} + \mathrm{ESRV} + \mathrm{EFED} + \mathrm{EGOV} + \mathrm{OE}$	....	....	....	....
(43)	ET	$= 1233\cdot2048 + 0\cdot0142\ \mathrm{GRO} + 0\cdot2349\ \mathrm{QGOV}$ $\quad(2\cdot0387)\qquad(5\cdot4974)$	0·9767	1·2352	21·5290	TSLS-6PC
		$= 1209\cdot7622 + 0\cdot0190\ \mathrm{GRO} + 0\cdot2047\ \mathrm{QGOV}$ $\quad(2\cdot9599)\qquad(5\cdot2346)$	0·9775	1·1254	21·1542	OLS
Block 5: Wages, price, and income						
(44)	AEM	$= 144\cdot2157 - 35\cdot7431\ \mathrm{UNR} + 15\cdot1797\ \mathrm{AEM}^* + 0\cdot9105\ \mathrm{AEM}_{-1}$ $\quad(-2\cdot4575)\qquad(2\cdot1829)\qquad(13\cdot7636)$	0·9976	1·5302	95·1210	TSLS-6PC
		$= 152\cdot1985 - 36\cdot8688\ \mathrm{UNR} + 15\cdot2852\ \mathrm{AEM}^* + 0\cdot9091\ \mathrm{AEM}_{-1}$ $\quad(-2\cdot6062)\qquad(2\cdot2019)\qquad(13\cdot7797)$	0·9976	1·5108	95·0501	OLS
(45)	AENM	$= 228\cdot6527 + 47\cdot5381\ \mathrm{AENM}^* + 0\cdot5465\ \mathrm{AENM}_{-1}$ $\quad(3\cdot0726)\qquad(3\cdot5061)$	0·9838	2·3860	169·2779	OLS
(46)	MTERN	$= (\mathrm{EM})(\mathrm{AEM}) + (\mathrm{ENM})(\mathrm{AENM})$	....	....	....	....
(47)	MTWB	$= \mathrm{MTERN} - (\mathrm{OLY})(\mathrm{P}) - (\mathrm{PYR})(\mathrm{P})$	....	....	....	....
(48)	RTWB	$= \mathrm{MTWB}/\mathrm{P}$	....	....	....	....
(49)	OLY	$= -550\cdot8636 + 1\cdot0221\ (\mathrm{RTWB}/\mathrm{ET}) + 0\cdot0340\ \mathrm{GRO}$ $\quad(4\cdot7917)\qquad(6\cdot1220)$	0·9826	1·5798	21·2968	TSLS-6PC
		$= -538\cdot5123 + 0\cdot8719\ (\mathrm{RTWB}/\mathrm{ET}) + 0\cdot0377\ \mathrm{GRO}$ $\quad(4\cdot3407)\qquad(7\cdot1606)$	0·9831	1·5074	21·0036	OLS
(50)	PRY	$= 577\cdot5570 + 0\cdot0686\ \mathrm{PY}_{-1} - 64\cdot6881\ \mathrm{CBR}^*$ $\quad(8\cdot0841)\qquad(-4\cdot3126)$	0·8653	1·2124	37·5592	OLS

Table 1 (continued).

Block 5 (continued)

No.	Var	Equation				Method
(51)	PTY	$= -1206 \cdot 3015 + 0 \cdot 0579$ MVP $+ 0 \cdot 1291$ GRO $(3 \cdot 0164)\quad(10 \cdot 9657)$	$0 \cdot 9844$	$0 \cdot 8442$	$54 \cdot 8126$	TSLS-6PC
		$= -1203 \cdot 9159 + 0 \cdot 0573$ MVP $+ 0 \cdot 1296$ GRO $(3 \cdot 1319)\quad(11 \cdot 5142)$	$0 \cdot 9844$	$0 \cdot 8462$	$54 \cdot 8199$	OLS
(52)	TP	$= -103 \cdot 6944 + 19 \cdot 6314$ TP* $+ 62 \cdot 2597$ CBR*$_{-1}$ $(7 \cdot 8729)\quad(2 \cdot 3371)$	$0 \cdot 9892$	$1 \cdot 8911$	$34 \cdot 1970$	OLS
(53)	PSI	$= -963 \cdot 1505 + 0 \cdot 0345$ PY $- 11 \cdot 9904$ UNR $+ 0 \cdot 4926$ LF $(3 \cdot 2612)\quad(-2 \cdot 5963)\quad(2 \cdot 1087)$	$0 \cdot 9670$	$1 \cdot 6343$	$29 \cdot 3278$	TSLS-6PC
		$= -971 \cdot 8451 + 0 \cdot 0347$ PY $- 11 \cdot 0277$ UNR $+ 0 \cdot 4935$ LF $(3 \cdot 7214)\quad(-2 \cdot 4688)\quad(2 \cdot 3913)$	$0 \cdot 9671$	$1 \cdot 6151$	$29 \cdot 2883$	OLS
(54)	PY	$=$ RTWB $+$ OLY $+$ PRY $+$ PTY $+$ TP $-$ PSI	....	....	....	....
(55)	PRFT	$=$ GRO $-$ (RTWB $+$ OLY $+$ PRY)	....	....	....	....
(56)	P	$= 39 \cdot 7756 + 128 \cdot 0721$ MTWB/GRO $- 1 \cdot 3476$ UNR $(29 \cdot 4815)\quad(-4 \cdot 7448)$	$0 \cdot 9796$	$1 \cdot 3058$	$1 \cdot 9980$	TSLS-6PC
		$= 40 \cdot 0169 + 127 \cdot 2384$ MTWB/GRO $- 1 \cdot 3071$ UNR $(29 \cdot 5717)\quad(-4 \cdot 7542)$	$0 \cdot 9798$	$1 \cdot 3035$	$1 \cdot 9910$	OLS
(57)	AVERN	$=$ (RTWB $+$ OLY $+$ PRY)/ET	....	....	....	....

Block 6: Demographic

No.	Var	Equation				Method
(58)	POP	$= 1585 \cdot 2195 + 0 \cdot 4056$ AVERN $+ 0 \cdot 0353$ GRO $+ 4 \cdot 0941$ NATG $(6 \cdot 8272)\quad(1 \cdot 9298)\quad(2 \cdot 1128)$	$0 \cdot 9789$	$1 \cdot 3280$	$59 \cdot 7983$	TSLS-6PC
		$= 1580 \cdot 9835 + 0 \cdot 3680$ AVERN $+ 0 \cdot 0466$ GRO $+ 4 \cdot 8264$ NATG $(6 \cdot 5303)\quad(2 \cdot 6784)\quad(2 \cdot 5631)$	$0 \cdot 9795$	$1 \cdot 1876$	$58 \cdot 8902$	OLS
(59)	UNR	$= 0 \cdot 8986 + 0 \cdot 4296$ UNR$_{-1} - 0 \cdot 0211$ (ET $-$ ET$_{-1}$) $+ 0 \cdot 5656$ UNR* $(4 \cdot 9696)\quad(-3 \cdot 9538)\quad(3 \cdot 3816)$	$0 \cdot 8932$	$0 \cdot 9220$	$0 \cdot 5358$	OLS
(60)	UNNO	$=$ (UNR)(LF) $=$ (UNR)(ET)/(1 $-$ UNR)	....	....		
(61)	LF	$=$ ET $+$ UNNO	....	....		

Table 1 (continued).

Equation	Dependent variable	Regression estimates and identities	$\bar{R}^2$	DW	SEE	Estimation method
Block 7: Federal and local government						
(62)	FIT	$= -1852\cdot7296 + 0\cdot1553$ PY $+ 105\cdot4791$ FETR* $\quad(12\cdot4827)\qquad\qquad(3\cdot5966)$	0·9356	0·3435	126·7178	TSLS-6PC
		$= -1860\cdot6476 + 0\cdot1542$ PY $+ 107\cdot0288$ FETR* $\quad(12\cdot4385)\qquad\qquad(3\cdot6546)$	0·9356	0·3420	160·9278	OLS
(63)	QFED	$= -372\cdot5577 + 0\cdot0482$ GRO $+ 11\cdot9766$ QFED* $- 20\cdot7957$ TIME $\quad(2\cdot7182)\qquad(11\cdot2045)\qquad(-3\cdot3054)$	0·9466	1·0150	41·1290	TSLS-6PC
		$= -336\cdot6648 + 0\cdot0436$ GRO $+ 12\cdot1160$ QFED* $- 19\cdot2498$ TIME $\quad(2\cdot5462)\qquad(11\cdot4486)\qquad(-3\cdot1570)$	0·9468	0·9933	41·0534	OLS
(64)	EFED	$=$ exogenously determined	.....	.....	.....	.....
(65)	EGOV	$= 64\cdot0546 + 0\cdot5918$ QFED* $+ 561\cdot0100$ GTE/POP $\quad(6\cdot0048)\qquad(21\cdot5989)$	0·9839	1·4600	4·7666	TSLS-6PC
		$= 64\cdot1663 + 0\cdot6106$ QFED* $+ 553\cdot9600$ GTE/POP $\quad(6\cdot2383)\qquad(21\cdot5647)$	0·9840	1·4525	4·7525	OLS
(66)	ELGOV	$=$ EGOV $-$ EFED	.....	.....	.....	.....
(67)	MTE	$= -125\cdot6916 + 0\cdot0682$ POP $+ 0\cdot5373$ MTR $+ 0\cdot8290$ MIR $\quad(3\cdot5647)\qquad(5\cdot1744)\qquad(2\cdot1777)$	0·9859	2·2252	17·0335	TSLS-6PC
		$= -129\cdot2904 + 0\cdot0683$ POP $+ 0\cdot5529$ MTR $+ 0\cdot7576$ MIR $\quad(3\cdot8397)\qquad(7\cdot5075)\qquad(2\cdot9053)$	0·9860	2·1986	16·9949	OLS
(68)	STE	$= -94\cdot5554 + 0\cdot1483$ SE $+ 0\cdot9430$ STR $\quad(1\cdot4676)\qquad(8\cdot7694)$	0·9926	1·6396	13·7037	TSLS-6PC
		$= -118\cdot3112 + 0\cdot2224$ SE $+ 0\cdot8619$ STR $\quad(2\cdot5372)\qquad(9\cdot2715)$	0·9929	1·4402	13·4440	OLS
(69)	MTR	$=$ MTXR $+$ MIR	.....	.....	.....	.....
(70)	STR	$=$ STXR $+$ SIR	.....	.....	.....	.....
(71)	MIR	$= -11\cdot5490 + 7\cdot6265$ GIR* $\quad(14\cdot4526)$	0·9082	1·8075	11·3696	OLS

Table 1 (continued).

Block 7 (continued)

(72)	SIR	$= -8 \cdot 1568 + 13 \cdot 2982 \text{ GIR}^*$ $\qquad (22 \cdot 5849)$	0·9586	1·2812	13·0150	OLS
(73)	MTXR	$= -1118 \cdot 8921 + 0 \cdot 6722 \text{ ET} + 0 \cdot 0200 \text{ MVP}$ $\qquad\qquad (5 \cdot 1539) \quad (1 \cdot 7919)$	0·8760	1·2292	46·0518	TSLS-6PC
		$= -1100 \cdot 9809 + 0 \cdot 6467 \text{ ET} + 0 \cdot 0219 \text{ MVP}$ $\qquad\qquad (5 \cdot 0531) \quad (2 \cdot 0063)$	0·8762	1·2111	46·0100	OLS
(74)	STXR	$= -101 \cdot 4126 + 0 \cdot 0079 \text{ MVP} + 0 \cdot 0102 \text{ GRO} + 0 \cdot 2975 \text{ STE}_{-1}$ $\qquad\qquad\quad (1 \cdot 8147) \qquad (1 \cdot 9519) \qquad (3 \cdot 5823)$	0·9778	2·1668	12·4364	TSLS-6PC
		$= -114 \cdot 9766 + 0 \cdot 0103 \text{ MVP} + 0 \cdot 0087 \text{ GRO} + 0 \cdot 3003 \text{ STE}_{-1}$ $\qquad\qquad\quad (2 \cdot 5122) \qquad (1 \cdot 7694) \qquad (3 \cdot 7857)$	0·9782	2·1299	12·3152	OLS
(75)	METR	$= \text{MTXR/MVP}$	....	....	....	....
(76)	SETR	$= \text{STXR/MVP}$	....	....	....	....
(77)	SE	$= -93 \cdot 0214 + 0 \cdot 0349 \text{ POP} + 0 \cdot 9464 \text{ SE}_{-1}$ $\qquad\qquad (2 \cdot 7136) \quad (26 \cdot 6217)$	0·9882	1·9100	6·6208	TSLS-6PC
		$= -79 \cdot 6471 + 0 \cdot 0296 \text{ POP} + 0 \cdot 9605 \text{ SE}_{-1}$ $\qquad\qquad (2 \cdot 4670) \quad (28 \cdot 8250)$	0·9982	1·9795	6·5410	OLS
(78)	MVP	$= -2893 \cdot 5781 + 3 \cdot 9882 \text{ POP}$ $\qquad\qquad\quad (27 \cdot 9232)$	0·9723	1·4181	274·5273	TSLS-6PC
		$= -2763 \cdot 6531 + 3 \cdot 9577 \text{ POP}$ $\qquad\qquad\quad (27 \cdot 9016)$	0·9725	1·4225	273·8159	OLS
(79)	GTE	$= \text{MTE} + \text{STE}$	....	....	....	....
(80)	GTXR	$= \text{MTXR} + \text{STXR}$	....	....	....	....

Block 8: Manufacturing investment

(81)	IM	$= -167 \cdot 2634 + 0 \cdot 1311 \text{ QM} + 0 \cdot 4943 \text{ IM}_{-1} - 0 \cdot 1198 \text{ KM}_{-1}$ $\qquad\qquad\quad (4 \cdot 8884) \qquad (3 \cdot 8578) \qquad (-3 \cdot 8676)$	0·8642	2·3189	31·3213	TSLS-6PC
		$= -171 \cdot 4277 + 0 \cdot 1336 \text{ QM} + 0 \cdot 4913 \text{ IM}_{-1} - 0 \cdot 1224 \text{ KM}_{-1}$ $\qquad\qquad\quad (5 \cdot 2904) \qquad (3 \cdot 8502) \qquad (-4 \cdot 1618)$	0·8643	2·3237	31·3146	OLS

Table 1 (continued).

Equation	Dependent variable	Regression estimates and identities	$\bar{R}^2$	DW	SEE	Estimation method
Block 8 (continued)						
(82)	KM	$= KM_{-1} + (IM - D)$	....	....	....	....
(83)	D	$= 0 \cdot 0667\ KM_{-1}$	....	....	....	....
Block 9: Retail sales						
(84)	RETS	$= -339 \cdot 4551 + 0 \cdot 1626\ GRO + 0 \cdot 7737\ POP$ (5·2589) (3·7857)	0·9697	2·1601	125·2851	TSLS-6PC
		$= -155 \cdot 2128 + 0 \cdot 1736\ GRO + 0 \cdot 6945\ POP$ (5·8805) (3·5700)	0·9700	2·1702	124·5300	OLS
(85)	AUTS	$= 237 \cdot 7282 + 0 \cdot 0560\ PY$ (9·5225)	0·8109	1·6855	68·0447	TSLS-6PC
		$= 237 \cdot 6810 + 0 \cdot 0560\ PY$ (9·5424)	0·8109	1·6857	68·0399	OLS
(86)	FOOD	$= 963 \cdot 3533 + 0 \cdot 0692\ PY$ (16·5045)	0·9282	1·8136	48·5015	TSLS-6PC
		$= 964 \cdot 7845 + 0 \cdot 0691\ PY$ (16·5106)	0·9282	1·8141	48·4850	OLS
(87)	DRUG	$= -192 \cdot 1168 + 0 \cdot 0816\ POP$ (18·7152)	0·9427	1·4707	7·7992	TSLS-6PC
		$= -188 \cdot 5369 + 0 \cdot 0808\ POP$ (18·6444)	0·9429	1·4717	7·7872	OLS
(88)	GAS	$= -313 \cdot 0760 + 0 \cdot 0191\ PPY + 0 \cdot 1060\ POP$ (2·4336) (5·8038)	0·9798	1·9706	8·3964	TSLS-6PC
		$= -348 \cdot 7508 + 0 \cdot 0090\ PPY + 0 \cdot 1292\ POP$ (1·6437) (10·0512)	0·9829	1·8718	7·7170	OLS
(89)	GMRCH	$= -1177 \cdot 4760 + 0 \cdot 4847\ POP$ (9·2183)	0·7996	1·3683	94·0066	TSLS-6PC
		$= -1164 \cdot 8045 + 0 \cdot 4818\ POP$ (9·2087)	0·7996	1·3682	94·0066	OLS

Table 1 (continued).

Block 9 (continued)

(90)	ORETS	$=$ RETS $-$ (AUTS + FOOD + DRUG + GAS + GMRCH)	.....	.....	.....	.....
Block 10:	**City of Philadelphia**					
(91)	PQM	$= -665\cdot4909 + 0\cdot3216$ PPY $+ 1181\cdot1933$ PROD $\quad\quad(5\cdot5690)\quad\quad\quad\quad(2\cdot5661)$	0·8224	1·2411	84·9458	TSLS-6PC
		$= -119\cdot6725 + 0\cdot2816$ PPY $+ 870\cdot7806$ PROD $\quad\quad(7\cdot1511)\quad\quad\quad\quad(2\cdot7815)$	0·8314	1·2637	82·7562	OLS
(92)	PPY	$= 2444\cdot9787 + 0\cdot3585$ PY $\quad\quad\quad(19\cdot7426)$	0·9465	1·3026	224·1938	TSLS-6PC
		$= 2451\cdot4463 + 0\cdot3579$ PY $\quad\quad\quad(19\cdot7653)$	0·9466	1·3031	224·1666	OLS
(93)	PEM	$= 17\cdot6406 + 0\cdot0544$ PQM $+ 0\cdot6299$ PEM$_{-1} - 3\cdot7214$ TIME $\quad\quad(2\cdot5039)\quad\quad(3\cdot2908)\quad\quad\quad\quad(-3\cdot0921)$	0·9558	1·1397	8·9876	TSLS-6PC
		$= 51\cdot7308 + 0\cdot0435$ PQM $+ 0\cdot6019$ PEM$_{-1} - 3\cdot6350$ TIME $\quad\quad(2\cdot5146)\quad\quad(3\cdot2328)\quad\quad\quad\quad(-3\cdot0694)$	0·9569	1·2569	8·8757	OLS
(94)	PENM	$= 58\cdot1698 + 0\cdot3317$ ENM $\quad\quad(15\cdot9165)$	0·9303	1·4980	11·1977	TSLS-6PC
		$= 57\cdot4788 + 0\cdot3322$ ENM $\quad\quad(15\cdot9165)$	0·9303	1·4988	11·1928	OLS
(95)	PET	$=$ PEM + PENM	.....	.....	.....	.....
(96)	PMWB	$= -348\cdot8034 + 0\cdot0774$ PY $+ 1\cdot2297$ PET $\quad\quad(21\cdot5754)\quad\quad(3\cdot7168)$	0·9616	1·8850	37·1048	TSLS-6PC
		$= -339\cdot3459 + 0\cdot0771$ PY $+ 1\cdot2204$ PET $\quad\quad(21\cdot5505)\quad\quad(3\cdot8163)$	0·9616	1·8899	37·0921	OLS
(97)	PMTE	$= 92\cdot7074 + 0\cdot4819$ PMTR $+ 6\cdot8092$ GIR* $\quad\quad(2\cdot3164)\quad\quad\quad(2\cdot3770)$	0·9586	1·2681	13·0744	TSLS-6PC
		$= 82\cdot1183 + 0\cdot5495$ PMTR $+ 5\cdot9014$ GIR* $\quad\quad(2\cdot9057)\quad\quad\quad(2\cdot2550)$	0·9589	1·2888	13·0249	OLS

Table 1 (continued).

Equation	Dependent variable	Regression estimates and identities	$\bar{R}^2$	DW	SEE	Estimation method
Block 10 (continued)						
(98)	PSTE	$= -16 \cdot 9660 + 0 \cdot 9733 \text{ PSTR} + 3 \cdot 3798 \text{ GIR}^*$ (4·3569) (2·1846)	0·9790	1·8491	6·9599	TSLS-6PC
		$= -10 \cdot 4389 + 0 \cdot 8689 \text{ PSTR} + 4 \cdot 0852 \text{ GIR}^*$ (5·0861) (3·3983)	0·9794	1·7414	6·8843	OLS
(99)	PMTR	$= \text{PMTXR} + \text{PMIR}$	::::	::::	::::	::::
(100)	PSTR	$= \text{PSTXR} + \text{PSIR}$	::::	::::	::::	::::
(101)	PMTXR	$= -205 \cdot 9793 + 0 \cdot 0796 \text{ POP} + 55 \cdot 9872 \text{ PRMTR}$ (3·6187) (2·2981)	0·8698	0·8747	16·7626	TSLS-6PC
		$= -195 \cdot 6510 + 0 \cdot 0760 \text{ POP} + 59 \cdot 4725 \text{ PRMTR}$ (3·5324) (2·4831)	0·8686	0·8709	16·7731	OLS
(102)	PSTXR	$= -61 \cdot 5911 + 0 \cdot 1249 \text{ PET} + 30 \cdot 1672 \text{ PRMTR}$ (2·0502) (6·0189)	0·7054	1·3974	6·7131	TSLS-6PC
		$= -67 \cdot 8284 + 0 \cdot 1335 \text{ PET} + 30 \cdot 0364 \text{ PRMTR}$ (2·2705) (6·0033)	0·7058	1·4076	6·7090	OLS
(103)	PMIR	$= -102 \cdot 7775 + 0 \cdot 0154 \text{ PPY} + 0 \cdot 1176 \text{ PMTE}$ (3·6345) (2·1656)	0·9054	1·7183	6·3019	TSLS-6PC
		$= -95 \cdot 4903 + 0 \cdot 0131 \text{ PPY} + 0 \cdot 1439 \text{ PMTE}$ (3·4629) (2·9318)	0·9072	1·6681	6·2396	OLS
(104)	PSIR	$= -37 \cdot 8659 + 166 \cdot 0815 \text{ PSTE/PSE}$ (11·3780)	0·8686	1·4397	8·4289	TSLS-6PC
		$= -36 \cdot 3812 + 162 \cdot 6379 \text{ PSTE/PSE}$ (11·2702)	0·8690	1·4369	8·4158	OLS
(105)	PMDOE	$= -13 \cdot 7560 + 0 \cdot 8063 \text{ PMTE}$ (20·5706)	0·9567	1·3265	10·8845	TSLS-6PC
		$= -11 \cdot 3231 + 0 \cdot 7973 \text{ PMTE}$ (20·5501)	0·9568	1·3073	10·8690	OLS

Table 1 (continued).

Block 10 (continued)

(106)	PMEGV	$= 15049\cdot0307 + 68\cdot6815$ PMDOE (13·6462)	0·9070	1·3474	1144·7610	TSLS-6PC
		$= 15083\cdot8142 + 68\cdot5103$ PMDOE (13·6516)	0·9070	1·3481	1144·5623	OLS
(107)	PSE	$= 43\cdot0075 + 0\cdot0571$ POP $- 3\cdot9583$ UNR (12·4350) (−4·0735)	0·9104	1·0819	6·7873	TSLS-6PC
		$= 47\cdot1740 + 0\cdot0561$ POP $- 3\cdot9815$ UNR (12·3727) (−4·2044)	0·9109	1·0903	6·7699	OLS
(108)	PWEN	$= 25\cdot8994 + 0\cdot7342$ PWE $+ 1\cdot7822$ TIME (11·8442) (4·0901)	0·9724	0·6816	6·6477	OLS
(109)	PWE	= exogenously determined	....	....	....	....
(110)	PUR	$= 7\cdot8096 + 0\cdot6382$ PUR$_{-1}$ (8·0999)	0·7727	1·5083	2·2046	OLS
(111)	PUE	$= -36\cdot1597 + 0\cdot0130$ POP $- 0\cdot3396$ TIME (3·7130) (−1·6541)	0·8620	1·1963	1·0190	TSLS-6PC
		$= -30\cdot8868 + 0\cdot0115$ POP $- 0\cdot2537$ TIME (3·7798) (−1·4131)	0·8639	1·1959	1·0121	OLS
(112)	PROD	$= $ QM/AEM	....	....	....	....
Block 11: Suburban						
(113)	SQM	$= $ QM − PQM	....	....	....	....
(114)	SPY	$= $ PY − PPY	....	....	....	....
(115)	SEM	$= $ EM − PEM	....	....	....	....
(116)	SENM	$= $ ENM − PENM	....	....	....	....
(117)	SET	$= $ ET − PET	....	....	....	....
(118)	SMWB	$= $ (AWM)(EM) − PMWB	....	....	....	....
(119)	SMTE	$= $ MTE − PMTE	....	....	....	....

Table 1 (continued).

Equation	Dependent variable	Regression estimates and identities	$\bar{R}^2$	DW	SEE	Estimation method
Block 11 (continued)						
(120)	SSTE	= STE − PSTE	...	...	...	...
(121)	SMTR	= MTR − PMTR	...	...	...	...
(122)	SSTR	= STR − PSTR	...	...	...	...
(123)	SMTXR	= MTXR − PMTXR	...	...	...	...
(124)	SSTXR	= STXR − PSTXR	...	...	...	...
(125)	SMIR	= MIR − PMIR	...	...	...	...
(126)	SSIR	= SIR − PSIR	...	...	...	...
(127)	SSE	= SE − PSE	...	...	...	...
Block 12: Banking						
(128)	DD	= 789·9983 + 0·3363 GRO + 133·8955 CBR* (8·3925) (1·8297)	0·9665	1·4045	200·7645	TSLS-6PC
		= 851·3416 + 0·3267 GRO + 149·9692 CBR* (8·2598) (2·0726)	0·9667	1·4109	200·3497	OLS
(129)	TD	= −4046·4067 + 0·5063 PY + 593·6093 CBR* (3·9159) (2·5553)	0·9249	0·2715	614·1929	TSLS-6PC
		= −4049·2855 + 0·5006 PY + 602·9626 CBR* (3·9369) (2·6323)	0·9249	0·2743	614·1304	OLS
(130)	TOTD	= DD + TD	...	...	...	...
(131)	LIN	= −1308·1420 + 1·0436 TOTD (94·1496)	0·9975	0·7983	107·6324	TSLS-6PC
		= −1296·0718 + 1·0424 TOTD (94·5509)	0·9975	0·8032	171·1674	OLS

Table 1 (continued).

Block 13: Consumption

(132)	CTOT	$= 0 \cdot 8320\ PY$	⋮	⋮	⋮
(133)	CFOOD	$= 0 \cdot 2159\ PY$	⋮	⋮	⋮
(134)	CHSE	$= 0 \cdot 2395\ PY$	⋮	⋮	⋮
(135)	CCLTH	$= 0 \cdot 0865\ PY$	⋮	⋮	⋮
(136)	CPC	$= 0 \cdot 0241\ PY$	⋮	⋮	⋮
(137)	CMC	$= 0 \cdot 0484\ PY$	⋮	⋮	⋮
(138)	CREC	$= 0 \cdot 0338\ PY$	⋮	⋮	⋮
(139)	CED	$= 0 \cdot 0165\ PY$	⋮	⋮	⋮
(140)	CTA	$= 0 \cdot 0906\ PY$	⋮	⋮	⋮
(141)	CTO	$= 0 \cdot 0144\ PY$	⋮	⋮	⋮
(142)	CREAD	$= 0 \cdot 0076\ PY$	⋮	⋮	⋮

Equilibrium and Catastrophic Modes of Urban Growth

J.C.AMSON
University of St. Andrews, Scotland

Part I: Equilibrium modes

1 Introduction

Let C denote a plane abstract city having only a single species P of civic matter [see Amson (1972a) for a formal account of these ideas]. For definiteness we may take C to have circular symmetry in the city's civic space X (= $\mathbf{R}^2$, the euclidean plane), and P to be a population of 'citizens' distributed smoothly at a density $\tau(r)$ $(r \geqslant 0)$ throughout X. I have shown (Amson, 1972b) that if the population is exposed to two kinds of competing coercions (civic forces)—namely (a) a cohesive coercion (civic attraction) of gravity type with the coercion law km_1m_2/d of the two-dimensional (note, not three-dimensional) Newtonian form having a logarithmic potential function $k\log(1/r)$, and (b) a relocation inducement of potential type given by the gradient $\mathrm{grad}\,p$ $(= -\mathrm{d}p/\mathrm{d}r$ in the outward radial direction) of a civic pressure function (potential) $p(r)$ $(r \geqslant 0)$, for which the price or rental of a bundle of housing commodities is a paradigm—then the relocation coercions experienced by every portion of the population P could exactly balance each other provided the rental p was functionally related to the density τ. We may call such an abstract civic system in which p and τ are suitably related a *coercion city*.

The typical (p, τ)-relations investigated were of the so-called 'polytropic' type:

$$p = K\tau^\gamma , \tag{1}$$

where the constants K and γ are such that $K > 0$ and $-\infty \leqslant \gamma \leqslant \infty$, and are called the rental coefficient and rental exponent respectively. The resulting *equilibrium configurations* (τ, p) for the coercion city C were determined by solving for τ and p the *fundamental civic equilibrium equation*:

$$k\tau(r)M(r)+r\frac{\mathrm{d}}{\mathrm{d}r}p(r) = 0 , \qquad (r \geqslant 0) \tag{2}$$

[where

$$M(r) = \int_{r'=0}^{r'=r} 2\pi r'\tau(r')\mathrm{d}r'$$

is the total mass of population occupying the central disc $D(r)$ of radius r] subject to the relation (1), and the central conditions $\tau(0) > 0$ and $(\mathrm{d}\tau/\mathrm{d}r)_{r=0} = 0$. Explicit solutions are available in only four cases: when $\gamma = 1$ (mesotropic or middle-type cities), $\gamma = 2$ (Bessel cities), $\gamma = \infty$

(constant density cities), or when $\gamma = 0$ (constant rental cities). The corresponding equilibrium configurations are illustrated in figure 1. Approximate numerical solutions are also available in the intermediate cases with $1 < \gamma < 2$ (epitropic cities) and $0 < \gamma < 1$ (hypotropic cities).

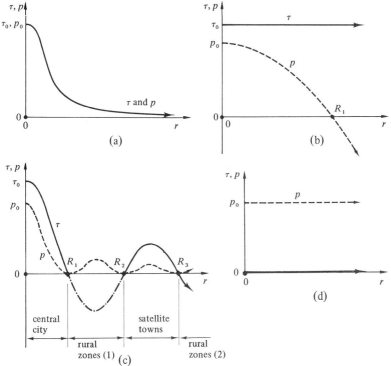

Figure 1. Distributions of population density (τ) and rental (p) as functions of the radial distance (r) from the city centre in four different classes of coercion cities:

(a)   Mesotropic city ($\gamma = 1$)
$$p = K\tau$$
$$\tau(r) = \tau_0 \left(1 + \frac{\tau_0}{\rho^2}p^2\right)^{-2}, \text{ where } \rho^2 = \frac{4K}{\pi k};$$

(b)   Constant density city ($\gamma = \infty$)
$$p(r) = p_0 - \tfrac{1}{2}k\tau_0^2\pi r^2,$$
$$\tau(r) = \tau_0, \text{ constant;}$$

(c)   Bessel city ($\gamma = 2$)
$$p = K\tau^2, \tau(r) = \tau_0 J_0(r/\alpha),$$
where $\alpha^2 = \frac{1}{\pi}\frac{K}{k}$ and J_0 is the Bessel function of the first kind and zeroth order;

(d)   Constant rental city ($\gamma = 0$)
$$p(r) = p_0, \text{ constant,}$$
$$\tau(r) \equiv 0 \text{ (the trivial zero solution, corresponding to no population at all).}$$
[γ is the 'rental exponent' whose values determine the different classes of coercion cities.]

Since the civic attraction is assumed to be two-dimensional Newtonian [1], we have the following situation. A ring of population mass dM_r at radius r is attracted by each inner ring of population mass dM_s at radius $s < r$ (with a coercion of magnitude $k\,dM_r\,dM_s/r$), but each inner ring is *not* attracted by the outer (because the net attraction on each element of the inner ring in response to the outer ring is identically zero). Moreover we have required the equilibrium to be local [see condition (2)], that is, the net coercion on each element of population (each citizen) must be nil. Consequently any equilibrium configuration (τ, p) can be *truncated* at any radius $R > 0$ to give a *finite* coercion city with its city edge along the circle of radius R (see figure 2).

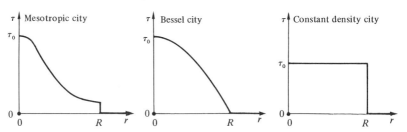

Figure 2. Population density distributions in truncated versions of coercion cities.

2 Equilibrium growth modes
Suppose we are given a coercion city C in a state of equilibrium and we simultaneously impose on it the following five kinds of uniform change:

(a) *A uniform territorial expansion* $r \mapsto \hat{r} = cr$ with a fixed expansion factor $c > 0$, under which the population becomes redistributed so that the mass of population $\hat{M}(\hat{r})$ over a new disc $D(\hat{r})$ remains the same as the mass $M(r)$ over the old disc $D(r)$. For this to happen it is not difficult to show that it is necessary and sufficient that we replace the old distribution of population density $\tau(r)$ by a new one $\hat{\tau}(\hat{r}) = \tau(r)/c^2$, or, in terms of the old distance r,

$$\hat{\tau}(r) = \frac{\tau(r/c)}{c^2} \ . \tag{3}$$

(b) *A uniform mass expansion* $M(r) \mapsto \hat{M}(r) = aM(r)$, with a fixed expansion factor $a > 0$, over each central disc $D(r)$. For this to happen we need only replace the old density distribution $\tau(r)$ by a new one:

$$\hat{\tau}(r) = a\tau(r) \ . \tag{4}$$

---

[1] This is done largely for the analytical convenience of being able to evaluate the inevitably encountered integrals. But we also note that coercions under this '$1/d$' law fall off more slowly with distance than do those under the more familiar '$1/d^2$' law frequently discussed by social geographers; hence the former, being much less sensitive to changes in distance especially at close range, are likely to describe more accurately actual perceptions of the distance effect.

(c) *A uniform rental expansion* $p(r) \mapsto \hat{p}(\hat{r}) = bp(r)$ (where $\hat{r} = cr$), with
a fixed expansion factor $b > 0$. In terms of the old distances r we then
have

$$\hat{p}(r) = bp(r/c) .$$ (5)

(d) *A rental coefficient change* $K \mapsto \hat{K} = fK$, $f > 0$ fixed.

(e) *An attraction coefficient change* $k \mapsto \hat{k} = gk$, $g > 0$ fixed.
Then the following is a natural question to ask: since the old
distributions $\tau(r)$ and $p(r)$ formed an equilibrium configuration with
respect to the civic coefficients (K, k), what conditions must we place on
the expansion factors, a, b, c, f, g, in order that the new distributions $\hat{\tau}(\hat{r})$
and $\hat{p}(\hat{r})$ should also form an equilibrium configuration with respect to the
new civic coefficients $(\hat{K}, \hat{k})$?

The answer, as has been shown before (Amson, 1972b), is not difficult
to find. The old quantities, $\tau(r), M(r), p(r), r, k, K$, satisfied the two
conditions (1) and (2), and so must the new ones. Hence we must have

$$\hat{p} = \hat{K}\hat{\tau}(\hat{r})^{\gamma}$$

and

$$\hat{k}\hat{\tau}(\hat{r})\hat{M}(\hat{r}) + \hat{r}\frac{d}{d\hat{r}}\hat{p}(\hat{r}) = 0$$

for all $\hat{r} \geq 0$. Substituting cr for $\hat{r}$, etc., and using equations (1) and (2),
it follows at once that when $\gamma \neq \infty$ we must necessarily have

$$b = \left(\frac{a}{c^2}\right)^{\gamma} f \qquad\qquad \text{and} \quad bc^2 = a^2g .$$ (6)

These two conditions are plainly also sufficient. Again, if $\gamma = \infty$ and we
replace (1) by

$$\tau(r) = \tau_0 = \frac{1}{K} ,$$ (1')

then a similar argument shows that the necessary and sufficient conditions
are now

$$c^2 = af , \qquad\qquad \text{and again} \quad bc^2 = a^2g .$$ (6')

Now any change

$$T : (\tau, p, r, K, k) \mapsto (\hat{\tau}, \hat{p}, \hat{r}, \hat{K}, \hat{k}) ,$$

from one list of civic quantities to a new list, can be regarded as the
result of a transformation T of the function space $S \times S \times D \times \mathbf{R} \times \mathbf{R}$ into
itself. This function space is the cartesian product of the spaces S of all
smooth (or, at least, twice differentiable) functions $\mathbf{R}^2 \rightarrow \mathbf{R}$ (to which
τ and p both belong), the space D of dilations $r \rightarrow cr : \mathbf{R} \rightarrow \mathbf{R}$ (to which
uniform territorial expansions belong), and the space $\mathbf{R} \times \mathbf{R}$ of all pairs of

real numbers (K, k). We shall call this function space the *configuration space* for the coercion city C, and denote it by $\mathbf{F}(C)$; each point $(\tau, p, r, K, k) \in \mathbf{F}(C)$ is a *configuration* of the coercion city C.

The subset $\mathbf{E}(C) \subset \mathbf{F}(C)$, consisting of all configurations for which (τ, p) is an equilibrium configuration for C (in the sense used in section 1), we shall call the *equilibrium configuration space* for C. Amongst all the possible transformations $T : \mathbf{F}(C) \to \mathbf{F}(C)$ on the configuration space for C there are some which are particularly important, namely those which leave the subspace $\mathbf{E}(C)$ invariant. By this we mean a transformation T such that, for each equilibrium configuration $(\tau, p, r, K, k) \in \mathbf{E}(C)$, its transform

$$T(\tau, p, r, K, k) = (\hat{\tau}, \hat{p}, \hat{r}, \hat{K}, \hat{k}) \in \mathbf{E}(C)$$

that is,

$$T[\mathbf{E}(C)] \subseteq \mathbf{E}(C) .$$

Transformations which have this property we shall call *equilibrium growths* for the coercion city C.

Our earlier results in this section now provide us with the following theorem.

Theorem: If the transformation $T : \mathbf{F}(C) \to \mathbf{F}(C)$ is given in terms of the uniform expansions (a), (b), ..., (e) listed previously (so that $T \equiv T_{a, b, c, f, g}$ say), then T is an equilibrium growth for C if and only if the conditions (6) (for $\gamma \neq \infty$) or (6$'$) (for $\gamma = \infty$) are satisfied.

What other transformations $T : \mathbf{F}(C) \to \mathbf{F}(C)$, more general than the uniform expansion ones, are equilibrium growths for C is an open question. Still other interesting problems arise when we extend the notion of equilibrium growths firstly to a theory of equilibrium growth *processes*, by introducing a time axis $\mathbf{R}^+$ to parametrize the set of all equilibrium growths for the city C, and secondly to a theory of *continuous processes*, by equipping the configuration space $\mathbf{F}(C)$ with a suitable metric topology. These generalisations will be taken up in a later study.

3 Locational wealth of an abstract city

The capacity to undertake physical activity ('work') depends on the availability of a physical wealth ('energy'); in an analogous manner it can be claimed that the possession of economic wealths of various kinds is necessary to be able to undertake economic activities. We now postulate that the capacity of a 'citizen' in our abstract city to undertake a generalised kind of 'civic activity' depends on the availability to him of 'civic wealths' of various kinds. For instance the relocation of a citizen within the city is a typical civic activity which consumes a variety of civic wealths of an economic, social, physical, and even psychological kind.

To relocate a citizen outwards, against the cohesive coercion experienced by him in response to the civic attraction of the population mass lying closer to the city centre than him, consumes civic wealth. Conversely a relocation nearer to the city centre can release civic wealth for other activities; for example the shorter daily trip time to the Central Business District releases the civic wealth 'time' for other gainful civic activities. Though there is no clear evidence that such a consumption or release of civic wealth would be proportional to the distance of the relocation and the strength of the coercion experienced, we shall assume that it is, if only for a temporary analytical convenience.

These notions lead us to the idea of a 'locational wealth' analogous to that of potential energy in a mass of gravitating matter. Consider two concentric circular rings of radii r and s $(r > s)$ of population masses dM and dm respectively in our circular abstract city C. As has previously been remarked, our assumption of a two-dimensional Newtonian form of civic attraction implies that the inner mass dm attracts the outer mass dM inwards, but not *vice versa*, the magnitude of the coercion in question being $k\,dM\,dm/r$, since the inner mass may be regarded as being condensed at the centre of the city. The total coercion on the outer ring due to all such inner rings of radii up to s is simply

$$k\,dM \int_0^s \frac{dm}{r} = \frac{k\,dM\,M(s)}{r} \ .$$

Now if we assume the city to have a finite edge at radius $R > 0$, we may imagine the city to have been 'assembled' piecemeal by 'bringing in' rings of population of mass dM from the edge of the city. Let us enquire to what extent this hypothetical process would involve an absorption or expenditure of locational wealth. Suppose a population of mass $M(s)$ has already been 'brought in' so as to cover the central region $D(s)$ of radius s; then 'bringing in' another ring of mass dM will release civic wealth in the ring's population for other activities. By our assumption of proportionality, the amount released during an infinitesimal step in the relocation, from radius r to $r - dr$, is $[kM(s)\,dM/r] \times (-dr)$, exactly the opposite of what would be expended in moving the mass out again. Hence the civic wealth released by the relocation inwards of the population mass dM from radius R to radius s is the integral

$$-\int_{r=R}^{r=s} kM(s)\,dM\,\frac{dr}{r} = -kM(s)\,dM \int_R^s \frac{dr}{r} = kM(s)\,dM \log\left(\frac{R}{s}\right).$$

Thus the total civic wealth that would be released by assembling the whole city, from the outer edge inwards, has the value obtained by summing the last expression over the elemental rings of mass dM at radius s as s increases from 0 to R. Writing dM as $ds[dM(s)/ds]$, we then have

$$L = \int_{s=0}^{s=R} kM(s)\frac{dM(s)}{ds}\log\left(\frac{R}{s}\right)ds \ .$$

Putting this another way: L is the civic wealth that would be needed to *disperse* the whole population of the city to the city's edge *against* the mutual civic attractions of all the citizens within the city.

We may now formalise these ideas by making the following definition.

Definition. The *locational wealth* of a finite abstract city C with a population mass distribution $M(r)$ $(0 \leqslant r \leqslant R)$ is the quantity

$$L \equiv L(R, k) = \int_{r=0}^{r=R} k\log\left(\frac{R}{r}\right)M(r)dM(r) \ . \tag{7}$$

An alternative way of looking at locational wealth is through the notion of the 'potential' of the distribution $M(r)$ of the population in the city. We have seen that, if a population of mass $M(s)$ already occupies the central disc $D(s)$, then the civic wealth released by moving a ring of population of mass dM from the city's edge R to any other radius $r \geqslant s$ is $kM(s)dM\log(R/r)$. Writing $U(r, s)$ for the quantity $kM(s)\log(R/r)$, we see that its negative derivative

$$-\frac{\partial}{\partial r}U(r, s) = \frac{kM(s)}{r} \ .$$

Thus $-\partial U(r, s)/\partial r$ is precisely the coercion due to the civic attraction of the central mass $M(s)$ on a ring of unit mass located at radius $r \geqslant s$. Hence, by the usual definition of a potential function as a scalar function whose directional derivative is a gradient force (coercion), we may regard $U(r, s)$ as the 'attraction potential' of the population mass $M(s)$ at a distance $r \geqslant s$. The presence of the constant $\log R$ in the quantity $U(r, s)$ ensures that the attraction potential vanishes at what is the most convenient place for us, namely the edge of the city at radius R. Now letting $s = r$ in the definition of the function $U(r, s)$ defines for us a function

$$U(r) = kM(r)\log\left(\frac{R}{r}\right) \qquad (0 \leqslant r \leqslant R) \ , \tag{8}$$

which we shall call the *attraction potential of the population distribution* $M(r)$. We then have the following important connexion between the locational wealth L and the attraction potential U in our abstract city:

Theorem: The locational wealth of an abstract city is proportional to the integral of the attraction potential throughout the city, namely

$$L = +\frac{1}{2}\int_{r=0}^{r=R} U(r)dM(r) \ . \tag{9}$$

Proof: from equation (7),

$$L = \frac{k}{2} \int_0^R \log\left(\frac{R}{r}\right) d[M^2(r)]$$

$$= \frac{k}{2}\log\left(\frac{R}{r}\right)M^2(r)\bigg|_0^R + \frac{k}{2}\int_0^R \frac{1}{r}M^2(r)\,dr \qquad \text{(integrating by parts)}$$

$$= \frac{1}{2}\int_0^R \frac{kM(r)}{r}M(r)\,dr \qquad \text{(since the first member vanishes identically).}$$

But, from equation (8),

$$\frac{kM(r)}{r} = -\frac{dU(r)}{dr} \; ;$$

hence

$$L = -\frac{1}{2}\int_0^R \frac{dU(r)}{dr}M(r)\,dr = -\frac{1}{2}U(r)M(r)\bigg|_0^R + \frac{1}{2}\int_0^R U(r)\,dM(r) \,,$$

and again the first member vanishes identically, since $U(R) = 0$ and $M(0) = 0$, hence the result.

As an illustration, we calculate the locational wealth of a truncated mesotropic city (cf. section 1), the density and population distributions for which are:

$$\tau(r) = \tau_0\left(1 + \frac{\tau_0 r^2}{\rho^2}\right)^{-2} \qquad (0 \leqslant r \leqslant R) \,,$$

$$M(r) = \pi\tau_0 r^2\left(1 + \frac{\tau_0 r^2}{\rho^2}\right)^{-1} \qquad (0 \leqslant r \leqslant R) \; ;$$

here $\rho^2 = 4K/\pi k$, and $dM(r) = 2\pi r\tau(r)\,dr$. Hence, from equation (7) we have

$$L(R) = \int_0^R k\log\left(\frac{R}{r}\right)\frac{2\pi^2\tau_0^2 r^3}{(1 + \tau_0 r^2/\rho^2)^3}\,dr \,.$$

This integral can be evaluated explicitly to give

$$L(R) = \frac{k\rho^4\pi^2}{4}\left[\log\left(1 + \frac{\tau_0 R^2}{\rho^2}\right) - \left(1 + \frac{\rho^2}{\tau_0 R^2}\right)^{-1}\right]$$

(see figure 3). We infer at once from this expression that, as a function of the city radius R, the locational wealth of a truncated mesotropic city is monotonicly increasing (that is, wider mesotropic cities have greater locational wealth, all other things being equal). It varies like $\log R$ for all large values of the city radius R, and so is unbounded above (that is, a wide enough mesotropic city will have a locational wealth greater than any preassigned amount). And when R is small enough, the locational wealth behaves like πR^2 (that is, a mesotropic city occupying only half the area of another such city will have only about half the locational wealth of the larger one).

In the case of a constant density city, the locational wealth assumes a much simpler form. It is readily calculated that

$$L(R) = \tfrac{1}{8}k(\pi R^2 \tau_0)^2 = \tfrac{1}{8}kM^2(R) \; ;$$

thus the locational wealth increases as the square of the total population $M(R)$ in the city.

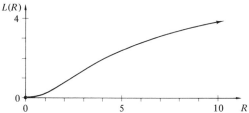

Figure 3. Locational wealth $L(R)$ as a function of city radius R in a finite mesotropic city (dimensionless units).

4 Invariance of locational wealth

We have just noted how the locational wealth can vary with an increase in the radius of some particular cities. However, such simple expansions of an abstract city do not in general comprise an equilibrium growth for the city. A natural question to ask now is: what happens to the locational wealth of a given coercion city C when the latter undergoes an equilibrium growth? The answer is simple. Suppose a coercion city C undergoes an equilibrium growth with expansion factors (a, b, c, f, g). Since

$$L(R) = \int_0^R k \log\!\left(\frac{R}{r}\right) M(r)\,dM(r) \; ,$$

we must compute the value of

$$\hat{L}(\hat{R}) = \int_0^{\hat{R}} \hat{k} \log\!\left(\frac{\hat{R}}{\hat{r}}\right) \hat{M}(\hat{r})\,d\hat{M}(\hat{r}) \; ,$$

where the accented variables satisfy the conditions given in (a), (b), ..., (e) in section 2. Hence we have

$$\hat{L}(\hat{R}) = \int_0^{cR} gk \log\!\left(\frac{cR}{cr}\right) aM(cr)a\,dM(cr)$$

$$= a^2g \int_0^R k \log\!\left(\frac{R}{r}\right) M(r)\,dM(r) = a^2 g L(R) \; .$$

Thus, regardless of the values given to the expansion factors b, c, and f, the locational wealth changes only by a factor a^2g (this of course could have been inferred at once from dimensional considerations).

From this result we see that if the locational wealth is to remain invariant during an equilibrium growth, then we must have $a^2g = 1$. Evidently this is also a sufficient condition, but it is not independent of the equilibrium growth conditions given in equations (6) and (6'). Taking note of these, we at once obtain the following theorem.

Theorem: For an equilibrium growth with expansion factors (a, b, c, f, g) to leave invariant the locational wealth of a coercion city, it is necessary and sufficient that in every case we have $a^2g = 1 = bc^2$, and that $b = (a/c^2)f$ (when $\gamma \neq \infty$) and $c^2 = af$ (when $\gamma = \infty$).

A typical sequence of density profiles of a truncated mesotropic city, undergoing equilibrium growths which leave the locational wealth invariant, is illustrated in figure 4.

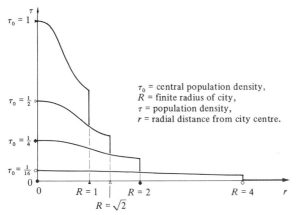

τ_0 = central population density,
R = finite radius of city,
τ = population density,
r = radial distance from city centre.

Figure 4. A typical sequence of equilibrium growths, which leaves both the locational wealth $L(R)$ and the total population $M(R)$ invariant, in a finite mesotropic city of radius R (dimensionless units).

Part II: Catastrophic modes

5 Urbanitic systems
We now introduce a more general idea of an abstract city which we shall refer to as an urbanitic system.

An *urbanitic system* C again consists of a distribution of civic matter (typically a population of citizens) in a civic space X (typically the euclidean plane) at a density τ, together with a distribution of civic pressure p (typically the rental or price of a bundle of housing commodities). For the present discussion it will be enough to regard τ and p as having only constant values over some finite region of the space X and zero values elsewhere, though the values and the region are not fixed. Unlike the previous case of an abstract coercion city, we shall place no special emphasis here on the presence of the cohesive coercions (civic attractions) that hold the population together in competition with the relocation inducements from other sources.

We again take it as a matter of observation that in any actual city there exists 'civic wealths' of one kind or another, the expenditure of which is a consequence of civic activities of various kinds, and which may be increased both by exogenous inputs and by internal activities. In the first part of this paper we have noted one particular kind of civic wealth—locational wealth—which exists in the presence of attraction coercions between the elements of the population. It is quite feasible to develop notions of other kinds of civic wealth—for example, 'banked' or 'stored wealth' (internal energy), 'activity wealth' arising in connexion with economic, commercial, and social activities (heat energy), 'mobility wealth' arising in connexion with transportation and other 'kinetic field' activities (kinetic energy), etc.—all of which can be gained, possessed, or expended by elements of the civic matter in the city. (The references to thermodynamic energies are to be regarded more as metaphors than as direct analogies.) But at this stage of the study it is preferable to be no more specific than to think of a generalised kind of civic wealth, the possession of which increases a city's capacity to undertake civic activities of a general kind [see for example, Woldenberg (1968), and Wilson (1968, 1970) for other comments on these notions].

Thus we shall now postulate that there is a distribution throughout our urbanitic system C of civic wealth, and that, as a measure of the 'wealthiness' or possession of this entity, we can describe the distribution by a positive measure function Ω, such that to each portion of the population of mass M in the city we can assign a positive numerical value $\Omega(M)$ of its wealthiness. To avoid any preconceptions as to what kind of wealth we are referring to, we shall call Ω the *opulence* distribution, and its reciprocal $1/\Omega$ the *poverty* distribution, in the urbanitic system C. Again, for the present, we regard Ω as having only a constant (but not fixed) value throughout any region of the system over which the population density is not zero, and a zero value elsewhere.

The values of the density τ, rental p, and opulence Ω which occur simultaneously in an urbanitic system C will be called a *state* of the system C, and we shall use the notation $C(\tau, p, \Omega)$ to denote that C is in the state (τ, p, Ω). Since we are only assuming that each value of each of τ, p, and Ω is a constant throughout C, we see that the *state space* of the urbanitic system [that is, the collection of all triples (τ, p, Ω)] is merely the euclidean space $\mathbf{R}^3$. We now define the system C to be in an *equilibrium state* (τ, p, Ω) if the net resultant of all the inducements on C to depart from this state has vanished; this state is then *stable* if C will always return to it following any small perturbation away from it; it is *neutrally stable* if C remains in any neighbouring perturbed state after the perturbation has ceased; it is *unstable* if it is neither stable nor neutrally stable. (We cannot at present discuss the nature of the inducements which can cause C to change from one state to another except to assume that they arise either in the ongoing civic activities connected with the possession of civic wealth, or from external sources.)

6 Urbanitic laws

We further postulate that throughout our urbanitic system C the three distributions, of density τ, rental p, and opulence Ω, satisfy certain functional relations which characterise the abstract city in question. We shall call these relations *urbanitic laws* for the abstract city C. The particular laws we shall investigate here are:

$$p = K\Omega\tau \qquad \text{('simple city')}, \qquad (10)$$

$$p = \frac{K\Omega\tau}{1 - \beta\tau} \qquad \text{('congested city')}, \qquad (11)$$

$$p + \alpha\tau^2 = K\Omega\tau \qquad \text{('evanescent city')}, \qquad (12)$$

$$p + \alpha\tau^2 = \frac{K\Omega\tau}{1 - \beta\tau} \qquad \text{('saccadic city')}. \qquad (13)$$

Thus an urbanitic law u is simply a constraint $u(\tau, p, \Omega) = 0$ on the possible states available to an urbanitic system. The locus

$$U = \{(\tau, p, \Omega) \in \mathbf{R}^3 | \ u(\tau, p, \Omega) = 0\} \qquad (14)$$

of states of C, which satisfy a given urbanitic law u, is a surface U in the state space $\mathbf{R}^3$ of the urbanitic system C; we shall call U the *urbanitic sheet* for C. A knowledge of the sheet U will permit a description of the behaviour of the urbanitic system in question.

The simple city law postulates that the housing rental borne by the city is directly proportional (with proportionality constant $K > 0$, the rental coefficient) to the population density and the opulence. Alternatively it expresses the fact that, at any given level of rental, the density varies inversely as the city's opulence (that is, directly as its poverty): the more opulent the city the more spread out, at lower densities, is its population. Or, at a fixed level of opulence, the city will contract in the face of rising rentals, bringing about higher densities (ghettoes). Or again, in two comparable urbanitic cities, the rental is higher in that one with the greater opulence. Thus the 'simple' urbanitic law is not an implausible relation, however ideal it may appear.

In any given urbanitic city C for which the opulence is a fixed constant, we may absorb its value into the proportionality constant K, and write equation (10) merely as

$$p = K\tau. \qquad (10')$$

This relation—the urbanitic version of Boyle's law for physical gases—is then of course a particular case (cf. the 'mesotropic city') of the polytropic relation employed in the previous abstract coercion city theory.

From equation (10) we see that the ratio p/τ has the value $K\Omega$. Now τ has the dimensions of 'citizens per unit area', and the rental p is strictly speaking a 'price density' with dimensions of 'price per unit area'. Hence the ratio p/τ has the dimensions of 'price per citizen'. Consequently, whatever dimensions for K and Ω are ultimately decided upon, changes in the opulence Ω are directly proportional to changes in the housing commodity costs that can be borne by individuals in the city. Greater opulence goes with the capacity to bear greater individual housing costs. Or again, greater poverty goes with a lesser capacity of the system's citizens to bear the costs of the housing commodity consumed. (We observe in passing that any of the above densities and quantities involving 'citizens' may be generalised by replacing 'citizens' by 'households' after introducing further ratios such as h = housing price per household, H = average number of citizens per household, etc. But we shall not enlarge on this development here.)

The second urbanitic law (11) is a refinement of the first, and corresponds with an 'imperfect gas law' in physics. The motivation is as follows. Since $1/\tau$ has the dimensions of 'area per citizen', it is a measure of the specific area or specific spatial extent of the citizens in the urbanitic city C. We shall refer to $1/\tau$ as the *specific space* in the system C. The simple urbanitic law then postulated that the rental p varied inversely as the specific space $1/\tau$ in the city: the larger the rental the smaller the specific space accepted by an individual. If the system is one which puts a premium on specific space—insofar as the residual space available to a citizen is of significant importance in determining the value of the housing commodity consumed—then it becomes important to consider the *net specific space*, $(1/\tau)-\beta$, of the citizen. Here $\beta > 0$ is the area ('personal-bubble space') occupied by an individual. In the simple city the specific space depended directly on the opulence and inversely on the rental: $1/\tau = K\Omega/p$. In the congested city the second urbanitic law (11) postulates that it is not the gross specific space $1/\tau$ which is so determined by the prevailing opulence and the rental, but the net specific space, thus: $(1/\tau)-\beta = K\Omega/p$. This means that the density determined by a given level of opulence and rental is less in the congested city than it would have been in the simple city. Expressed differently: in the congested city the rental that would have prevailed for a given level of opulence and density in the simple city has now been increased in the ratio,

$$\frac{1}{\tau}\bigg/\left(\frac{1}{\tau}-\beta\right) = \frac{1}{1-\beta\tau} > 1\ ,$$

of the gross to the net specific space. This ratio we may call the 'occupancy factor'. It has values typically in the range from $1\cdot02$ in small towns up to $1\cdot25$ in the central zones of large cities. For values of τ in the range $40 < \tau < 400$ persons per hectare (40 persons/ha $\approx$ 10000 persons/mile^2),

$1/\tau$ lies between 250 and 25 m², whilst β is of the order of 5 m² and represents between 2 and 20 *percent* of the gross specific space $1/\tau$.

The third urbanitic law (12) is also a refinement of the first, but is independent of the second. The motivation this time lies in the observation that p/τ, the price of housing commodity per citizen that can be borne by an individual, may itself be influenced by the prevailing local population density. Thus, in highly crowded zones, an individual may desire to pay less for the housing consumed (or more, according to the social and urban economic attitudes of the community in question). To a first approximation, it is reasonable to assume that the ratio p/τ (given by $K\Omega$ in the simple city) is modified by an amount proportional to the local density, so that we must replace $K\Omega$ by $K\Omega - \alpha\tau$, where α is a constant which we shall call the 'density response factor'. Consequently the urbanitic law (10) becomes $(p/\tau) = K\Omega - \alpha\tau$, which we may rewrite as in equation (12).

The fourth urbanitic law (13) is simply the result of combining the two previous modifications—which are independent of each other. It may be rewritten in the form

$$(p + \alpha\tau^2)\left(\frac{1}{\tau} - \beta\right) = K\Omega \,,$$

in which it can be recognised (after writing V for the specific space $1/\tau$) as having the same form as the van der Waals' law for imperfect physical gases. The motivation behind the choice of the name 'saccadic' (having a jumping or jerking motion) for this law is made clear in detail in the next section. But briefly it is because an urbanitic system obeying such a law can exhibit discontinuous changes in the density in response to continuous changes in the opulence and the rental, abrupt changes analogous to the phase changes in a van der Waals' gas in response to continuous changes in the gas temperature and pressure. Such discontinuities have been included amongst the class of system singularities termed 'catastrophes' in the work of René Thom (compare for example Thom, 1969, 1972; Zeeman, 1971, 1972; Fowler, 1972).

7 Catastrophic growth modes
The behaviour of an urbanitic system C is determined by the changes in the states (τ, p, Ω). The changes that are available to C depend of course on which urbanitic law the city is obeying. The system's possible range of behaviour can thus be understood by examining the system's urbanitic sheet U, and by observing how the available values of the population density τ are determined by the prevailing values of the rental p and the opulence Ω, under each urbanitic law. Obviously we need only consider that part of the urbanitic sheet which lies over the positive (p, Ω)-quadrant $\{(p, \Omega) \in \mathbf{R}^2 \mid p > 0, \Omega > 0\}$, since we do not envisage at this stage the presence of negative rental and opulence {though we note that there are

no *a priori* reasons for not doing so, or even for not including negative densities [cf.Amson (1972b), for other comments on 'urban–rural' and 'polarised' populations]}. We now describe the characteristic features of the urbanitic sheet in each of the four cases defined in section 6.

(1) *Simple cities* Here we have, from equation (10),

$$\tau = \frac{p}{\Omega K} \ ,$$

so that over the positive (p, Ω)-quadrant the urbanitic sheet U is a smooth unfolded surface having a constant upwards slope in the direction of increasing rentals p, and a downwards slope in the direction of increasing opulence Ω (a slope whose steepness decreases rapidly). There are no singularities in the density τ in a simple city: smooth changes of (positive) rental and opulence are always accompanied by smooth changes of density. If the total mass of population in the city remains constant, the city's total spatial extent contracts as the density increases in response to any increase in housing rental; it expands as the density decreases in response to an increase in the city's opulence.

(2) *Congested cities* From equation (11) we now have

$$\tau = \frac{p}{\beta p + K\Omega} \ ,$$

so that at low rentals p, and great opulence Ω, the population density behaves very much like it did in the simple city. However, as the opulence decreases (and the poverty increases), or as the rental increases substantially, the density tends to increase towards a maximum fixed value $1/\beta$. In other words the specific space in the city tends to decrease towards its lowest possible value, β, the 'personal-bubble space' of the individual citizen. Thus in extreme cases of great poverty and high rentals, the city becomes densely crowded and practically all of an individual's residual specific space $(1/\tau) - \beta$ disappears. No matter how much further the rental is raised or the city's poverty increased, no further crowding can take place—unless the personal-bubble space β of each individual is allowed to shrink. The city has become *congested*.

(3) *Evanescent cities* Since the law (12) is quadratic in the density τ, there must be a constraint,

$$K^2 \Omega^2 \geqslant 4\alpha p \ , \tag{15}$$

on the values of the rental p and the opulence Ω in order that they correspond to real values of the density. If the density-response factor $\alpha < 0$ (that is, if at high densities individuals are willing to pay more for the housing commodity they consume than in the simple city), then condition (15) is satisfied for every rental $p > 0$, no matter what the opulence of the city is. But if $\alpha > 0$ (that is, if individuals perceive high densities as a disadvantage to their enjoyment of the housing commodity consumed), then condition (15) can only be satisfied in sufficiently opulent cities, or in cities with sufficiently low rentals. We shall discuss these two cases separately.

Case 1: $\alpha > 0$

Because there are two values (both positive) of τ which satisfy the law (12) when $K^2\Omega^2 > 4\alpha p$, the urbanitic sheet U for the city is a folded surface over the 'critical region',

$$K = \{(p, \Omega) \in \mathbf{R}^2 \mid K^2\Omega^2 \geqslant 4\alpha p \,,\, p > 0 \,,\, \Omega > 0\} \,,$$

in the positive quadrant of the (p, Ω)-plane; the fold occurs over the 'critical line',

$$K^* = \{(p, \Omega) \in \mathbf{R}^2 \mid K^2\Omega^2 = 4\alpha p \,,\, p > 0 \,,\, \Omega > 0\} \,.$$

It is likely (cf.section 8) that the lower sheet of U will correspond with unstable equilibrium states of the urbanitic system, and that only the upper surface (the larger values of τ) will correspond to stable equilibrium states and hence be accessible to the system. If that be so, then we need only consider the upper values of τ given by

$$\tau = \frac{K\Omega}{2\alpha}\left[1 + \left(1 - \frac{4\alpha p}{K^2\Omega^2}\right)^{\frac{1}{2}}\right] \,.$$

Over the critical line K^* the density τ has its least value, $K\Omega/2\alpha$, and over the interior of the critical region K the density lies between once and twice its least value. Thus high densities can only be reached in such a city as this [which finds high densities an economic disadvantage $(\alpha > 0)$] by the city becoming very opulent. But looked at in quite a different way we see that, at fixed rentals, this city tends to expand to lower densities as the opulence Ω falls—and the poverty $1/\Omega$ increases. This dispersal of the population persists until the poverty reaches the critical level $1/\Omega^*$ (at the critical line K^*, where $\Omega^* = 2(\alpha p)^{\frac{1}{2}}/K$]. If the poverty should increase beyond that level, the population density τ becomes imaginary—the city has become *evanescent*. This situation—of a city becoming evanescent with increasing poverty—we shall refer to as a *catastrophic growth* (or rather *decay*) *of the first kind* (cf.'Fold catastrophe', section 8).

Case 2: $\alpha < 0$

This is a less interesting case. There are two real values of τ corresponding to every pair of values (p, Ω) in the positive (p, Ω)-quadrant, but only one of these is positive. Thus so far as we are concerned here, the urbanitic sheet U consists only of a single surface over the whole positive (p, Ω)-quadrant. But the behaviour of the city in this case differs essentially from that of the simple city in that the density now increases with increasing opulence instead of decreasing.

(4) *Saccadic cities* Despite the fact that the saccadic law (13) is a simple compound of the laws of the two previous types, laws (11) and (12), the behaviour of a saccadic city is by no means a combination of the separate behaviours of a congested city and an evanescent city. In order to analyse clearly the relation between population density τ, and the values of the rental p and opulence Ω in a saccadic city, it is helpful to make a number of preliminary transformations of the urbanitic relation (13). After writing $\tau = 1+t$, $p = 1+q$, $\Omega = 1+w$, and choosing temporary values of $\alpha = 9$, $\beta = \frac{1}{3}$, $K = \frac{8}{3}$, equation (13) transforms to

$$3t^3 + (8w + q)t + 8w - 2q = 0 .$$

Further, writing $8w + q = y$ and $8w - 2q = z$ (so that $3q = y - z$ and $24w = 2y - z$), we transform the last cubic equation into the form

$$3t^3 + yt + z = 0 . \tag{16}$$

To each pair of values (p, Ω) there corresponds a unique pair of values (y, z) and either one, two, or three values of t which satisfy the saccadic law in the form of equation (16). The critical ('cusp') set,

$$K = \{(y, z) \in \mathbf{R}^2 \mid 4y^3 + 27z^2 \leqslant 0 , \; y \neq 0 , \; z \neq 0\} ,$$

is the subset of the (y, z)-plane for which equation (16) is satisfied by more than one value of t for each of its pairs (y, z); its boundary,

$$K^* = \{(y, z) \in \mathbf{R}^2 \mid 4y^3 + 27z^2 = 0 , \; y \neq 0 , \; z \neq 0\} ,$$

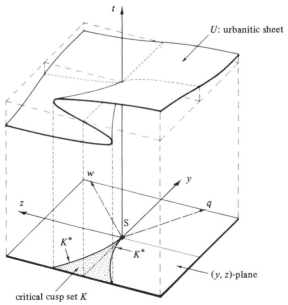

Figure 5. The urbanitic sheet U and the critical cusp set K for a saccadic city.

is the critical line on which equation (16) is satisfied by two distinct
values of t for each pair (y, z); its interior $K - K^*$ is the critical region
on which equation (16) is satisfied by three distinct values of t for each
pair (y, z). At the 'cusp point' $(y, z) = (0, 0)$, these three values have
coincided at the single value $t = 0$.

The urbanitic sheet U for the city is uniquely determined as the set of
all triples (t, y, z) which satisfy equation (16). From the foregoing
remarks it follows that U is a surface covering the (y, z)-plane with a
double fold over the critical cusp set K, the edges of the folds lying over
the cusp line K^*, and with a singularity at the cusp point $(0, 0)$—as
illustrated in figure 5. By transforming back to the original variables
(p, Ω), it can be shown that the critical cusp set K in the (y, z)-plane is
transformed as illustrated in figure 6.

Using figures 5 and 6 we can describe the behaviour of a system
obeying the saccadic law (13) by following what happens to the density τ
as we change the rental p and the opulence Ω along, say, the rectangular
path A B C D E F A shown in figure 7, first in an anticlockwise direction,
then in a clockwise one. The changes in density are illustrated in
figure 8. As the path enters the critical region K, in either direction, no
significant change in the steady fall in density occurs until the path
leaves the region K. As the path passes over the critical cusp line K^*, on
its way out of K, the density undergoes a discontinuous ('saccadic') leap
up (at F), or down (at D), depending on which way the path is being
traversed. This situation—in which saccadic behaviour in the density can
result from smooth changes in either the rental or the opulence in the
city—we shall refer to as a *catastrophic growth of the second kind*
(cf.'cusp catastrophe', section 8).

It is also clear from figures 5 and 6 that saccadic behaviour cannot occur
in cities which are opulent enough, or which have high enough rentals,
since the states of such a city lie away from the critical cusp set K in the
(p, Ω)-plane. Moreover, by considering a path such as G F in figure 7, we

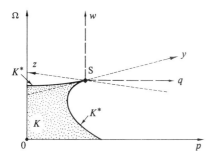

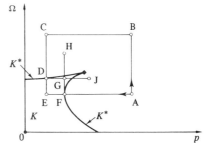

Figure 6. The critical cusp set K in the
(p, Ω)-plane [transformed from the
(y, z)-plane]. p = rental; Ω = opulence.

Figure 7. Typical catastrophic growth
paths in the (p, Ω)-plane (see figure 8 for
the associated changes in population
densities). p = rental; Ω = opulence.

see that a city may suffer a saccadic increase in density when its opulence
falls from Ω_G to Ω_F, but that the density never returns to its earlier low
value when the opulence returns to its earlier high value Ω_G (since the
higher density is still on the upper surface of the cusp fold in the urbanitic
sheet U). Lower densities are only recoverable once again if the city can
further increase its opulence to Ω_H, say, and so permit the density to
drop saccadically over the edge of the cusp fold in U down to the lower
surface again. Analogous remarks apply to a decrease in rental from p_G
to p_D, say; the density drops saccadically across the critical cusp line K^*,
and no fresh increase in rental will bring about a return to the old high
densities until the rentals have grown large enough, to p_J say, for the
saccadic increase to reappear as the increasing rental crosses the critical
line K^* at the other side of the region K.

[Although the natural 'inertia' in any actual city would prohibit any
truly saccadic jumps in density, in real time, it is thought that examples of
such growth can be found in the case where the opulence is regarded as a
measure of the mobility ('kinetic wealthiness') of the city's population.
Many European and North American cities have exhibited 'approximately
saccadic' expansions of territory, with attendant falls in density, as the
mobility increased and housing rentals fell in response to technological
innovations in transportation.]

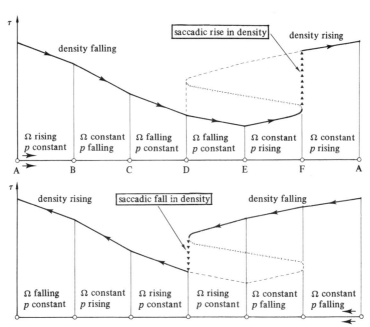

Figure 8. Two typical catastrophic growth diagrams for a saccadic city. The changes
in population density τ, opulence Ω, and housing rental p are shown as the growth
path A B C D E F A in the (p, Ω)-plane (see figure 7) is traversed in opposite directions.

8 General theory of catastrophic growth

It is reasonable to ask whether more complicated urbanitic laws than those introduced in section 7 would lead to yet more complicated behaviour in an urbanitic system. The answer would be negative—that is, the kinds of singular behaviour available to an urbanitic city C with the *three* parametric distributions τ, p, Ω, say, could only *essentially* be of the two kinds of catastrophic growth discussed in section 7—provided certain circumstances were satisfied. These we now discuss.

We have already defined (in section 3) one particular kind of civic wealth in an abstract city, namely locational wealth ('potential energy'), and have mentioned (in section 5) the possibility of defining other kinds. Going into no further details, suppose that to each urbanitic system C there corresponds a finite family $(W_i)_{i \in I}$ of different kinds of civic wealths W_i, each one a function of the three civic parameters τ, p, and Ω. Let W denote the *total wealth* $\sum_{i \in I} W_i$ of the system. Now either we postulate the existence of a 'principle of conservation of civic wealth': "For every accessible state (τ, p, Ω) of the urbanitic system, the total wealth $W = W(\tau, p, \Omega)$ is invariant"; or we do not. If we do, then the family $(W_i)_{i \in I}$ is not independent, and we must postulate that there exists at least one subfamily $(W_i)_{i \in J \subset I}$, consisting of all but one of the original wealths W_i, which is an independent family. And then we postulate that the behaviour of the urbanitic system can be determined by the total wealth $W_0 = \sum_{i \in J} W_i$ of this subfamily. If we do not, we must postulate that the original family is independent, and that the behaviour of the system can be determined by the total wealth $W = \sum_{i \in I} W_i$. To fix our ideas and to simplify the notation, we shall adopt the latter hypothesis. Then the total wealth is a function $W : (\tau, p, \Omega) \mapsto W(\tau, p, \Omega) : \mathbf{R}^3 \to \mathbf{R}$ of the system's state space into the real numbers, and we assume it to be smooth (that is, infinitely differentiable).

We have also required each urbanitic system to be constrained by an urbanitic law, $u(\tau, p, \Omega) = 0$ (cf.section 6), from which we may determine values of the density corresponding to some or all pairs of values (p, Ω) of the rental and opulence. Hence it is now profitable for us to regard our urbanitic system C as a control system, one in which the control is measured by the two *control* parameters, rental p and opulence Ω, and the state of the system is then measured by the single *state* parameter, density τ; and, moreover, one in which the system's behaviour is determined by the total wealth function W using the criteria that the stationary (that is, critical) values of W correspond to the equilibrium states of C—minima of W to stable ones, maxima of W to unstable ones, and inflexions of W to neutral ones (cf.Zeeman, 1972).

It is then a theorem in the catastrophe theory introduced by Thom that the singularities ('catastrophes') in the system's behaviour are

then precisely of the two types (cf.Thom, 1969, table 1):
(1) the *fold* catastrophe (catastrophe of dimension 1 and codimension 1),
(2) the *cusp* or *Riemann–Hugoniot* catastrophe (catastrophe of dimension 1 and codimension 2).
{In our examples in section 7, the 'dimension' refers to the fact that the wealth function W has a one-dimensional range R, and 'codimension' refers to the presence either of only one of the two control parameters p and Ω (cf.the evanescent city case in which only the parameter p exercises an essential control), or of both of them (cf.the saccadic city, controlled by both p and Ω). The behaviour-determining function V in Thom's theory corresponds to our wealth function W. Equating to zero the derivative $\partial V/\partial x$ of the 'universal unfolding' of the fold and the cusp catastrophe (Thom, *loc. cit.*) gives $x^2 + u = 0$ and $x^2 + ux + v = 0$, respectively. These two relations determine the equilibria in the corresponding systems: for each value of the control parameter u, or pair of values (u, v), they determine the corresponding equilibrium value of the state parameter x. Our urbanitic laws (12) and (13) [cf.equation (16)] are in fact topologically equivalent to these relations.}

This theorem allows us to state our conclusion: in any urbanitic system of the kind we have discussed here—in which only two parameters, p and Ω say, control a third, τ—the only kinds of catastrophic growth available to the system are essentially of the first and second kind (cf.section 7), associated with the evanescent city and the saccadic city respectively. In more elaborate systems we would expect the catastrophic growth behaviour to be of the more complicated kind associated with elementary catastrophes of higher dimension and codimension.

Acknowledgement. This essay is based on research financed during 1970-1971 by a Research Grant from the Centre for Environmental Studies, London.

References
Amson, J. C., 1972a, "Equilibrium models of cities: 1. An axiomatic theory", *Environment and Planning*, 4, 429-444.
Amson, J. C., 1972b, "Equilibrium models of cities: 2. Single species cities", *Environment and Planning*, 5, 295-338.
Fowler, D. H., 1972, "The Riemann–Hugoniot catastrophe and van der Waals equation", in *Towards a Theoretical Biology: 4 Essays*, Ed. C. H. Waddington (Edinburgh University Press, Edinburgh), pp.276-282.
Thom, R., 1969, "Topological models in biology", *Topology*, 8, 313-335.
Thom, R., 1972, *Stabilité Structurelle et Morphogenèse* (Benjamin, New York).
Wilson, A. G., 1968, "Notes on some concepts in social physics", *Papers, The Regional Science Association XXII* (Budapest Conference, 1968), 159-193.
Wilson, A. G., 1970, *Entropy in Urban and Regional Modelling* (Pion, London), Chapter 7.
Woldenberg, M. J., 1968, "Energy flow and spatial order", *Geographical Review*, 58, 552-574.
Zeeman, E. C., 1971, "The geometry of catastrophe", *Times Literary Supplement*, number 3641 (December 10th, 1971), 1556-1557.
Zeeman, E. C., 1972, "A catastrophe machine", in *Towards a Theoretical Biology: 4 Essays*, Ed. C. H. Waddington (Edinburgh University Press, Edinburgh), pp.1-7.

Spatial Equilibrium in an Ideal Urban Setting with Continuously Distributed Incomes

E.CASETTI
Ohio State University

This paper reports an investigation of the spatial equilibrium distribution of households with identical preferences but different incomes, in an ideal urban setting. An income distribution into a finite number of classes is considered first, and then continuous distributions of incomes are discussed. Spatial equilibrium distributions of incomes, land values, and population densities are investigated. The model in the paper is related to earlier work by Beckmann (1969), Montesano (1972), and Casetti (1970, 1971). Its potential usefulness in connection with some phases of empirical research is noted.

The model

Assume a homogeneous urban area with all places of employment concentrated in a central location, called the Central Business District (CBD). The urban area is circular in shape and has a radius of $\bar{\bar{s}}_n$. All the urban land is available for residential use, and belongs to landowners who strive to obtain for it the highest rent possible. The urban area is inhabited by one person households, identical in preferences but different in incomes. Let the households' preferences be indicated by a utility function u,

$$u = u(z, q, s) = z^a q^b f(s) , \tag{1}$$

specifying the combinations of a composite good z, of quantity of residential land q, and of the distance s of their residences from the CBD, this giving to a household the same aggregate 'utility'; a and b are parameters; $f(s)$ is an unspecified function of s, identifying the positive (or negative) preference of the households for a central location. The function $f(s)$ should be a monotonically decreasing function of s if it is assumed that the households are influenced only by accessibility to place of work and possibly to the amenities located at the CBD. If congestion and pollution, which are greater near the CBD, are entered into the model, then $f(s)$ should be either monotonically increasing, or increasing at first and then decreasing as s is increased (Mirrlees, 1972; Papageorgiou, 1972a). Let p, $r(s)$, and k be respectively unit price of the composite good, unit price of residential land at distance s from the CBD, and commuting costs per unit of distance. Assume that the households are differentiated into n income classes with incomes y_i ($i = 1, 2, ..., n$), where $y_i < y_{i+1}$, and let P_i denote the number of households with an income of y_i. Each household of the ith class is confronted by a budget constraint,

$$y_i = pz + r(s)q + ks ,\qquad(2)$$

stating that the sum of the outlays for the purchase of the composite good, for the rent of a parcel of residential land, and for commuting must equal its income. The value of p is given, and is assumed to be spatially invariant. The households strive to maximize their income, subject to the condition that their budget constraints are not violated.

Define a state of spatial equilibrium, of an ideal (spatial) system identified by a set of assumptions, as a state of the system such that the actors in it are not motivated to change if they act in accordance with the rules of behavior attributed to them. Here, therefore, an equilibrium exists if neither landowners nor households are permitted to increase respectively their rent or the degree of satisfaction of their preferences by initiating or promoting a change. Specifically a state of spatial equilibrium will exist, within the urban system defined by the assumptions above, if the following conditions are met:

1 no household may increase its optimal utility level by relocating within the urban area or by changing its consumption mix of z and q;
2 the land value distribution is such that no landowner may increase his rent by forcing the households residing on his land to relocate;
3 the market is cleared, because all the land available is occupied at all distances from the CBD, and all urban residents are housed somewhere within the urban area.

Equilibrium within a spatial setting wider than the urban area would require that no household, irrespective of its income, should be able to increase its optimum utility level by moving into or out of the urban area, and that the lowest land value in the urban area should be equal to value of the land in agricultural use. Here, by taking the total number of households and the urbanized area as given, only the within-city equilibrium is focussed upon.

The object of this paper is to identify the intraurban spatial equilibrium distribution of households according to income and the distributions of population densities and land values associated with this household distribution.

Let $\bar{z}_i$ and $\bar{q}_i$ be the values of z and q which give a constrained maximum of the utility function u, for a given value of s, to a household with an income of y_i. Thus $\bar{z}_i$ and $\bar{q}_i$ are such that

$$u(\bar{z}_i, \bar{q}_i, s) = \text{maximum} ,$$

and

$$p\bar{z}_i + r(s)\bar{q}_i + ks = y_i ;$$

$\bar{z}_i$ and $\bar{q}_i$ are demands for the composite good and for residential land respectively, and are functions of p, z, y_i, and s, as well as of the parameters of the utility function. By using standard optimization procedures, we obtain

$$\bar{z}_i = \bar{z}(r, y_i, s) = \frac{a(y_i - ks)}{vp} \, , \tag{3}$$

$$\bar{q}_i = \bar{q}(r, y_i, s) = \frac{b(y_i - ks)}{vr} \, , \tag{4}$$

where $v = a + b$.

Let $\bar{u}(r, y_i, s)$ be the optimum utility level attainable by a household with an income of y_i, residing at distance s from the CBD, and confronted by a land value of r, where

$$\bar{u}_i = u(\bar{z}_i, \bar{q}_i, s) = \left(\frac{a}{p}\right)^a \left(\frac{b}{r}\right)^b \left(\frac{y_i - ks}{v}\right)^v f(s) \, . \tag{5}$$

According to equilibrium condition '1', at equilibrium no household should be able to increase its optimum utility level by relocating. This implies that at equilibrium the optimum utility level $\bar{u}_i$, attainable by households with an income of y_i, is the same in all locations where these households reside. By imposing the condition

$$u(\bar{z}_i, \bar{q}_i, s) = \bar{\bar{u}}_i = \text{constant} \, , \tag{6}$$

a land-value–distance function $\bar{\bar{r}}_i(s)$, where

$$\bar{\bar{r}}_i(s) = \left[\left(\frac{a}{p}\right)^a b^b \left(\frac{y_i - ks}{v}\right)^v \frac{f(s)}{\bar{\bar{u}}_i}\right]^{1/b} \, , \tag{7}$$

is implicitly defined, capable of insuring that the households with an income of y_i attain an identical level of satisfaction of their preferences $\bar{\bar{u}}_i$. That is to say, if the rent levels $\bar{\bar{r}}_i(s)$ exist throughout the areas where the ith class of households reside, these households have no motivation to relocate within these areas. Therefore at equilibrium the rent paid by households of the ith class in the area where they reside is $\bar{\bar{r}}_i(s)$. By replacing r by $\bar{\bar{r}}$ in equation (4), we obtain the quantity of land $\bar{\bar{q}}_i$, consumed by a household of income y_i, when a state of equilibrium exists, where

$$\bar{\bar{q}}_i = \left\{\left[\frac{a(y_i - ks)}{vp}\right]^a \frac{f(s)}{\bar{\bar{u}}_i}\right\}^{-1/b} \, . \tag{8}$$

Equilibrium condition '2' requires that landowners may not attain greater rents by forcing households to relocate. This implies that, at equilibrium, all residential land is released to the households who are willing to pay the highest rent for it. Therefore, at equilibrium, households of classes i and j, where $j = i + 1$, may be found in the same annulus, bounded by circles at distances s^* and s^{**} ($s^{**} > s^*$) from the CBD, only if

$$\bar{\bar{r}}_i(s) = \bar{\bar{r}}_j(s) \qquad \text{for} \qquad s^* \leqslant s \leqslant s^{**} . \tag{9}$$

By using equation (7), equation (9) can be reduced to the following:

$$\frac{(y_i - ks)^v}{\bar{\bar{u}}_i} = \frac{(y_j - ks)^v}{\bar{\bar{u}}_j} . \tag{10}$$

Since y_i, y_j, $\bar{\bar{u}}_i$, and $\bar{\bar{u}}_j$ are given constants, equation (10) may be solved for one value of s, which will be denoted $\bar{\bar{s}}_i$,

$$\bar{\bar{s}}_i = \frac{\tilde{u}_j y_i - \tilde{u}_i y_j}{k(\tilde{u}_j - \tilde{u}_i)} , \tag{11}$$

where

$$\tilde{u}_i = \bar{\bar{u}}_i^{1/v} .$$

However, equation (10) cannot possibly hold for all the s values in an interval (s^*, s^{**}). Therefore, at equilibrium, households from two consecutive income classes cannot be found simultaneously in the same annulus. Instead they reside in distinct regions with a boundary in common and $\bar{\bar{s}}_i$ is the equilibrium boundary between these regions. Since $\bar{\bar{s}}_i$ is the distance from the CBD of the boundary separating the residential areas occupied by the households with incomes y_i and y_{i+1}, the $\bar{\bar{s}}_i$ values have to be positive. By the use of equation (11), it may easily be checked that

$$\bar{\bar{s}}_i > 0 ,$$

if

$$\tilde{u}_j y_i > \tilde{u}_i y_j . \tag{12}$$

Inequality (12) is therefore a restriction that should be satisfied for all y_i, $\tilde{u}_i$, y_j, and $\tilde{u}_j$, for all i and j, where $j = i+1$.

Since households from classes i and j may not be found at the same distance from the CBD, except at $\bar{\bar{s}}_i$, the question arises as to which households' residential area, at equilibrium, is closer to the CBD. Clearly the households who reside closer to or farther from the CBD must be prepared to pay higher rent. In order to tell who resides where, let us take a small interval $\bar{\bar{s}}_i + \mu\Delta s$ near the boundary $\bar{\bar{s}}_i$, and determine whether

$$\bar{\bar{r}}_i(\bar{\bar{s}}_i + \mu\Delta s) < \bar{\bar{r}}_j(\bar{\bar{s}}_i + \mu\Delta s) \qquad \text{for } \mu \neq 0 . \tag{13}$$

Since

$$y_j > y_i , \tag{14}$$

it is reasonable to assume that

$$\bar{\bar{u}}_j > \bar{\bar{u}}_i . \tag{15}$$

From equations (13) and (7) we obtain

$$\frac{[y_i - k(\overline{\overline{s}}_i + \mu \Delta s)]^v}{\overline{\overline{u}}_i} < \frac{[y_j - k(\overline{\overline{s}}_i + \mu \Delta s)]^v}{\overline{\overline{u}}_j} . \tag{16}$$

By definition,

$$\frac{(y_i - k\overline{\overline{s}}_i)^v}{\overline{\overline{u}}_i} = \frac{(y_j - k\overline{\overline{s}}_i)^v}{\overline{\overline{u}}_j} . \tag{17}$$

Equation (17) may be rewritten as

$$\frac{y_i - k\overline{\overline{s}}_i}{\tilde{u}_i} = \frac{y_j - k\overline{\overline{s}}_i}{\tilde{u}_j} , \tag{18}$$

and inequality (16) may be rewritten as

$$\frac{y_i - k\overline{\overline{s}}_i}{\tilde{u}_i} - \frac{k\mu \Delta s}{\tilde{u}_i} < \frac{y_j - k\overline{\overline{s}}_i}{\tilde{u}_j} - \frac{k\mu \Delta s}{\tilde{u}_j} ,$$

which because of equation (18) reduces to

$$\frac{\mu}{\tilde{u}_i} > \frac{\mu}{\tilde{u}_j} . \tag{19}$$

Inequality (19) holds for any μ greater than zero. Therefore inequalities (13) and (19) imply that, at equilibrium, the richer households of class $i+1$ will be prepared to pay higher rent in the area at a distance from the CBD greater than $\overline{\overline{s}}_i$. Therefore any two classes of households with incomes y_i and y_{i+1} will reside in two nonoverlapping residential areas separated by a circular boundary at distance $\overline{\overline{s}}_i$ from the CBD. The richer households will reside farther from the CBD than the boundary, while the households with an income of y_i will reside closer to the CBD than the boundary. At the boundary the rent bid value for the two classes of households is identical. By applying this reasoning to all consecutive classes of households, the ordering of households, at equilibrium, is easily obtained. The households of the lowest income class y_1 will locate in a circular area centered on the CBD with boundary at a distance $\overline{\overline{s}}_1$ from the CBD. The households of the next lowest class will be located in a ring bounded by two circles of radius $\overline{\overline{s}}_1$ and $\overline{\overline{s}}_2$, and so on up to the class of households with the highest income y_n. The latter will be located in the outermost ring bounded by the limit of the urban area $\overline{\overline{s}}_n$ on the outside, and the boundary with the next highest class of households at distance $\overline{\overline{s}}_{n-1}$ from the CBD. For any two consecutive classes of households the equilibrium land values are identical at the boundary between their respective areas.

Equilibrium condition '3' requires that all households of any class i should be provided with residential space and that all residential area should be allocated. The requirement, that the market be cleared, may be expressed as follows:

$$\int_{\bar{\bar{s}}_i}^{\bar{\bar{s}}_{i+1}} \frac{2\pi s}{\bar{\bar{q}}_i(s)} ds = P_i , \qquad i = 0, 1, ..., n-1 , \tag{20}$$

where $\bar{\bar{s}}_0 = 0$ and $\bar{\bar{s}}_n$ is the radius of the urbanized area. In fact, equation (20) insures that all P_i households with an income of y_i are allocated to the annulus bounded by circles of radius $\bar{\bar{s}}_i$ and $\bar{\bar{s}}_{i-1}$ and vice versa.

To sum up, at equilibrium the urban area is divided into concentric rings, each occupied by households with the same income. The higher the income the more distant the respective ring is from the city center. The equilibrium land values paid by households of consecutive income classes is identical at the boundary between their respective areas. At equilibrium all households are housed and all the urban residential areas are allocated. The outer boundary $\bar{\bar{s}}_n$ of the outermost ring, inhabited by the households belonging to the highest income class, is identified by the radius of the urbanized area and, within the context considered, is given.

Continuous income distribution

The distribution of the households into discrete income classes provides a convenient starting point to investigate the equilibrium patterns corresponding to a setting where the households have continuously distributed incomes.

A continuous distribution of incomes may be construed as the limiting case approached by decreasing the separation of the households' income classes and increasing their number. Clearly the size of income classes considered in the first part of this paper does not affect the household spatial distribution patterns. That is to say, if the number of classes, whatever that might be, is doubled while the size of each class is halved, the spatial equilibrium distribution of the households will still be characterized by rings, with households of the ith class being assigned to the ith ring, counting the innermost one first. In other words the location of the higher-income households further away from the downtown area constitutes the equilibrium pattern irrespective of the number of discrete income classes considered. But incomes are measured in some currency unit, and a continuous income distribution may be construed only as an approximation to a discrete income-class distribution in which classes differ at most by the smallest monetary unit available. Therefore we have to assume that in an ideal setting, characterized by continuously distributed incomes, households with the same income still locate at the same distance from the CBD, and that this distance increases, the greater the income. Therefore let us assume here that in the continuous case the distance s, where the households with an income of y are located at equilibrium, is a monotonically increasing function of y, namely

$$s = s(y) \,, \tag{21}$$

and

$$\frac{ds}{dy} > 0 \,. \tag{22}$$

The basic difference of having discrete income classes as against continuously distributed incomes is that in the former case some points in the urban area lay in homogeneously settled residential rings and some on boundaries, while in the latter case every point in the urban area is on a boundary. The setting with continuously distributed incomes is in fact the limit of a process whereby the income classes increase in number and decrease in 'size', while the circular boundaries of the annuli of residential land that they occupy approach one another and coalesce in the limit. This implies that, in the continuous setting, equation (11), specifying $\bar{s}_i$ as function of y_i, $\bar{u}_i$, y_j, and $\bar{u}_j$, reduces to a relationship between $\bar{u}$, y, and s which will be derived in the following section.

Equation (11) specifies in the discrete case the location of the boundary $\bar{s}_i$ between the areas occupied by the households of classes i and $i+1$. $\bar{s}_i$ is a function of incomes and optimum utility level attained at equilibrium by the two classes of households. In the discrete case it was assumed that if $y_j > y_i$ then $\bar{\bar{u}}_j > \bar{\bar{u}}_i$, since richer households should be capable of a higher level of satisfaction of their preferences. Here let us assume that $\bar{\bar{u}}$ is some well-behaved monotonically-increasing function of y, namely

$$\bar{\bar{u}} = \bar{\bar{u}}(y) \,, \tag{23}$$

and

$$\frac{d\bar{\bar{u}}}{dy} > 0 \,. \tag{24}$$

Let us now replace the income classes y_i and y_j, considered in the earlier portion of this paper, with the income classes y and $y + \delta y$. The relationship between $\bar{s}_i$, y_i, $\bar{\bar{u}}_i$, y_j, and $\bar{\bar{u}}_j$, specified by equation (11), may then be rewritten as follows:

$$k\bar{s} = \frac{y\bar{u}(y + \delta y) - (y + \delta y)\bar{u}(y)}{\bar{u}(y + \delta y) - \bar{u}(y)} \,, \tag{25}$$

where

$$\bar{u}(y) = \bar{\bar{u}}(y)^{1/v} \,.$$

By dividing the numerator and denominator of the right hand side of equation (25) by δy, we have

$$k\bar{s} = \frac{y\bar{u}(y + \delta y) - (y + \delta y)\bar{u}(y)}{\delta y} \bigg/ \frac{\bar{u}(y + \delta y) - \bar{u}(y)}{\delta y} \,, \tag{26}$$

which can be rearranged as

$$k\overline{\overline{s}} = y\left[\frac{\tilde{u}(y+\delta y)-\tilde{u}(y)}{\delta y}-\frac{\tilde{u}(y)}{y}\right]\bigg/\frac{\tilde{u}(y+\delta y)-\tilde{u}(y)}{\delta y}. \tag{27}$$

For $\delta y \to 0$, equation (27) yields the following differential equation,

$$(y-k\overline{\overline{s}})\frac{\mathrm{d}\tilde{u}}{\mathrm{d}y} = \tilde{u}, \tag{28}$$

the solution of which is

$$\overline{\overline{u}} = h(y-k\overline{\overline{s}})^{v}, \tag{29}$$

where h is an integration constant. Equation (29) is the equivalent of equation (11) in the continuous case. Since $\overline{\overline{s}}$ was defined as the equilibrium boundary between the areas occupied by households with incomes y and $y+\delta y$, in the limit, as $\delta y \to 0$, all distances s are also equilibrium boundaries $\overline{\overline{s}}$, and therefore equation (29) may be rewritten as

$$\overline{\overline{u}} = h(y-ks)^{v}. \tag{30}$$

Equation (30) does not contradict the equilibrium condition that households with the same income should attain the same optimum utility level wherever they reside, which is specified in the case of discrete income classes by equation (6). That no contradiction arises becomes obvious by considering that $\overline{\overline{u}}$ in equations (29) and (30) is the optimum utility level of households with an income of y, and that households with this income can only be found at s, by assumption.

In a setting characterized by a continuous income distribution, the equivalents of the equilibrium land-value function of equation (7) and of the equilibrium quantity of land consumed by a household of equation (8) are respectively

$$\overline{\overline{r}}(s) = \left[\left(\frac{a}{p}\right)^{a}b^{b}\left(\frac{y-ks}{v}\right)^{v}\frac{\mathrm{f}(s)}{\overline{\overline{u}}}\right]^{1/b}, \tag{31}$$

and

$$\overline{\overline{q}}(s) = \left\{\left[\frac{a(y-ks)}{vp}\right]^{a}\frac{\mathrm{f}(s)}{\overline{\overline{u}}}\right\}^{-1/b}. \tag{32}$$

By replacing $\overline{\overline{u}}$ from equation (30) in equation (31), the spatial-equilibrium rent in the continuous case is obtained:

$$\overline{\overline{r}}(s) = \left[\left(\frac{a}{p}\right)^{a}b^{b}hv^{-v}\mathrm{f}(s)\right]^{1/b}. \tag{33}$$

Equation (33) shows that in this context the equilibrium rent at s is not a function of the income of the households locating there. A similar result from different assumptions and in different contexts is given in Montesano (1972) and Papageorgiou (1972b). The value of the integration constant h is determined by imposing a suitable boundary condition, for instance, by specifying the land value at the city center or at the city's boundary. By replacing $\bar{\bar{u}}$ from equation (30) in equation (32), we obtain the equilibrium quantity of land consumed at distance s from the CBD by households with an income of y:

$$\bar{\bar{q}}(s) = \left[(y - ks)\left(\frac{pv}{a}\right)^a \frac{h}{\mathrm{f}(s)} \right]^{1/b} . \tag{34}$$

Equations (33) and (34) hold for any continuous distribution of incomes. However, in order to determine the function $y(s)$, identifying the equilibrium distribution of households of different incomes over the urban area, a specific income-distribution function is required. Assume that the households' incomes follow a Pareto distribution with parameters A and α, so that with $N(y)$ is the number of households with an income of y or larger:

$$N(y) = Ay^{-\alpha} . \tag{35}$$

Then the density of households per foot is $\alpha A y^{-\alpha-1} \, dy/ds$, and the equation insuring that the residential land market is cleared at all distances from the CBD may be shown to be (Beckmann, 1969, p.64; Montesano, 1972, p.331)

$$\bar{\bar{q}} \alpha A y^{-\alpha-1} \frac{dy}{ds} = 2\pi s . \tag{36}$$

Equation (36) is the equivalent of equation (20) in the continuous case. From equations (34) and (36) the following differential equation is obtained:

$$\frac{H(y - ks)y^{-\alpha-1}}{\mathrm{f}(s)} \frac{dy}{ds} = s , \tag{37}$$

where

$$H = \frac{\alpha A}{2\pi} \left[\left(\frac{pv}{a}\right)^a h \right]^{1/b} .$$

The solution of equation (37) is the equilibrium distribution of households of different incomes along s.

Equation (37) does not have any obvious solution. Its investigation could be carried out by assigning simple and plausible values to at least some of its parameters, and then obtaining an analytical solution for the simplified differential equation so obtained. Alternatively, numerical values for all parameters and initial conditions could be assumed, and a numerical solution over a suitable range of s derived. However, these lines of research will not be pursued here.

Equations (33), (34), and (37) constitute the results of the preceding discussion in that they define the equilibrium distribution of land values

and of consumption of land [1], and the equilibrium distribution of
households according to income in an ideal urban setting with incomes
following a Pareto distribution. Equilibrium distributions corresponding
to alternative utility functions and/or income-distribution functions could
be readily arrived at by reasoning analogous to that in the sections above.
Models incorporating continuous income distributions are potentially
useful, as regards empirical research, in that they provide a more realistic
frame of reference for interpreting the results of empirical investigations
of relationships between urban population densities and land values on
the one hand, and distance from the CBD on the other. It should be
pointed out, however, that the assumption which places all jobs at the
CBD, still hinders considerably the empirical relevance of models of this
type. In fact it limits their validity to those situations in which this
assumption does actually reflect to some significant degree the spatial
distribution of jobs in the real world. Work in which this assumption is
relaxed, perhaps by introducing a hierarchy of centers in place of a
single CBD (Papageorgiou, 1971), is indeed called for. As regards the
significance to empirical research of the specific results obtained here,
attention is called to the equilibrium land-value–distance relationship of
equation (33), which holds for any continuous distribution of incomes.
This relationship contains the function f(s) which represents, in the utility
function of the households, the extent of the households' positive or
negative preferences for residential locations at distance s from the CBD.
If f(s) is specified, equation (33) yields functions for which the parameters
may be estimated using real world data. A suitable specification of f(s)
might for instance be f(s) = exp($c_0 - c_1 s$), where c_0 and c_1 are constants,
c_1 positive. Substitution of this f(s) into equation (33) yields a negative-
exponential equilibrium land-value–distance function. This provides a
justification for fitting negative exponential functions to land-value–
distance data which do not depend upon stringent assumptions regarding
income distributions.

Differences with respect to earlier related work
In the following section, this paper's model is related to earlier work by
Beckmann (1969) and Casetti (1970, 1971). Beckmann assumes
households which are 'rational', in that they maximize their utility subject
to a budget constraint. The households have incomes following a Pareto
distribution, and live in a homogeneous urban area with all jobs
concentrated at the CBD. Beckmann's strategy hinges upon requiring that
the residential land market be cleared at all distances from the CBD, and
that all households be located so as to maximize their utility. His paper
focuses upon the derivation of the spatial distribution of households, and

[1] In this setting the equilibrium consumption of land is the reciprocal of equilibrium
population densities.

of land values, that satisfy these requirements. Mathematically this is accomplished (1) by the constrained maximization of the households' utility functions with respect to the composite good z, the quantity of land q, and the distance s from the CBD, and (2) by imposing the condition that, at all distances from the CBD, all available land is demanded. A set of differential equations is obtained and solved. The fact that the constrained maximization of the households utilities is carried out with respect to the distance from the CBD is one of the major differences with respect to this paper. Beckmann's approach appears to rest on a form of welfare optimality, since it involves maximizing the sum of the households' 'locational utilities'. In other words it would seem that Beckmann's strategy yields spatial distributions which correspond to the optimum of a welfare function consisting of the sum of the utilities of the households in the system. Of course, the spatial distributions of households and land value generated in this manner are not necessarily different from the ones corresponding to a state of equilibrium. However, the possibility should not be excluded that for some utility functions optimum and equilibrium distributions would differ.

The model discussed in this paper extends to a setting involving households with continuously distributed incomes, an approach employed in some earlier work by Casetti (1970, 1971). Alonso (1964), in his well-known contribution to the theory of urban land rent, discussed equilibrium in a context characterized by 'rational' households living in a homogeneous urban area with all jobs concentrated at a central location. However, in Alonso's work the problem of deriving equilibrium land-value–distance functions remains unsolved. In fact, Alonso (1964, p.150) is able to obtain "points of the price structure function but not the function itself". In Casetti (1971) an equilibrium land-value–distance function was arrived at by assuming households identical in preferences, consumption, and income, and by imposing the equilibrium condition that the households' optimal utility levels be equal to a spatially invariant constant. This spatial invariance insures that the households are not motivated to relocate within the urban area, under the rules of behavior (utility maximization) attributed to them. In a subsequent paper (Casetti, 1970) this setting was modified by assuming rich and poor households, identical in preferences and composition but equal in income only to the members of the same class, and by introducing explicitly into the model rent maximizing landowners. The condition, that the optimum utility level attainable by the rich and poor households be spatially invariant in their respective areas of residence, was complemented by an additional equilibrium condition requiring that the spatial distribution of rich and poor be such as to produce maximum rent. The combination of the two conditions insures that the households are not motivated to move, and that the landlords are not motivated to force them to move, under the rules of behavior specified in the model. This paper extends to the limit the differentiation of the households according to income, à la Beckmann, but it retains spatial equilibrium as its focus, and uses rent maximization and the spatial invariance of the maximum utility level of each class of households within their area of residence, as the basic equilibrium conditions.

Acknowledgement. The author wishes to thank Dr. R. Solow, Department of Economics, MIT, for calling his attention to a major mathematical shortcoming in an earlier version of this paper. The comments and criticisms of Dr. G. Papageorgiou, Department of Geography, McMaster University, are gratefully acknowledged. Any errors remaining in the text are the responsibility of the author.

References
Alonso, W., 1964, *Location and Land Use* (Harvard University Press, Cambridge, Mass.).
Beckmann, M. J., 1969, "On the distribution of urban rent and residential density", *Journal of Economic Theory*, 1, 60-67.
Casetti, E., 1970, "Spatial equilibrium distribution of 'rich' and 'poor' households in an idealized urban setting", Discussion Papers number 13, Department of Geography, Ohio State University, Columbus, Ohio.
Casetti, E., 1971, "Equilibrium land values and population densities in an urban setting", *Economic Geography*, 47, 16-20.
Mirrlees, J. A., 1972, "The optimum town", *The Swedish Journal of Economics*, 74, 114-135.
Montesano, A., 1972, "A restatement of Beckmann's model on the distribution of urban rent and residential density", *Journal of Economic Theory*, 4, 329-354.
Papageorgiou, G. J., 1971, "The population density and rent distribution models within a multicentre framework", *Environment and Planning*, 3, 267-282.
Papageorgiou, G. J., 1972a, "Population density and quality of the environment", in *International Geography, volume 2*, Eds. W. P. Adams, F. M. Helleiner (University of Toronto Press, Montreal), pp.921-922.
Papageorgiou, G. J., 1972b, "Spatial equilibrium within a hierarchy of centers with distributed incomes", manuscript.

Disaggregated Residential Location Models: Some Tests and Further Theoretical Developments

M.L.SENIOR, A.G.WILSON
University of Leeds

1 Introduction

In this paper we are primarily concerned with the empirical testing and further development of a residential location model derived from entropy maximising methods (Wilson, 1970a, 1970b), though one section of the paper is devoted to a discussion of an alternative model, at a similar level of resolution, obtained by modifying the model of Herbert and Stevens (1960). We will not give a detailed discussion of the derivation of the original model here: the reader is referred to the works mentioned above, and to a review of the model in a wider context in another paper (Senior, 1973). Here we simply define the variables and equations of the model as originally formulated. Let

T_{ij}^{kw} be the number of working heads of household resident in a type k house in zone i earning wage w in a job in zone j [1];

H_i^k be the number of type k houses in zone i;

E_j^w be the number of wage w jobs in zone j;

c_{ij} be the generalised cost of work trips between zones i and j;

c_{ij}' be the money cost of work trips between zones i and j;

p_i^k be the cost of a type k house in zone i; and

q^w be the average proportion of income, after deduction of journey to work costs, spent on housing by a w-income household.

Then the model is

$$T_{ij}^{kw} = A_i^k B_j^w H_i^k E_j^w \exp(-\beta^w c_{ij}) \exp\{-\mu^w [p_i^k - q^w(w - c_{ij}')]^2\}, \tag{1}$$

where

$$A_i^k = \left(\sum_j \sum_w B_j^w E_j^w \exp(-\beta^w c_{ij}) \exp\{-\mu^w [p_i^k - q^w(w - c_{ij}')]^2\} \right)^{-1} \tag{2}$$

to ensure that

$$\sum_j \sum_w T_{ij}^{kw} = H_i^k, \tag{3}$$

and

$$B_j^w = \left(\sum_i \sum_k A_i^k H_i^k \exp(-\beta^w c_{ij}) \exp\{-\mu^w [p_i^k - q^w(w - c_{ij}')]^2\} \right)^{-1} \tag{4}$$

to ensure that

$$\sum_i \sum_k T_{ij}^{kw} = E_j^w; \tag{5}$$

[1] Here we assume, in effect, one worker per household, who is also head of household; this assumption is relaxed in the next section.

β^w and μ^w are Lagrangian multipliers (which can be estimated directly through some calibration procedure) associated with the equations

$$\sum_i \sum_j \sum_k T_{ij}^{kw} c_{ij} = C^w \tag{6}$$

and

$$\sum_i \sum_j \sum_k T_{ij}^{kw} [p_i^k - q^w(w - c'_{ij})]^2 = \sigma^{w^2} \tag{7}$$

respectively.

In the next section of this paper we show how to modify the model to include workers who are not heads of households—whom we have called dependent workers. It is the model with this modification which has been the subject of most of our empirical work. Section 2.2 develops the model further to include households with no workers. In section 3 we discuss data needs, the associated spatial system, and computational feasibility, and in section 4 we describe our calibration and the results of our tests. Most of the theoretical developments which have been suggested to us by this empirical work are concerned with the housing budget mechanism, the term $\exp\{-\mu^w[p_i^k - q^w(w - c'_{ij})]^2\}$ in equation (1), and section 5 is concerned with these. It has always been of interest that the resolution level of the model tested here is similar to that of the Herbert–Stevens model, and we show in section 6 how the latter can be modified in a way which may make it more realistic at this level of resolution, and which makes the models even more directly comparable. We hope to report tests of this model in a later paper. In section 7 we make a number of concluding comments and outline further possible theoretical developments.

2 Towards a more comprehensive formulation of the original model
2.1 The model as tested: coping with dependent workers
The assumption of one worker per household implicit in equation (1) was modified before empirical testing. In an earlier paper (Wilson, 1970a) two ways of doing this were suggested: the first rested on the assumption that only the income of the head of the household is relevant to the residential location decision, the second that all household income is relevant. We decided to make the former assumption for the present tests: the 'household income assumption' has been used by Cripps and Cater (1972). The following derivation of a model distinguishing heads of households from dependent workers is a modification of that originally presented.

We now add a superscript n to the variable T_{ij}^{kw} to give T_{ij}^{kwn}, with $n = 1$ indicating heads of households, and $n = 0$ dependent workers. If we let r_i be the ratio of *all workers*[2] to heads of households in zone i, then we can represent the number of available residential places as follows,

[2] Including heads of households.

to replace equation (3):

$$\sum_j \sum_w T_{ij}^{kw1} = H_i^k , \tag{8}$$

$$\sum_j \sum_w T_{ij}^{kw0} = (r_i - 1)H_i^k . \tag{9}$$

In effect constraint (9) ensures that within each zone i sufficient accommodation is made available for dependent workers within the houses for which only the heads of households compete.

All workers compete for employment, so

$$\sum_i \sum_k \sum_n T_{ij}^{kwn} = E_j^w , \tag{10}$$

and all incur journey-to-work costs, so

$$\sum_i \sum_j \sum_k \sum_n T_{ij}^{kwn} c_{ij} = C^w . \tag{11}$$

However, heads of households only are assumed to pay for housing and so the housing-budget–house-price mechanism equation is modified accordingly:

$$\sum_i \sum_j \sum_k T_{ij}^{kw1} [p_i^k - q^w(w - c_{ij}')]^2 = \sigma^{w^2} . \tag{12}$$

In addition experience gained during calibration suggests the need for a constraint to ensure that the numbers of heads and dependent workers by income group (w) do not vary. This is particularly important for the calibration of the μ^w parameters in the model which depend on normalised versions of constraints (12) for calibration statistics. Note that constraints (10) ensure only the constancy of the number of *all* workers in a w-group. Therefore all that is needed is a constraint on the numbers of heads in each group, that is

$$\sum_i \sum_j \sum_k T_{ij}^{kw1} = M^w . \tag{13}$$

Maximising entropy subject to constraints (8)–(13) gives

$$T_{ij}^{kw1} = A_i^{k1} B_j^w D^w H_i^k E_j^w M^w \exp(-\beta^w c_{ij}) \exp\{-\mu^w [p_i^k - q^w(w - c_{ij}')]^2\}, \tag{14}$$

$$T_{ij}^{kw0} = A_i^{k0} B_j^w (r_i - 1) H_i^k E_j^w \exp(-\beta^w c_{ij}) , \tag{15}$$

where

$$A_i^{k1} = \left(\sum_j \sum_w B_j^w E_j^w D^w M^w \exp(-\beta^w c_{ij}) \exp\{-\mu^w [p_i^k - q^w(w - c_{ij}')]^2\} \right)^{-1} , \tag{16}$$

$$A_i^{k0} = \left[\sum_j \sum_w B_j^w E_j^w \exp(-\beta^w c_{ij}) \right]^{-1} , \tag{17}$$

$$B_j^w = \left(D^w M^w \sum_i \sum_k A_i^{k1} H_i^k \exp(-\beta^w c_{ij}) \exp\{-\mu^w [p_i^k - q^w (w - c_{ij}')]^2\} \right.$$
$$\left. + \sum_i \sum_k A_i^{k0} (r_i - 1) H_i^k \exp(-\beta^w c_{ij}) \right)^{-1}, \qquad (18)$$

$$D^w = \left(\sum_i \sum_j \sum_k A_i^{k1} H_i^k B_j^w E_j^w \exp(-\beta^w c_{ij}) \exp\{-\mu^w [p_i^k - q^w (w - c_{ij}')]^2\} \right)^{-1}. \qquad (19)$$

The two A_i^k balancing factors in equations (16) and (17), A_i^{k1} and A_i^{k0}, deal separately with competition among heads of households and competition among dependent workers for residential places. However, all workers compete for jobs as the common B_j^w term indicates. D^w is associated with constraints (13).

Some empirical difficulties with this version of the model are mentioned in section 4. Here we briefly speculate about the locational decisions of dependent workers. If we assume that the residential location decision of a household is made with reference to the income *and* workplace location of the head of the household, then it may well be unrealistic to hypothesise that dependent workers themselves make residential location decisions in relation to their workplaces. Equation (15) may well be inappropriate, and perhaps in some future model we should explore the possibility that the residential location of dependent workers is fixed by the accessibility needs of the head of the household, in which case we might profitably apply a job location model to dependent workers, allocating them to jobs around fixed residences. This possibility has previously been suggested in a dynamic model context in an earlier paper (Wilson, 1970a). However, even with this hypothesis, we either have to use something like equation (15), or estimate the distribution of jobs of dependent workers separately from E_j^w as a whole, which may be difficult or impossible.

2.2 Incorporating nonworker households

The inclusion of nonworker households in the model is important for policy reasons, but even more fundamentally to achieve a comprehensive picture of residential choice—namely that worker households compete with nonworker households for residential opportunities.

This immediately suggests a reformulation of the housing stock constraint (8). Let us extend the notation T_{ij}^{kwn}, adding $n = 2$ to represent 'heads' of nonworking households. To represent the complete competition for housing we amend constraint (8) as follows:

$$\sum_w \left(\sum_j T_{ij}^{kw1} + T_{i*}^{kw2} \right) = H_i^k, \qquad (20)$$

where for $n = 2$ we have replaced j by an asterisk, as by definition workplace is irrelevant. The total number of nonworker households within the system can be regarded as fixed and can hence be constrained by

$$\sum_i \sum_k T_{i*}^{kw2} = E_*^{w2} \ . \tag{21}$$

With the introduction of equation (21), constraint (10) needs to be made to refer explicitly to worker categories only; so

$$\sum_i \sum_k \sum_{n=0}^1 T_{ij}^{kwn} = E_j^w \ . \tag{22}$$

Similarly with the travel cost constraint

$$\sum_i \sum_j \sum_k \sum_{n=0}^1 T_{ij}^{kwn} c_{ij} = C^w \ . \tag{23}$$

The housing budget term needs extending to include nonworker households and the following constraint is the obvious counterpart of constraint (12) for nonworker households:

$$\sum_i \sum_k T_{i*}^{kw2} [p_i^k - q^w(w)]^2 = \sigma^{w2} \ . \tag{24}$$

Clearly there is no c_{ij}' term in equation (24). Constraint (13) remains unaltered.

With these amendments to the constraint equations, the resulting entropy-maximising model becomes:

$$T_{ij}^{kw1} = A_i^{k1/2} B_j^{w1/0} D^w H_i^k E_j^w M^w \exp(-\beta^w c_{ij}) \exp\{-\mu^w [p_i^k - q^w(w - c_{ij}')]^2\} \ , \tag{25}$$

$$T_{ij}^{kw0} = A_i^{k0} B_j^{w1/0} (r_i - 1) H_i^k E_j^w \exp(-\beta^w c_{ij}) \ , \tag{26}$$

$$T_{i*}^{kw2} = A_i^{k1/2} B_*^{w2} H_i^k E_*^{w2} \exp\{-\mu^w [p_i^k - q^w(w)]^2\} \ , \tag{27}$$

where

$$A_i^{k1/2} = \left(\sum_j \sum_w B_j^{w1/0} D^w E_j^w M^w \exp(-\beta^w c_{ij}) \exp\{-\mu^w [p_i^k - q^w(w - c_{ij}')]^2\} \right.$$
$$\left. + \sum_w B_*^{w2} E_*^{w2} \exp\{-\mu^w [p_i^k - q^w(w)]^2\} \right)^{-1} \ , \tag{28}$$

$$A_i^{k0} = \left(\sum_j \sum_w B_j^{w1/0} E_j^w \exp(-\beta^w c_{ij}) \right)^{-1} \ , \tag{29}$$

$$B_j^{w1/0} = \left(M^w D^w \sum_i \sum_k A_i^{k1/2} H_i^k \exp(-\beta^w c_{ij}) \exp\{-\mu^w [p_i^k - q^w(w - c_{ij}')]^2\} \right.$$
$$\left. + \sum_i \sum_k A_i^{k0} (r_i - 1) H_i^k \exp(-\beta^w c_{ij}) \right)^{-1} \ , \tag{30}$$

$$B_*^{w2} = \left(\sum_i \sum_k A_i^{k1/2} H_i^k \exp\{-\mu^w [p_i^k - q^w(w)]^2\} \right)^{-1} \ , \tag{31}$$

and

$$D^w = \left(\sum_i \sum_j \sum_k A_i^{k1/2} B_j^{w1/0} H_i^k E_j^w \exp(-\beta^w c_{ij}) \right.$$
$$\left. \times \exp\{-\mu^w [p_i^k - q^w(w - c_{ij}')]^2\} \right)^{-1} \ . \tag{32}$$

This discussion could be carried a stage further, and dependent nonworkers could be included explicitly. A method for doing this is reported in Wilson (1972a).

3 Data needs, and the associated spatial system
3.1 Introduction
It is inappropriate that we should duplicate the detailed discussion of data requirements of, and data availability for, the model, as this was thoroughly dealt with by Cripps and Cater (1972). Rather, we briefly discuss our own decisions regarding data collection, classification, and aggregation. The objective in these preliminary tests was to quickly obtain experience with the 'behaviour' of the model from a situation where data provision was poor. It is hoped to improve the data base for future work.

We first discuss how data needs and availability led to the definition of our spatial system; secondly we mention the data available and our manipulations of it; and finally we discuss computational feasibility in the light of our decisions.

3.2 The spatial system
In our case reliable interaction data was available only for Leeds County Borough, and unfortunately not for the more ideal city-region[3]. Hence the journey-to-work system was arbitrarily closed at the C.B. boundary by subtracting any in-commuters from E_j^w and any out-commuters from H_i^k, and some simple measures of closure using aggregative journey-to-work data from the 1966 census were calculated for the County Borough and city-region.

The first two measures of 'closure' are identical to those employed in the Cheshire study (Barras et al., 1971):

1 $\dfrac{Persons\ living\ and\ working\ in\ study\ area}{Total\ persons\ living\ in\ study\ area\ and\ working\ anywhere}$.

2 $\dfrac{Persons\ living\ and\ working\ in\ study\ area}{Total\ persons\ working\ in\ study\ area\ and\ living\ anywhere}$.

As there are only partial measures of the degree of 'closure' of our system of interest, we can obtain a more realistic measure by combining them to give,

3 $\dfrac{Persons\ living\ and\ working\ in\ area\ (totally\ internal\ trips)}{All\ interactions\ affecting\ study\ area\ (all\ trips)}$.

These closure measures for Leeds C.B. and Leeds city-region are presented in table 1.

The Cheshire study took an arbitrary 80% closure based on measures 1 and 2 as being satisfactory, and the Leeds C.B. system satisfies this requirement. The lower type 2 measure reflects Leeds' greater importance

[3] This would typically include the Local Authorities of Morley, Pudsey, Horsforth, Aireborough, Otley, Wharfedale, Wetherby, Harrogate, Tadcaster R.D., Garforth, Rothwell, and possibly Ilkley.

as a provider of employment for residents of neighbouring local authorities, rather than a supplier of labour to these L.A.'s. However, in terms of total interaction crossing the system boundary, we are ignoring nearly 25% of the trips affecting Leeds C.B.

In effect we find ourselves in a similar position to Anthony and Baxter (1971) in having reliable data only for a spatial system smaller than desirable. We appreciate that our spatial system leads to an under-representation of longer trips, a large proportion of these probably being made by workers of high socio-economic status. It is therefore essential to interpret carefully the β^w parameters in relation to the spatial system for which they are determined (see section 4). In addition the spatial system understates the full variety of housing opportunities by location available in the local housing market.

In partitioning our spatial system into zones for our preliminary model tests, considerations of computational feasibility (see section 3.4) have weighed more heavily with us than the need to maximise interzonal interaction (Broadbent, 1970). Furthermore, very high levels of spatial resolution militate against obtaining adequate samples of the disaggregated interaction variable T_{ij}^{kw} and of house prices by type. Consequently it was convenient for us to use the 28 wards of the city as our zoning system, bearing in mind that in future we would wish to achieve a suitable compromise between the need to minimise intrazonal interaction and obtain homogeneous residential zones on the one hand, and on the other have reliable data samples for a computationally feasible model.

The existing wards vary in their amount of intrazonal interaction, largely because of spatial concentrations of employment and residences. For example, City Ward which contains the Central Business District (CBD) and a lot of industry south of the River Aire accounts for about a

Table 1. Measures of closure for the Leeds C.B. and the Leeds city-regional systems.

Closure measure	% Closure for Leeds C.B.	% Closure for Leeds city-region
1	90·95%	92·4%
2	81·56%	91·7%
3	75·44%	84·726%

Table 2. Some example measures of intrazonal interaction.

Social class	% Intrazonal interaction by ward		
	City	Middleton	Cross Gates
Professional	1·3	7·5	11·6
Intermediate	1·65	7·5	13·2
Skilled manual	1·17	7·9	15·0
Semi-skilled manual	2·01	8·1	15·2
Unskilled manual	3·55	8·0	14·8

third of Leeds' employment but very little of the city's housing stock. Consequently intrazonal interaction is minute compared with interzonal interaction. Similarly wards with small amounts of employment but substantial amounts of housing (for example, Middleton) tend to have relatively small intrazonal interaction. Wards which have more of a mixture of employment and housing tend to be the least satisfactory (for example, Cross Gates), and will require future disaggregation. Table 2 presents the percentage of all interaction (by social class) which is intrazonal for the three wards mentioned above as examples.

3.3 The data base

In general our data sources were much the same as those used by Cripps and Cater (1972), except that we did not have specially tabulated disaggregated journey-to-work data. In the short term this has led to difficulties because our initial data for calibration has been of the form T_{ij}^{*w} (where the asterisk as usual denotes summation, in this case over k) and the lack of disaggregation by house type (k) has posed increasing problems as empirical and theoretical work has progressed (as described in section 4).

Because of these difficulties we attempted to make some conditional probability estimates of T_{ij}^{kw} using, for example, cross-tabulations of social groups by house type for the West Yorkshire Conurbation from the 1966 census. As data on housing stock by type is available for small areas in the 1966 Ward and Parish Library, we have of course been able to predict values of T_{ij}^{kw} with the model.

The housing stock (H_i^k) can be differentiated by a multiplicity of characteristics which can quickly lead to an unmanageable number of submarkets. Faced with this situation we have adopted a very simple classification designed to reflect the main features. A tenure breakdown is obviously essential to any residential model, and so a threefold breakdown into owner-occupied, public rented, and private rented sectors is used. Within each of these tenure groups we have split housing into low price and high price groups using this very coarse classification as a rough proxy for age, condition, and structural type. On examination of the price and rent data (p_i^k) obtained from estate agents and the City Housing Department there does seem to be a clear division by price into lower and higher price sectors, particularly for owner-occupied and local authority housing. Obviously in more refined tests of the model we would wish to have a more sensitive classification, again subject to computational feasibility. In our particular study area we could not adopt the classification used by Cripps and Cater (1972), as we could neither treat all owner-occupied housing as of good condition nor regard local authority housing as being relatively homogeneous.

The definition of income groups (w) poses even greater problems. At present the model is formulated in terms of discrete income categories.

[As an alternative, it would be possible to produce a continuous formulation of the model perhaps following the method of Hyman (1970) in an equivalent transport model.] However, even with the discrete version of the model, some fairly severe compromises have to be made to obtain income data. Ideally we would wish to define employment by actual wage (E_j^w). Without this, the next alternative would be some sensitive proxy for wage earnings by employment category, perhaps a very highly disaggregated occupational classification of employment, so that the corresponding wage levels could be aggregated into discrete wage categories. In fact as we are restricted to highly aggregate occupational proxies for earnings it is virtually impossible to obtain discrete wage categories. Although we might obtain mean wages which differ significantly between occupational groups, it is certain that the corresponding distributions will overlap because of the variety of occupations within an aggregate social classification and the different levels of skill, experience, and hours worked within an occupation.

As long as we have to rely on census data for small area disaggregated journey-to-work data then we are obliged to accept aggregate social groupings for confidentiality reasons. In addition, without information on local wage levels, we have to rely on *national* earnings data. In this study we have used five social class groupings (professional, intermediate, skilled manual, semi-skilled manual, and unskilled manual) as proxies for wage earnings. We have persisted with the threefold disaggregation of the manual (or blue collar) sector of employment in an attempt to incorporate more explicitly those people who are at the lower end of the housing expenditure scale (q^w). We would expect that the future inclusion of pensioner households (as proposed in section 2.2) will be another step in incorporating the widest possible range of housing expenditures within the model. The importance of this will hopefully be manifest when the model is employed in policy contexts.

We can briefly conclude this subsection by noting that c_{ij} was measured as the cost of travel between i and j, and was assumed to be proportional to distance. In calculating the weekly travel cost c'_{ij}, five return journeys per week were assumed. Obviously when measuring c_{ij} it is difficult to be satisfied with anything less than some suitable modal split disaggregation, and this possibility is discussed in section 7.

3.4 Computational feasibility of the model

We have made frequent reference in previous sections of the need to keep the model within manageable bounds for computational reasons. This seems quite reasonable at this preliminary stage of model development when experience with the model and an understanding of its mechanisms are sought. Inevitably this leads to aggregations of variables, in both sectoral and spatial dimensions, which display lower levels of resolution than desirable.

As yet, however, we have not experienced any storage difficulties with the model, chiefly because there has been no pressing need to store all of the predicted trip matrix T_{ij}^{kw}, with dimensions of $28 \times 28 \times 6 \times 5$, at any one time. Moreover, with the installation of 'paging hardware' on the Leeds University 1906A computer, up to 200 K cells of storage are available on the 'virtual core'. Although the 'actual core' has a storage limit of 30 K, transfers between the 'actual' and 'virtual' core stores enable very large programs to be run, provided that these 'transfers' are not excessive owing to inefficient layout of data with respect to program instructions. Naturally this augurs well for testing increasingly disaggregated and extended versions of the model.

Use of computer time is the other major factor in assessing model computability. In particular we are using a doubly-constrained model which typically requires at least 4 iterations of the balancing factors, A_i^k and B_j^w, for convergence to within a 1% limit. At present a run of the model for one parameter takes on average 3 to 5 minutes. In the future we hope to use faster calibration routines such as those of Batty and Mackie (1972) to minimise the number of runs.

4 Preliminary model tests
4.1 Calibration
Interaction measures lead to the most sensitive measures of goodness-of-fit, and we have decided to proceed on this basis as follows in finding best values of β^w and μ^w. We have measured the relationship between T_{ij}^{*w} (observed) and T_{ij}^{*w} (predicted) for each income group by regression, using the coefficient of determination (R^2). This was done both for *all* workers and *heads* of households, as it will be recalled from section 2.1 that the housing expenditure equation (12), to which the μ^w parameters are related, refers only to heads of households.

However, as Cripps and Cater (1972) point out, we can use normalised measures of the constraint equations (11) and (12), which give rise to the β^w and μ^w parameters, to assess goodness-of-fit. For β^w we compare observed and predicted mean trip lengths or costs $(\overline{C^w})$ calculated from

$$\overline{C^w} = \frac{\sum_i \sum_j \sum_k T_{ij}^{kw} c_{ij}}{\sum_i \sum_j \sum_k T_{ij}^{kw}} \ . \tag{33}$$

For μ^w the appropriate statistics are the housing expenditure variances calculated from

$$\sigma^{w2} = \frac{\sum_i \sum_j \sum_k T_{ij}^{kw1} [p_i^k - q^w(w - c_{ij}')]^2}{\sum_i \sum_j \sum_k T_{ij}^{kw1}} \ . \tag{34}$$

The latter measures offer the advantage of separate calibration statistics for the β's and μ's, whereas the trip variables alone are related to both parameters. We present our current best estimates of the parameters in sections 4.3 and 4.5. Before examining these, we need to recount our experiences with this model by way of introduction to the important modification we need to make to the model.

On embarking on model calibration we were well aware that some *negative* μ^w parameters had been obtained by Cripps and Cater (1972). The question arose as to whether this implied either general deficiencies with the model, or turned out to be related to Cripps and Cater's particular study area and data base. Quite by accident, by some error which is completely irrelevant to the following arguments, we initially found that μ^w parameters tended towards negative values, and naturally this fostered the idea that there was some fundamental deficiency with the housing budget term in the model. On examination of this term, which is repeated here for convenience as

$$\exp\{-\mu^w [p_i^k - q^w(w - c'_{ij})]^2\} \,, \tag{35}$$

it was postulated that if housing costs were aggregated for the whole system then the total housing cost should match the total housing expenditure in the system; that is

$$\sum_i \sum_k H_i^k p_i^k = \sum_i \sum_j \sum_k \sum_w T_{ij}^{kw1} q^w(w - c'_{ij}) \,. \tag{36}$$

However, it was quite likely that in assembling data on the variables in (35) from diverse sources and making assumptions about the weekly cost of owner-occupied housing, the two sides of equation (36) would not balance. Hence the need for a 'data consistency factor' K, to ensure the appropriate balance of costs and expenditure [4].

$$\sum_i \sum_k H_i^k p_i^k = K \sum_i \sum_j \sum_k \sum_w T_{ij}^{kw1} q^w(w - c'_{ij}) \,. \tag{37}$$

The value of K found for our study area was $0 \cdot 881644$, indicating that we had either overestimated housing expenditure, or had underestimated housing costs. The latter explanation seems more likely. The estimation of weekly housing costs for owner-occupiers is extremely problematical; rather than treating all owner-occupiers as paying off the first instalments of a mortgage we have tried to force dynamic considerations into a static model by recognising that owner-occupiers will be at different stages in their mortgage repayments, and that the actual capital cost of similar house types (on which interest is paid) will have varied over time due to inflation. These problems are taken up again in section 5.

Returning to equation (37) again, we thought it appropriate that housing costs should be balanced against housing expenditure for each social class as follows:

$$\sum_i \sum_j \sum_k T_{ij}^{kw1} p_i^k = K^w \sum_i \sum_j \sum_k T_{ij}^{kw1} q^w(w - c'_{ij}) \,, \tag{38}$$

[4] This discovery was made independently at Reading University at about the same time.

where the data consistency factor K becomes K^w. Hence it has turned
out that the model's housing budget formulation could easily lead to data
inconsistencies in empirical tests of the model. In section 5 we show how
the above arguments can be developed in a theoretical way. In section 4.3,
however, it remains to interpret the effects of such data inconsistencies
on the calibration process, and to examine the effects of introducing K^w.
Before that we note the deficiencies of our preliminary calibration data.

4.2 A note on calibration data
The chief deficiency of our original calibration data was the lack of a
house type (k) disaggregated interaction variable. This led to two
drawbacks. Firstly it entailed averaging over house type variability in
equation (34) used for calibrating μ^w, and this reduced the sensitivity of
the housing expenditure variances to changes in the μ's. Secondly the
same type of averaging over house type variability prevented us from
obtaining accurate values of the disaggregated data consistency factors K^w
(see section 4.3). In the short term we pursued some exploratory
calibration using K^w. However, we have also made some conditional
probability estimates of T_{ij}^{kw} to clear up the short term difficulties
associated with T_{ij}^{*w}. In section 4.3 we present values of the parameters
and calibration statistics obtained using T_{ij}^{*w} and associated K^w. The
results obtained do throw light on the problem of negative μ values, and
therefore allow some conclusions to be drawn about the effects of
inconsistencies in the model. Later we were able to obtain much more
satisfactory values for μ using T_{ij}^{kw}, and these results are reported in
section 4.5.

4.3 Results of the calibration process using T_{ij}^{*w}
The mean trip costs (table 3) indicate the expected values in the sense
that higher social class groups tend to travel further on average than other
groups. However, the differentials are not greater for two possible
reasons:
1 As mentioned in subsection 3.2 the study area 'cutoff' at the Leeds
   C.B. boundary probably causes an underrepresentation of long distance
   trips by higher social class groups.
2 The location of some of the city's largest council estates is on the
   urban periphery (for example, Seacroft, Middleton), and in the mid-

Table 3. β parameters and associated mean trip costs.

Social class	Mean trip costs (p)	β^w
Professional	6·383066	0·218
Intermediate	6·097297	0·245
Skilled manual	5·398874	0·29617
Semi-skilled manual	5·061384	0·3322
Unskilled manual	4·710698	0·382

1960's more council housing was located in the suburban, rather than inner urban, ring of Leeds, as noted by Leigh (1972). This inevitably gives rise to longer trips by a substantial number of workers in manual employment. More recent and substantial inner urban renewal is tending to even up this spatial differentiation.

The relative magnitudes of the β^w values are as expected. Of greater interest are the values of the μ^w parameters and the observed housing expenditure variances with and without the data consistency factor K^w (table 4). Firstly let us briefly note that the parameters do not seem to be inversely related to the magnitudes of the housing expenditure variation as would be expected. This is solely due to the deficiencies of T_{ij}^{*w} as calibration data, as shown by the results in section 4.5.

Of greater interest in relation to Cripps and Cater's (1972) empirical work is the finding that the K^w factors tend to reduce housing expenditure variation in balancing housing costs with housing expenditure. This inevitably tends to increase the value of the μ^w parameter for each social class group. It is clear now that we can offer one possible explanation for negative values of μ^w parameters. As the amount of imbalance between housing costs and housing expenditure becomes larger, μ^w will tend to become smaller and eventually negative. In fact the μ^w parameter is being forced to give a good fit of the predicted to the observed results with inconsistent data. In trying to correct for this inconsistency the value of μ has become nonsensical. To be more explicit what happens is that the mean housing expenditure for certain income groups (w) tends to be matched in price by only a few houses (for example, as in figure 1). In this hypothetical case the mean housing expenditure of income group 1 is matched by the prices of numerous housing opportunities so μ^1 would be positive. For income groups 2 and 3 the mean housing expenditure coincides with a 'depression' in the surface of housing opportunities by price. Hence, to obtain a fit, μ^2 and μ^3 must 'push' residential locators in such groups away from their mean

Table 4. Calibration of μ^w with and without the data consistency factor.

Social class	No K^w factor		With K^w factor	
	observed housing expenditure variance (p)	μ^w	observed housing expenditure variance[5] (p)	μ^w
Professional	345·0541	0·212	68·8284	0·385
Intermediate	183·7597	0·2876	61·8067	0·79
Skilled manual	56·6757	0·60002	51·4064	0·87
Semi-skilled manual	55·3378	0·279	51·2979	0·7
Unskilled manual	53·2056	0·356	51·4026	0·66

[5] For reasons mentioned in section 4.2, the K^w factor is overstating the reduction in housing expenditure variation for higher social class groups.

housing expenditure. So instead of obtaining the normal distribution of housing expenditure hypothesised in the housing budget mechanism (35), negative values of μ^2 and μ^3 imply an inverted normal distribution, hence matching housing expenditure to the peculiarities of the surface of housing opportunities by price. It is perhaps not surprising that Cripps and Cater (1972) obtained negative μ values for their higher socioeconomic groups, as the latter will display a higher propensity to live in owner-occupied housing and, as implied in subsection 4.1, it is extremely difficult to estimate an accurate average weekly housing cost for this type of housing when 'dynamic' factors are so prevalent.

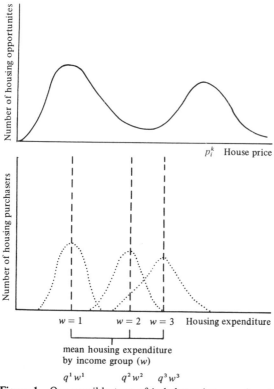

Figure 1. One possible type of imbalance between housing costs and housing expenditure.

4.4 Some model outputs

Model performance was also assessed using the coefficient of determination (table 5), and visually in map and histogram form. The maps and histograms are presented at the end of this paper as figures 4–14 for the reader to make his own visual assessment.

However, it is worth noting one effect of using the dependent worker model as given in section 2.1 [equation (15)]. The maps of observed and predicted trip flows to City Ward for professional workers (figures 4 and 5 respectively) indicate that a good fit is not achieved. The R^2 value of 0·7058 for *all* workers bears this out. However the R^2 value of 0·7912 for *heads* of households is an obvious improvement. This arises from the form of the model presented in section 2.1. As residences of professional workers are spatially concentrated in the northern, and to a lesser extent eastern sectors of Leeds, only the heads-of-households equation (14), with its housing budget term, tends to allocate workers to the higher cost housing concentrated in those sectors. The dependent worker equation (15) tends to allocate professional 'dependent' workers according to their mean trip cost. Consequently, as most professional employment is at the city centre, professional dependents tend to be allocated more symmetrically to the suburban ring of the city.

This inevitably casts further doubts on the utility of treating dependent workers as residential locators with respect only to their own workplace location. Given this sort of argument it is debateable whether we should amend the dependent worker equation to take account of the dominant residential decisions of the head of the household. However, it might be worth some brief experimentation.

Table 5. Coefficients of determination.

Social class	R^2—all workers	R^2—heads of households
Professional	0·7058	0·7912
Intermediate	0·7362	0·8042
Skilled manual	0·8873	0·8793
Semi-skilled manual	0·8672	0·8659
Unskilled manual	0·8027	0·8032

4.5 Calibration using T_{ij}^{kw}

For the reasons mentioned in section 4.2, we found it necessary to improve our data base for calibration by making some conditional probability estimates of T_{ij}^{kw}, subject to constraints on the known stock of housing by type in each residential zone i. In addition we wished to clear up any doubts about the erratic behaviour of the μ values, as between groups presented in section 4.3. Although these latter results were adequate for showing up internal inconsistencies in the model, the μ^w values did not show an inverse relationship with housing expenditure variances as the β^w values did with mean trip costs.

The parameter values obtained using T_{ij}^{kw}, and presented in table 6, clear up the difficulties and doubts mentioned, and confirm the consistent action of the K^w scaling factor in reducing housing expenditure variances.

The Newton–Raphson method was used to find the parameter values which minimised the differences between observed and predicted housing expenditures for each group. The largest difference between these statistics was of the order of $0 \cdot 02$ np.

It should be emphasised that these values refer to the model as given in equations (14) and (15), where the H_i^k variable is constrained. We can as yet place no confidence in parameter values obtained when H_i^k is used as an unconstrained attractiveness term for residential zones.

Table 6. Results of the calibration using T_{ij}^{kw}.

Social class	Housing expenditure variance without K^w (p)	Value of K^w	Housing expenditure variance with K^w (p)	Approximate μ^w values
Professional	$169 \cdot 152934$	$0 \cdot 74792851$	$83 \cdot 819862$	$0 \cdot 3595$
Intermediate	$130 \cdot 500811$	$0 \cdot 80529483$	$94 \cdot 514906$	$0 \cdot 3217$
Skilled manual	$77 \cdot 016837$	$0 \cdot 87035435$	$69 \cdot 784189$	$0 \cdot 6317$
Semi-skilled manual	$51 \cdot 97662$	$1 \cdot 03614706$	$51 \cdot 698192$	$0 \cdot 8024$
Unskilled manual	$40 \cdot 42773$	$0 \cdot 99074228$	$40 \cdot 397817$	$0 \cdot 9745$

5 Further developments with the housing budget mechanism

5.1 Introduction

We said at the outset in this paper that our main concern was the testing of the model, more or less as originally proposed, in a situation where data provision was far less than ideal. However, in the course of this empirical work, we have had to undertake further theoretical developments to make the model work at all, and other notions have materialised as the empirical work forced us to consider more deeply our interpretation of the mechanisms of the model.

One theoretical development has already been reported—the introduction of dependent workers and nonworker households. Our thoughts for the near future, however, are mainly concerned with the housing budget mechanism. The consequences of tackling one problem, the cost–expenditure balance, have already been built into the model, as noted in section 4, but we reserved the full theoretical discussion until this point. This is discussed in section 5.2.

In section 5.3 we introduce a two parameter version of the housing cost–expenditure function, and in 5.4 we have a further discussion of the problems of interpretation.

5.2 The overall balance of housing cost and expenditure

We have already noted in section 4 that, within our system, household expenditure on housing, as determined through our assumptions about q^w, should 'balance' our assumptions about the cost of housing through the p_i^k's. The problem is: at what sector-spatial level of resolution should we expect balance?

At first sight it seems that we might expect balance for each house type k, within each zone i. We have assumed that the cost of such housing is $H_i^k p_i^k$, and that expenditure is $\sum_j \sum_w T_{ij}^{kw} q^w (w - c_{ij}')$. However, since q^w and p_i^k are both average quantities, we cannot expect balance at this level. If type k houses in i are exceptionally expensive, for example, then the w-income people who live in them will be at the top end of the distribution of that population around the mean $q^w (w - c_{ij}')$. That is, for such house types and zones, $H_i^k p_i^k$ may considerably exceed $\sum_j \sum_w T_{ij}^{kw} q^w (w - c_{ij}')$.

A similar argument applies if we sum the above terms over i alone or k alone. However, we may expect balance within an income group. But now, rather than use $H_i^k p_i^k$, we have to use $\sum_j T_{ij}^{kw} p_i^k$, so that we can attach household type (w) to house type (i, k). Then we might expect our data to be such that $\sum_i \sum_k \sum_j T_{ij}^{kw} p_i^k$ balances $\sum_i \sum_k \sum_j T_{ij}^{kw} q^w (w - c_{ij}')$.

If it does not, then this implies deficiencies in our data or in assumptions about our data, and we may introduce a term K^w such that

$$K^w \sum_i \sum_k \sum_j T_{ij}^{kw} q^w (w - c_{ij}') = \sum_i \sum_k \sum_j T_{ij}^{kw} p_i^k \ . \tag{39}$$

Unfortunately, if basic data is not available to give an observed T_{ij}^{kw}, as in our case initially, then K^w cannot be estimated directly from data. Then we either aggregate over w in equation (39) and use K, where

$$K \sum_i \sum_k \sum_j \sum_w T_{ij}^{kw} q^w (w - c_{ij}') = \sum_i \sum_k \sum_j \sum_w T_{ij}^{kw} p_i^k \tag{40}$$

which we can translate into the form

$$K \sum_i \sum_j \sum_w T_{ij}^{*w} q^w (w - c_{ij}') = \sum_i \sum_k H_i^k p_i^k \tag{41}$$

in which equation all the quantities are available from data, or we would have to use an iterative procedure. This would involve setting $K^w = 1$, and estimating T_{ij}^{kw} from

$$T_{ij}^{kw} = A_i^k B_j^w H_i^k E_j^w \exp(-\beta^w c_{ij}) \exp\{-\mu^w [p_i^k - K^w q^w (w - c_{ij}')]^2\} , \tag{42}$$

then substituting this estimate of T_{ij}^{kw} into equation (39) and the new estimate of K^w into equation (42), and repeating until convergence is achieved.

To explore further what we are doing with these balancing procedures, let us make both p_i^k and q^w distributions explicit. Let $x = 1, 2, ...$, $y = 1, 2, ...$ be cells which record actual cost of a house within an (i, k) group, and actual proportions of income spent after deduction of transport costs. That is p_i^{kx} is the xth amount in the distribution of values around

$p_i^k (=p_i^{\overline{kx}})$, and q^{wy} the yth proportion in the distribution around $q^w (=q^{\overline{wy}})$. Assume that the p_i^{kx} and q^{wy} distributions are given as $N_x(p_i^{kx})$ and $N_{wy}(q^{wy})$. Then the interaction variable would become T_{ij}^{kxwy}, and the basic model equation would be

$$T_{ij}^{kxwy} = A_i^{kx} B_j^w C^{wy} H_i^{kx} E_j^w \exp(-\beta^w c_{ij}) \exp\{-\mu^w [p_i^{kx} - q^{wy}(w - c_{ij}')]^2\},$$

(43)

where

$$H_i^{kx} = H_i^k \frac{N_x(p_i^{kx})}{\sum_x N_x(p_i^{kx})}$$

(44)

(or alternatively we might simply assume that H_i^{kx} was given) and where C^{wy} was calculated to ensure that

$$\sum_i \sum_j \sum_k \sum_x T_{ij}^{kxwy} = N_{wy}(q^{wy}).$$

(45)

In such a formulation, μ^w would be very high, possibly even infinite, making the function a 0–1 function if p_i^{kx} and $q^{wy}(w - c_{ij}')$ groupings could be defined to match exactly—though this would be difficult because of the c_{ij}' term. μ^w would cease to be a very interesting parameter of the model. The interesting parameters would be those of the $N_x(p_i^{kx})$ (or H_i^{kx}) and $N_{wy}(q^{wy})$ distributions. The nature of these distributions can be discussed in terms of costs as perceived of (i, k) houses—which may vary with amount of capital available (the average of which would clearly vary with income group), and hence size of mortgage, time at which mortgages were taken out (or more simply, 'age' of house), and so on— and in terms of the range of perceived expenditure as a proportion of income less journey-to-work costs.

More empirical research on the nature of these distributions would obviously be desirable. Meanwhile the model we have is the equation (43) model aggregated over x and y, and the adjustment factor K^w (or K) introduced earlier is to be seen as something which gets perceived cost and perceived expenditure into balance. When our p_i^k's are rents, then the measure may be similar to perceived cost, but for the owner-occupied sector, there is likely to be a wider variation. This does suggest that it would be desirable to have a balancing factor which varied by tenure, but since this is part of our definition of k, the earlier argument against it applies. This could probably only be made to work if income groups could be divided by tenure in some way. This could be managed in part by replacing q^w by q^{wk}, where only the tenure part of k contributed to the variation of q^{wk}. Then from data we might seek a term L^k such that

$$q^{wk} = L^k q^w,$$

(46)

or simply estimate q^{wk} directly as

$$q^{wk} = \frac{\sum_i \sum_j \sum_{k \in V} T_{ij}^{kw} p_i^k}{\sum_i \sum_j \sum_{k \in V} T_{ij}^{kw}(w - c_{ij}')} .$$ (47)

where $\sum_{k \in V}$ means summation over k within a tenure group. Then q^w could be replaced by this q^{wk}, and a term K^w, also split by tenure [6], introduced by the procedures outlined earlier. This we have yet to explore empirically.

5.3 A two-parameter function
The argument about the housing expenditure mechanism can be developed in another way altogether, and this leads to some possibly interesting conclusions. The introduction of K or K^w terms stemmed from difficulties with the calibration procedure for μ^w. To some extent these difficulties may be caused because we are asking the μ parameters to do too much: to determine the dispersion about a mean, and in effect the mean as well. An alternative procedure is to add a constraint equation which determines mean expenditure within an income group, though, to avoid overcomplicating matters, for this particular term we will take no account of journey-to-work expenditure. A suitable equation is

$$\sum_i \sum_k \sum_j T_{ij}^{kw} p_i^k = C^{Hw} = \sum_i \sum_k \sum_j T_{ij}^{kw} q^w (w - c_{ij}') ,$$ (48)

where C^{Hw} is total group w expenditure on housing. The second equation shows how this can be estimated from data, though for forecasting purposes we have to project C^{Hw} directly. This constraint generates a term $\exp(-\lambda^w p_i^k)$ in the model equation. In other words, the usual housing expenditure function $\exp\{-\mu^w [p_i^k - q^w(w - c_{ij}')]^2\}$ is replaced by a two-parameter function $\exp(-\lambda^w p_i^k)\exp\{-\mu^w [p_i^k - q^w(w - c_{ij}')]^2\}$. This is what Tribus (1969) calls the truncated normal distribution. For a range of values of λ and μ, this family of functions takes a variety of shapes— from negative exponential ($\mu = 0$, λ positive) right skewed distributions (small μ), through the normal distributions ($\lambda = 0$) to the left skewed distributions (λ negative). We have not considered μ negative, nor would we expect λ to be negative. The most interesting cases are shown in figures 2 and 3.

Of course the arguments which have been used for housing expenditure could perhaps be used for journey-to-work expenditure, provided we could find a suitable equivalent of the dispersion term. We would have to say something like: let r_i^w be the mean expenditure on journey-to-work for income group w resident in zone i, and then generate a two-parameter

---

[6] Clearly we would need two subscripts for 'k' to do this, one of which would be tenure.

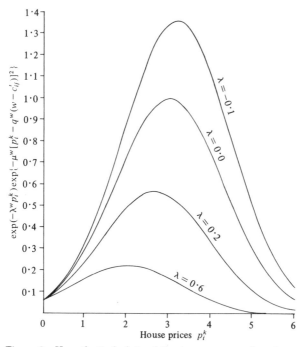

Figure 2. Hypothetical plots of the two-parameter housing expenditure function: constant μ [$\mu = 0 \cdot 3$; $q^w(w - \overline{c}_{ij}^T) = 3$].

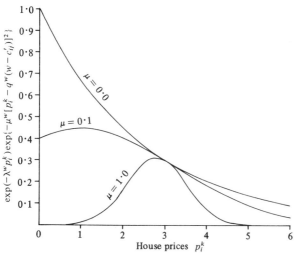

Figure 3. Hypothetical plots of the two-parameter housing expenditure function: constant λ [$\lambda = 0 \cdot 4$; $q^w(w - \overline{c}_{ij}^T) = 3$].

function $\exp(-\beta^w c_{ij})\exp\{-\nu^w[c'_{ij}-r^w_i w]^2\}$. Several authors have investigated the possibility of two-parameter distribution functions before for spatial analysis (Mogridge, 1969; March, 1971), but this particular family does not appear to have been used before, though it is introduced by Tribus (1969) as mentioned earlier.

In relation to the transport model, it has been argued in another paper (Wilson, 1973) that it should be possible to estimate transport expenditure by zone, and hence to replace β^w by β^w_i. The same argument could also be applied to housing expenditure. Instead of estimating C^{Hw}, we could estimate C^{Hw}_i, and thus replace λ^w by λ^w_i. Such an estimation procedure would take account of people in the top end of expenditure distributions living in more expensive houses [7].

5.4 Concluding discussion on interpretation and price determination

Whatever mechanism is used to match house prices and household expenditure, it is obviously crucial to a residential location model and its interpretation. It has been remarked before that this model is neither clearly a supply nor a demand model, as such, but represents the outcome of an allocation process, an (imperfect) market clearing procedure. In other words, it is an intersection of supply and demand. Ideally prices and expenditures should be determined endogenously within the model, and it is interesting to discuss this in relation to the housing budget mechanism.

At present we assume p^k_i and q^w to be given as averages, and we have explored the form the model would take if explicit distributions were incorporated. How can we extend the model so that prices and expenditures can be determined endogenously? The *level* of house prices for those in the market will be determined by the demand for and supply of housing, but also by supply, demand, and prices for many other goods in the economy as a whole. Thus it seems that the general level of house prices can only be determined within an overall economic model which is not yet available to us. However, we might expect to predict the spatial distribution of house prices. Formally we could write

$$p^k_i = p^k_i(H^k_i, E^w_j, c_{ij}, T^{kw}_{ij}),\tag{49}$$

showing p^k_i as a function of the distribution of housing and jobs, transport facilities, and the distribution of population itself. This suggests that house prices and residential distribution should be determined simultaneously within an iterative procedure. This is of course an expected result for this kind of system.

Suppose we proceed this way. Then what of expenditure? Again, as with the level of house prices, we can only determine say mean

[7] Note that in equation (48), the role of p^k_i and $q^w(w-c'_{ij})$ could in principle be reversed. This would lead to a term $\exp[-\lambda^w q^w(w-c'_{ij})]$ instead of $\exp(-\lambda^w p^k_i)$.

expenditure in an income group in an overall consumers' model in which other goods and prices also appeared. In the absence of this, we are saying: let us make an assumption about mean expenditure and the dispersion about the mean, within an income group, and we will relate our assumptions to empirical studies. Then q^w (which determines λ^w if a two-parameter function is in use) and μ^w can be considered to be functions of the kind of variable which would appear in the consumers' model if we had it, and the relationship can be explored empirically (using econometric techniques say). This procedure would not be too bad if time series data was available for these quantities, though unfortunately this is not usually the case. The argument used here for expenditure on housing is exactly analogous to that which has been used, and recently elaborated, in relation to expenditure on transport (Wilson, 1973).

In the above discussion the phrase 'those in the market' was used. It is possible to consider that everyone is in the market in the sense that all review their residential location continually, compare present location with all possible ones, and then decide to stay or move (and where to move to). There is a sense in which this account is obviously unrealistic. In order to change it, potential movers have to be identified, and this leads to various forms of dynamic model being explored in papers which are referred to later. This identifies the pool of people who are seeking accommodation in relation to current prices and their own resources (and our definition of income may have to be modified to reflect capital availability, for example). However, it seems worthwhile to attempt to justify the cross-section model, not by accepting the above assumption about everyone being in the market, but by modifying our interpretation of what the model does, and again the cost–expenditure mechanism is crucial.

Suppose the model tested, the total cross-section model, represents not the outcome of a market clearing process in a short time period, but the cumulation of many such processes over past time periods. Now the p_i^k's and w's which we use in the model are based on current data. So is q^w, though history is reflected in this in that some people may be paying amounts appropriate to mortgages taken out many years ago [8]. We use a K or a K^w term to bring costs and expenditures into balance. It is perhaps best conceptually to consider this done by factoring the p_i^k's, which are current averages, to bring them into line with average expenditures. Then the model gives T_{ij}^{kw}. What this actually means is that T_{i*}^{kw} heads of household live in a house in i whose *average* cost is p_i^k while they themselves pay an *average* of $q^w(w - c_{ij})$. For any particular household, perceived cost may be p_i^{kx} and expenditure $q^{wy}(w - c'_{ij})$, and these quantities are equal. However, p_i^{kx} could be above or below p_i^k, and

[8] In this discussion, as earlier, we are working with perceived expenditures. We guess that this is more like out-of-pocket expenditure than opportunity costs, though empirical work is needed on this topic.

$q^{wy}(w - c'_{ij})$ could be above or below $q^w(w - c'_{ij})$—the full variety of situations is possible. The model as we have it does not give us the distributions implied by the x and y superscripts, but we have now shown that the model, which is maximally consistent with what we do know, is compatible with a variety of such distributions which may hold in fact.

This analysis probably means that the cross-section model tested here is likely to give a good broad coherent picture of urban residential structure, but may be less accurate in detail than may be desirable for some purposes.

6 An entropy maximising version of the Herbert–Stevens model

It has always been recognised that it would be nice to build a residential location model using the economists 'theory of consumers' behaviour', and that Alonso's (1964) pioneering work had indicated how this might be done. The problem of building a comprehensive operational model using Alonso's concepts has proved a difficult one: it is another example of the mathematical problems associated with aggregation (Wilson, 1972b). However, the first model to utilise Alonso's concepts, produced in Philadelphia shortly after Alonso had first worked on his theory, was that of Herbert and Stevens (1960). They wrote of the relationship of their work to Alonso's as follows: "His method is difficult to apply directly, but we feel that our linear programming model provides an analogous approach that is both acceptable and workable". It has long been of some interest that in order to make spatial interaction models realistic they had to be disaggregated, in order to make consumers' theory models operational they had to be aggregated, and the resulting level of resolution is about the same. Thus comparisons are of interest. We shall show below, however, that it is possible to develop a version of the Herbert–Stevens model which is potentially more realistic than the original one, and which is then directly comparable with the disaggregated model which is the main subject of this paper. The new development is also of particular interest in relation to the discussion of the previous section on the determination of housing expenditures within a model.

In a notation as close as possible to that used previously in this paper, the Herbert–Stevens model can be presented as follows. Let T^{kw}_{i*} be the number of type w people living in a type k house in i (where the asterisk denotes summation over j which is not relevant to this model); let p^k_i be the cost of a type k house in i *exclusive of site cost,* s^k be the land area occupied by a type k house [9], L_i the total land area in i available for residential development, and P^w the total number of type w households.

---

[9] Herbert and Stevens use p^{kw}_i and s^{kw}, but for our definitions of k we are unlikely to need the w-superscripts (unless we include income related weights in some of the component costs). This alteration does not affect the number of constraint equations in the model.

As we saw in our earlier discussion some assumption has to be made about the level of household expenditure within a w-group. Herbert and Stevens solve the problem elegantly by defining quantities which are rather like Alonso's bid rents: b^{kw} is the budget allocated for a type k house by a w-income household. The cost of the journey to work does not appear explicitly in the model, but is included on an average basis as part of p_i^k [10]. Then T_{i*}^{kw} is determined by the following procedure. Maximise

$$Z = \sum_i \sum_k \sum_w T_{i*}^{kw}(b^{kw} - p_i^k) , \qquad (50)$$

subject to

$$\sum_k \sum_w s^k T_{i*}^{kw} \leqslant L_i \qquad (51)$$

and

$$\sum_i \sum_k T_{i*}^{kw} = P^w . \qquad (52)$$

Of course all the T_{i*}^{kw}'s must be greater than or equal to zero. The term $b^{kw} - p_i^k$ in the maximand represents the bidding power for site rent. An analysis of the dual shows that, when bid rent is maximised, actual rent paid is minimised.

It can be seen that the aggregation level is similar to the one used earlier. However, the difficult data estimation problem (relative to the earlier one) relates to b^{kw}, since, in effect, preferences measured by possible budgets have to be determined for each w-group for each house type. It is rather like our q^w disaggregated by k. However, this suggests that some estimate can be obtained for testing such a model from the kind of data we have available.

The problem with the operation of the Herbert–Stevens model is that there will be at most only as many nonzero T_{i*}^{kw}'s as there are constraints. This is a fundamental theorem of linear programming. This is presumably what Harris (1962) was referring to when he wrote: "... there is no cross-hauling, whereas this is prevalent in metropolitan interaction." This means that, in a situation of market imperfections, the linear programming model is unlikely to reflect the full variety of actual behaviour. Harris's response was to suggest that the model should only be applied to "a marginal group of new locators and relocators". However, even if this is done, the argument can still be used that there are likely to be more suboptimal allocations than a linear programming model could by its nature predict, for example because of market imperfections.

This problem disappears if we seek a solution which is less than optimal, and the suboptimality reflects real imperfections. An efficient

---

[10] This may be a good reason for having p_i^{kw} rather than p_i^k, as work trip costs may vary with w.

way of doing this is to use an entropy maximising procedure in which equation (50) is treated as a constraint with Z no longer being a maximand. We can then maximise

$$S = -\sum_i \sum_k \sum_w \ln T_{i*}^{kw}! , \qquad (53)$$

subject to

$$\sum_i \sum_k \sum_w T_{i*}^{kw}(b^{kw} - p_i^k) = Z , \qquad (54)$$

and equations (51) and (52), where Z now is some number. This gives

$$T_{i*}^{kw} = A^w P^w \exp(-\beta_i s^k) \exp[\mu(b^{kw} - p_i^k)] , \qquad (55)$$

where

$$A^w = \left(\sum_i \sum_k \exp(-\beta_i s^k) \exp[\mu(b^{kw} - p_i^k)] \right)^{-1} \qquad (56)$$

to ensure that equation (52) is satisfied, and β_i and μ are the Lagrangian multipliers associated with equations (51) and (54) respectively. A^w, β_i, and μ would have to be calculated in an iterative sequence with subiterations to solve the equations for β_i and μ. Z should be chosen so that the resulting T_{i*}^{kw} most accurately reflects the real world situation. $Z^{\max}$ could be calculated of course, and $Z^{\max} - Z$ would be a measure of suboptimality of some kind[11]. This model would not have any zero T_{i*}^{kw}'s, and so might provide an alternative to the Herbert–Stevens model which has an appropriately realistic 'blurring'—or Harris's cross-hauling—in its predictions.

It remains to identify the actual housing expenditure in the new model. To help in this task, we first look at the dual of the Herbert–Stevens maximisation problem. It is, minimise

$$Z' = \sum_i \beta_i L_i + \sum_w \nu^w P^w , \qquad (57)$$

subject to

$$s^k \beta_i + \nu^w \geqslant b^{kw} - p_i^k , \qquad (58)$$

where the β_i's are variables associated with the constraints (51) and ν^w are variables associated with constraints (52). The β_i's must be positive, but the ν^w's can be of either sign. They show that β_i can be interpreted as land rent in i, and ν^w as a surplus to a type-w household. This surplus can be collected by the landowner, but taxed away again. Thus the housing expenditure actually incurred by a w-income household in a type

---

[11] We might conjecture that T_{i*}^{kw} tends to the value which maximises Z when $\mu \to \infty$ in equation (55), rather as T_{ij} in a transport model probably tends to the linear programming solution as the parameter tends to infinity.

k house in i is

$$p_i^k + \beta_i s^k + \nu^w ,\tag{59}$$

where ν^w may actually be repaid through the tax system.

The entropy maximisation problem which leads to the new model also has a dual (Whittle, 1971, p.63). This is obtained as follows. Put

$$\xi_1 = \sum_i \sum_k \sum_w T_{i*}^{kw}(b^{kw} - p_i^k) ,\tag{60}$$

$$\xi_{2i} = \sum_k \sum_w s^k T_{i*}^{kw} ,\tag{61}$$

$$\xi_3^w = \sum_i \sum_k T_{i*}^{kw} ,\tag{62}$$

and define $\underline{\xi}$ as the vector made up of all the variables ξ_1, ξ_{2i}, ξ_3^w. Then a function $\psi(\underline{\xi})$ can be defined which is essentially the entropy function defined in terms of $\underline{\xi}$-variables, and the dual problem is to minimise

$$\psi(\underline{\xi}) + \mu\xi_1 - \sum_i \beta_i \xi_{2i} - \sum_w \nu^w \xi_3^w .\tag{63}$$

This maximand is the equivalent of equation (57) in the Herbert–Stevens model. So β_i and ν^w are rents and surpluses as before, and μ can be interpreted as a household-unit reduction due to suboptimality[12]. Thus the actual housing expenditure incurred by a w-household in a type k house in i is

$$p_i^k + \beta_i s^k + \nu^w + \mu ,\tag{64}$$

where in principle ν^w can be recovered from landowners, and redistributed through the tax system. Thus in this model expenditure *is* determined endogenously, though assumptions have to be made about costs p_i^k, and bids about these, b^{kw}, by w-households.

7 Concluding comments

It is perhaps most useful to conclude with some comments about ongoing research strategy in relation to the model we have been testing. The real world situation which is being modelled is obviously extremely complicated, and many detailed refinements of the model are possible and should be tested. For example, it is clear that such things as quality of schools may be an important determinant of residential location. We then have to decide whether this is reflected in the p_i^k-term, and in that sense covered, or whether we should be including another term, say $\exp(-\alpha^w u_i)$, where u_i is some measure of school provision, directly into the model. Of course if this argument can be used for schools, it can be used for a

[12] This interpretation should be considered as a conjecture, since the objective function (63) is not the 'resource cost' which usually turns up in these duals, because of the entropy term $\psi(\underline{\xi})$; but, since the linear programming solution is a limiting form of this problem, the conjecture is perhaps a reasonable one.

number of other services and environmental features. It would probably be better to subsume these in the p_i^k term for the residential location model, and to concentrate on relating p_i^k to these features in a separate submodel.

One feature which perhaps ought to be directly incorporated into the model is transport access *by mode*. There is no difficulty in doing this in principle: c_{ij} could be replaced by c_{ij}^m, for mode m, but there is the complicating feature that we would also have to amend our person type index, currently w, to reflect car availability. This could be done by introducing another person type superscript, l, in the manner of the model now used in transport studies (Wilson, 1967), but this would generate a variable T_{ij}^{kwml} which probably has too many indices for comfort. An alternative would be to build in a 'car available' probability, conditional on w.

We argued in section 5 that the 'total cross-section' model used here may involve reasonable assumptions if the terms of the model are carefully interpreted. However, it is likely in the longer run that a quasi-dynamic model, in which the current pool of potential movers is identified, will prove more fruitful. A mechanism for this was proposed in the original paper on the model discussed here (Wilson, 1970a), and some of the very complicated problems which arise (for example, amending the supply side mechanism to release houses made available by movers, as well as new houses) are discussed in a further paper (Wilson, 1972a). However, the empirical development of these concepts requires a data base which includes time series information which we do not have available at present, so that further development in this direction may have to be postponed.

Acknowledgements. The authors would like to thank Gordon Bryant, Tim Hadwin, and Geoff Hodgson for their cartographic assistance.

M. L. Senior would also like to thank the Social Science Research Council for financial support whilst undertaking research for this paper.

References
Alonso, W., 1964, *Location and Land Use* (Harvard University Press, Cambridge, Mass.).
Anthony, J., Baxter, R., 1971, "The first stage in disaggregating the residential submodel", WP-58, Land Use and Built Form Studies, Cambridge.
Barras, R., Broadbent, T. A., Cordey-Hayes, M., Massey, Doreen B., Robinson, K., Willis, J., 1971, "An operational urban development model of Cheshire", *Environment and Planning*, 3, 115–223.
Batty, M., Mackie, S., 1972, "The calibration of gravity, entropy, and related models of spatial interaction", *Environment and Planning*, 4, 205–233.
Broadbent, T. A., 1970, "Notes on the design of operational models", *Environment and Planning*, 2, 469–476.
Cripps, E. L., Cater, Erlet A., 1972, "The empirical development of a disaggregated residential location model: some preliminary results", in *Patterns and Processes in Urban and Regional Systems*, Ed. A. G. Wilson (Pion, London).

168   M.L.Senior, A.G.Wilson

Harris, B., 1962, "Linear programming and the projection of land uses", Penn Jersey Transportation Study, Paper Number 20, Philadelphia, Penn.
Herbert, D. J., Stevens, B. H., 1960, "A model of the distribution of residential activity in urban areas", *Journal of Regional Science*, 2, 21-36.
Hyman, G. M., 1970, "Trip distribution and modal split by categories of households", *Transportation Research*, 4, 71-76.
Leigh, C. M., 1972, *The Journey-to-work in Leeds: Its Influence upon the Spatial Structure of a City*, unpublished Ph. D. Thesis, Department of Geography, University of Leeds.
March, L., 1971, "Urban systems: a generalised distribution function", in *Urban and Regional Planning*, Ed. A. G. Wilson (Pion, London).
Mogridge, M. J. H., 1969, "Some factors influencing the income distribution of households within a city region", in *Studies in Regional Science*, Ed. A. J. Scott (Pion, London).
Senior, M. L., 1973, "Approaches to residential location modelling 1: Urban ecological and spatial interaction models (a review)", *Environment and Planning*, 5, 165-197.
Tribus, M., 1969, *Rational descriptions, Decisions and Designs* (Pergamon Press, Oxford).
Whittle, P., 1971, *Optimisation under Constraints* (John Wiley, London).
Wilson, A. G., 1967, "A statistical theory of spatial distribution models", *Transportation Research*, 1, 253-269.
Wilson, A. G., 1970a, "Disaggregating elementary residential location models", *Papers and Proceedings of the Regional Science Association*, 24, 103-125.
Wilson, A. G., 1970b, *Entropy in Urban and Regional Modelling* (Pion, London).
Wilson, A. G., 1972a, "Principles for building a general urban and regional model", WP-21, Department of Geography, University of Leeds.
Wilson, A. G., 1972b, "Behavioural inputs to aggregative urban system models", in Paper 5 *Papers in Urban and Regional Analysis* (Pion, London).
Wilson, A. G., 1973, "Further developments of entropy-maximising transport models", WP-20, Department of Geography, University of Leeds; published in *Transportation Planning and Technology*, 1 (2), 183-193.

Figure 4. Observed work trips to City Ward by professional workers.

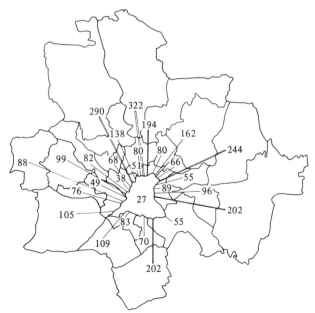

Figure 5. Predicted work trips to City Ward by professional workers; $\beta = 0 \cdot 21$, $\mu = 0 \cdot 385$.

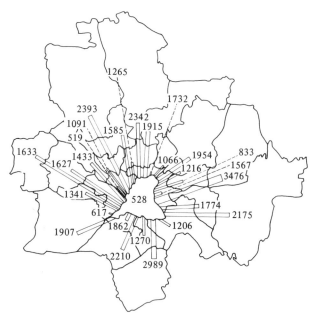

Figure 6. Observed work trips to City Ward by skilled manual workers.

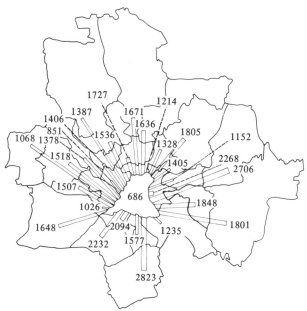

Figure 7. Predicted work trips to City Ward by skilled manual workers; $\beta = 0 \cdot 2964$, $\mu = 0 \cdot 87$.

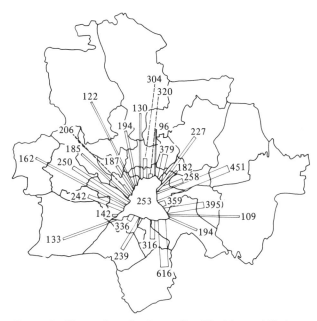

Figure 8. Observed work trips to City Ward by unskilled manual workers.

Figure 9. Predicted work trips to City Ward by unskilled manual workers; $\beta = 0\cdot402$, $\mu = 0\cdot66$.

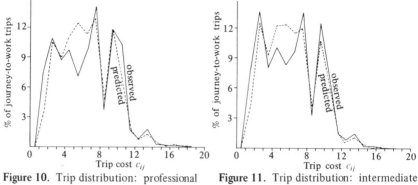

Figure 10. Trip distribution: professional workers. Mean = 6·383066.

Figure 11. Trip distribution: intermediate workers. Mean = 6·097297.

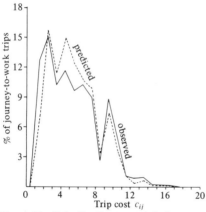

Figure 12. Trip distribution: skilled manual workers. Mean = 5·398874.

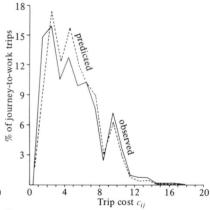

Figure 13. Trip distribution: semi-skilled manual workers. Mean = 5·061384.

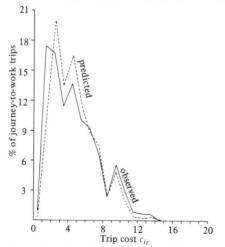

Figure 14. Trip distribution: unskilled manual workers. Mean = 4·710698.

On the Feasibility of Simulating the Relationship Between Regional Imbalance and City Growth

M.CORDEY-HAYES
Centre for Environmental Studies, London

1 Introduction

There is a need for simulation models in planning that focus more directly on policy analysis than do existing comparative static spatial methods. Such models would be used explicitly to 'conduct policy experiments' in an attempt to learn about possible conflicts between objectives, and to identify undesirable side effects and how these are phased over time. A framework that aims to provide a brief explanatory context for these simulation models in plan/programme or policy analysis is given in figure 1.

Specifically, the role of such simulation models is in the analysis of how well a policy is likely to achieve its objectives, and in the *explicit* exploration of the positive and negative side effects arising from the policy or programme of action; that is, in tracing the often unexpected repercussions of a policy so that a fuller assessment of the advantages and disadvantages of alternative policies may be examined. There are, however, two major difficulties in the development of these models. Firstly, planning goals are frequently not clearly specified; they are complex and the subject of conflicting interests amongst the people affected. Secondly, we lack an adequate science for the analysis of

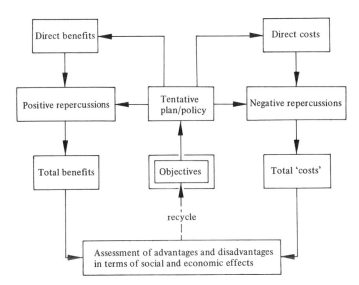

Figure 1. A framework for urban simulation models.

complex interacting systems over time. Therefore methods that aim to represent and understand the interrelationships between activities and objectives, and their subsequent trade offs currently tend to be empirical and iconic.

Acknowledging this, it is nevertheless of interest to examine tentatively the claims of those frameworks and urban simulation models that aim to look at the 'whole system', and to consider if these could be integrated with the essential method of science which is based on breaking down global problems into discrete and soluble ones, so that some rationale for the structured development of these methods can be achieved. This thesis is clearly expressed in the O.E.C.D. report *Science, Growth and Society*: "In the discussion of ecological or social systems, it is not enough simply to say that everything depends on everything else, and so we must look at the whole system. This too easily becomes a counsel for despair and, in the area of policy, a pretext for inaction. The essential method of science is to break down global problems into discrete and soluble problems, and we must be prepared to do this in tentative ways, realising that any particular breakdown is only a first approximation, and we may have to start over again after proceeding some considerable distance". The process is one of structured learning as well as identifying and testing policy options.

Within this general context, this paper aims at an assessment of the *feasibility* of developing simulation models for the study of the relationship between regional imbalance and city growth in a regional policy context. In some ways the paper is a *'pot-pourri'* of ideas and partially completed research, but the intended structure is:

1 A brief assessment of the methodology used in the urban dynamic models of Forrester (1969) and, to a lesser extent, of Kadanoff (1971).
2 An outline of a theoretical framework which attempts to give a more structured approach to experimental research on processes of urban growth and change.
3 A preliminary analysis of the migration movements between 20 *city regions* of England and Wales in terms of the concepts developed in '1' and '2'.

Thus section 2 of this paper gives a brief critical appraisal of Forrester's (1969) *Urban Dynamics*. The section is based on three months of experimental research in which the model was run in a modified and extended form, and was originally intended to stimulate discussion, but the section also aims to show the following:

(a) Forrester's results do not follow from counter-intuitive systems behaviour, but follow directly from the particular structure of his model, and from his evaluative measures (see section 2.1). In essence, the model is considered to be a novel way of expressing his subjective views.

(b) Minor modifications to the migration equations give rise to markedly different values for his evaluative measures, and at present there is scarcely sufficient understanding of urban processes to specify these equations adequately (section 2.2).

(c) Despite these major criticisms, the methodology is considered a potentially useful approach to simulation modelling, particularly as a contextual framework for more specific subsystem studies. For example, in this case a 'linked cities' model is examined as a framework for the study of the relationship between regional imbalance and city growth through the process of interurban migration (section 2.2.2).

Section 3 of the paper follows on from these conclusions and emphasises the importance of integrating dynamic simulation modelling with a serious programme of experimental research which is devoted to a more formal understanding of urban growth processes. It outlines a theoretical approach to this experimental research that was developed in more detail in an earlier paper (Cordey-Hayes, 1972). This paper aimed to explore which theoretical frameworks provide a useful orientation for this experimental research on growth processes, and concluded that the Markov property and kinetic theory allow a structuring of research by providing initially an accounting framework for the description of change through time; but the paper then emphasised that the experimentally observed transition parameters used in these approaches must be related to the causal variables that influence this change. In section 3 an outline of kinetic theory is given to illustrate this approach of *hypotheses making within a time-oriented accounting framework*, and it is shown how the approach gives useful insights on the introduction of behavioural inputs into aggregate models. Migration analysis is taken as a focus because the thesis of this paper is that a clearly based relationship between the economic and demographic sectors must be established before city or regional simulation models can be regarded as a feasible proposition.

The paper concludes with (section 4) a preliminary analysis of the migration flows between 20 city regions covering England and Wales in terms of the ideas and concepts developed in section 3, but highly pruned because the study is in its very early stages and also because of data constraints. Progress towards the longer-term aim of obtaining an experimentally-based link between the demographic and employment sectors is outlined, and the results indicate that the relationship between migration and city 'attractiveness' does not have the form used by Forrester (1969), nor that used in the more serious studies of Kadanoff (1972).

2 A brief assessment of the Forrester model
2.1 A critique of the structure of the model
2.1.1 *Sectors*
The Forrester model attempts to simulate city growth in three sectors, namely *population, housing,* and *industry*. Population is disaggregated

into three socioeconomic groups called in Forrester's notation labour (L),
managerial/professional (P), and underemployed (U) (sometimes in this
paper relabelled 'unskilled'). Housing is similarly broken down into three
groups and labelled by the socioeconomic group of the occupants. In
general, housing is considered to be built for the managerial/professional
and labour groups, and both of these types of housing 'age' into housing
for the 'lower' socioeconomic categories.

Industry is separately classified into new enterprises, mature business,
and declining industry. This classification is based entirely upon 'age';
new enterprises become mature businesses after ten years, and then after
a further period of ten years they are called declining industry. The
process of ageing is not considered. New enterprises are assumed by
Forrester to require twice as many managers as mature business, and the
latter twice as many managers as declining industry.

A specified land area (100000 acres) is assumed to be available for city
growth. After this area has been filled, then further growth can only
occur with clearance followed by new construction. Forrester suggests
that this fixed land constraint corresponds more closely to the central
part of the city than to a complete city. But it appears to be a poor
representation of either because all population is considered to live and
work in this constrained area, which is therefore unrepresentative of a city
centre, whilst a complete city would very rarely have such a rigid land-
availability constraint. It corresponds more closely to an island. [See
also Kadanoff (1971); Ingram (1970).]

2.1.2 *Interaction of the city with the outside world*
The only explicit interaction of the Forrester city with the outside world
is through population movements. Population in the three categories can
move into and out of the 'city' being considered. The flow to and from
the city depends on the 'relative attractiveness' of the city compared to its
surrounding environment. A specified attractiveness for this limitless
environment is taken as a reference, and the attractiveness of the city rises
and falls with respect to this reference. The attractiveness of the city is
indexed separately for each population group in terms of job and housing
opportunities, and the tax rate. In equation form the in-migration is
written:

$$I_u^{KM} = (U^K + L^K)A_u^K N .\qquad(1)$$

This states that the in-migration of underemployed (I_u^{KM}) into the city
during the time interval K to M is proportional to the total number of
underemployed (U^K) and labour (L^K) already in the city at time K, and to
the 'attractiveness' (A_u) of the city as perceived by an underemployed
resident outside the city; N is a constant which normalises the flow rate
with respect to the attractiveness of the surrounding environment. Similar
equations describe the arrivals and departures of the other two population

categories. The in-migration of underemployed (I_u) is one component of the overall rate of change of underemployed population; the total change is given by

$$\Delta U = I_u - O_u - S_u + B_u \ ,   \tag{2}$$

where O_u represents the out-migration of underemployed, S_u is the net flow of the group by social mobility into the labour category, and B_u is the change through births and deaths. O_u, S_u, and B_u have a similar equation format to that given in equation (1). Out-migration (O_u) is assumed to be inversely proportional to the 'attractiveness' of the city (but see section 4.2 for a test of this hypothesis).

Because so little is understood of all these development processes, they have been represented in their simplest form. That is, the rate of change of one variable depends directly on an earlier value of the variable that is itself undergoing change. For example, in equation (1) the rate of change of the number of underemployed by way of in-migration to a city is assumed to depend on the existing level of underemployed population in that city. This form of difference equation has an exponential solution, and has the consequence that urban growth processes are *assumed* to be exponential. This exponential growth together with a rigid constraint on land availability determines the essential features of Forrester's results, and it is argued in the next section that these results are in no way counter-intuitive as is suggested by Forrester.

Implicitly, the Forrester city also interacts with the outside environment through the demand for goods and services produced within the city. This interaction is not explicitly incorporated but, since it is assumed that the construction of new enterprise industry is constrained only by land availability and professional staff requirements, the implicit assumption is that the environment provides a limitless demand for the goods and services produced within the city.

2.1.3 *City growth process and the evaluative criteria*
With a model based on the above three sectors (population, housing, industry), the land area constraint, and the migration process, Forrester aims to simulate the process of the development of an urban area, initially unoccupied, and then to illustrate how the process of growth gives way to maturity and stagnation. Because of the form of the *hypothetical* growth equations, both population and employment develop exponentially until the stipulated land area for construction becomes filled at year 100. This 'filling up' triggers (within the equation system) an onset of stagnation. Stagnation is an equilibrium situation in which the ratios of underemployed to professionals and to labour are higher than in a freely growing city. The stagnation occurs because, in this model, new enterprises can only be created when there is vacant land available and in

a situation where the ratio of managers to other population groups is high, and neither of these conditions prevail at year 100.

When the stipulated land area for construction becomes filled, the managers and professionals begin to leave the city whilst the underemployed still enter the city. (This critical point is marked A in figure 2.) There are several reasons which can explain why this occurs. When the city reaches its physical limit, no further housing for professionals and managers can be constructed; yet (within this model) their housing is automatically 'ageing' into labour and underemployed housing, and therefore the housing available to professionals is in fact decreasing. Similarly, as new enterprise industry ages into mature business, the job opportunities for managers/professionals decline—the city is therefore less attractive to professionals and there is a net outward movement. Employment declines for all groups because there is no new construction, but in-migration of the underemployed still occurs since their housing opportunities remain good for some time, not only because of the ageing of professional and labour housing into this category, but also because they are considered by Forrester to perceive the city as it was 20 years previously.

The net result of these processes is that the number of professionals and managers within the city declines, whilst the underemployed increase in number for several years until the housing opportunities have declined sufficiently not to attract further population. This situation of constant

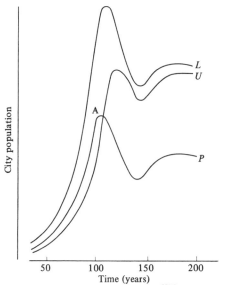

Figure 2. Migration equation: $I_u^{KM} = (U^K + L^K)A_u^K N$. U = underemployed; L = labour; P = professionals/managers. (The vertical scale for P is one-third that of L and U.)

levels of each population category but with a high ratio of underemployed is called stagnation (see figure 2).

In policy analysis it is important to define as clearly as possible the 'problems' that are to be tackled and to identify performance measures related to these. Forrester does not do this explicitly, and it is necessary to extract his perceived problems and evaluative criteria from the text. The foregoing discussion has shown that in Forrester's model 'stagnation' corresponds to a high proportion of unskilled jobs and of high unemployment compared to the equivalent proportions in the growing city. Forrester then examines a set of alternative strategies for what he calls the 'revitalisation' of the city, which appears to mean decreasing the proportion of underemployed workers within that city, and providing the conditions for growth (except in physical size). These policy programmes are inserted as changes in the values of certain variables, and the model is run for a further 100 years after the equilibrium state to see the long-term consequences of such changes. For example, the *underemployed job programme* instantaneously provides jobs for 10% of the underemployed population by creating public service types of employment without involving a change in any of the other levels or flow processes. It is instructive to quote from Forrester's assessment of this programme because it clarifies his evaluative criteria: "At first glance ... (there is) ... little change resulting from the underemployed job programme, but more careful examination discloses several unfavorable changes in the composition of the area ... The total number of underemployed has increased. Underemployed housing has increased while worker housing has decreased ... There is an excess of arrivals of underemployed to departures ... Taxes needed have risen by 14% because of the increase in underemployed workers".

Similarly a training programme to upgrade the skills of the underemployed is considered undesirable because it attracts more underemployed to the city. Also, because of the rigid city size constraint, no new enterprises can be created and therefore there are no new jobs to occupy the retrained underemployed. Thus, as a result of the retraining programme, there is an increased competition for available jobs, and there is an increased departure of labour, an increased underemployed arrival rate, and a rise in taxes.

Several other programmes are rejected by Forrester because they make the city attractive for unskilled workers—hence the proportion of unskilled to professionals within this particular city increases, as does the tax rate *per capita*, and this is regarded as bad in terms of evaluative criteria used.

Forrester's favoured programme comprises the "demolition of 5% per year of underemployed housing (slum housing)", the restriction of new housing construction, and an encouragement of new enterprise industry construction. The result of this can be predicted, as were the others, entirely intuitively from the structure of the model. A reduction of underemployed housing causes the underemployed population density to increase, thereby decreasing the relative attractiveness of the city for this population group, and there is no net in-migration of underemployed. New enterprise industry and professional housing are constructed on the cleared land; this attracts professionals into the city by raising its attractiveness for this group above that of the environmental reference attractiveness. These population movements directly improve Forrester's implicit evaluative factors, but also do so indirectly by providing jobs which can be filled by an upward mobility from the underemployed population within the city.

2.1.4 *Conclusions*
Forrester suggests that "these computer runs disclose reasons for the futility and frustration that characterises urban development programs. They demonstrate the counter-intuitive nature of complex social systems by showing that intuitively sensible policies can affect adversely the very problems they are designed to alleviate". But the present brief assessment has attempted to show that the results follow directly from the structure of the model (hypothesised exponential growth and a rigid land area constraint) and from the implied evaluative criteria (essentially the ratio of underemployed to professionals). Forrester appears only to be saying that if you increase the attractiveness of a city for a certain population group, then more of these will move in. When these are unskilled and his evaluative criteria applied only to one city, then this will appear detrimental to that city, particularly since the arrivals cannot be employed because new enterprise construction is prevented by the very rigid land availability constraint. The environment of the city is unlikely to be a limitless source of unskilled (or any other population category) as is assumed in the model, and also the evaluative criteria should be applied in a wider context than the single city. Perhaps one can usefully conclude that "programs for improving the lot of the unskilled should be applied nationally rather than locally in order to prevent the partial neutralisation of these policies as a result of the concentration of the unskilled in the program area" (Kadanoff, 1971). Forrester's model does not permit the analysis and evaluation of policies in a wider national or regional context. The feasibility of the design of a model which aims to study the relationship between regional imbalance and city growth for a number of linked city regions is considered in section 2.2.2 and in section 4.

Before this, in section 2.2.1, it is demonstrated that the equilibrium ratio of underemployed to professionals in a single city model is very sensitive to the explicit form of the in-migration equations used, and that equilibrium situations could exist (even within the rigid structure of the Forrester model) in which the ratio of unskilled to professionals is similar to that in a freely growing city.

2.2 Modifications to the Forrester model
2.2.1 *The structure of the migration equations*
In the Forrester model the flow of population in the underemployed category into the city depends on the relative attractiveness of the area compared to its surrounding environment, and on the number of labour and underemployed already within the city. Formally, the in-migration equation is, once again,

$$I_u^{KM} = (U^K + L^K)A_u^K N \qquad \text{[equation (1)]},$$

where I_u^{KM} is the in-migration of the underemployed during the time interval K to M, A_u^K is the 'perceived attractiveness' of the city from outside, and N normalises the inward flow with respect to the reference environment. The relative attractiveness of the city is assessed through components relating to job and housing availability, housing density, public services offered by the city (as assessed by the tax rate), and the opportunity for underemployed to move into the skilled labour category. The hypothesised relationship between 'attractiveness' and each of the above components is entered into the model as a table of numbers which are considered to be a plausible relationship. For example, as population density increases by 50%, the city is considered to be less attractive by a factor of approximately five.

Similar equations and table functions describe the inward migration of the labour and managerial categories. There are, however, differences in the details of the functions; for example, the attractiveness of the city for the underemployed is considered to increase with increasing tax rate (better welfare facilities offered), but for the professional category the attractiveness decreases with increasing tax rate. This section, however, will not consider the details of the attractiveness index but instead focuses on the general structure of the above equation (1).

Because the rate of change of the number of underemployed, through in-migration to the city is considered by Forrester to be dependent on the existing level of underemployed within the city, then the growth process is assumed to be exponential. The presence of this effect dominates the growth process and makes the above attractiveness hypotheses on in-migration comparatively insensitive (see Cordey-Hayes and Matheson, 1972). Further, the form of equation (1) is quite arbitrary and it may be reasonably hypothesised instead that the term $U^K + L^K$ should be replaced by L^K as the relevant measure of city size reflecting job prospects generally. Again it is quite arbitrary to say that the dependence is linear; for example, the overall attractiveness may be related as the square root of the labour force. These modifications were made to Forrester's in-migration equation for the underemployed population category. The resulting growth processes are shown in figures 2, 3 and 4, and the associated values of the underemployed to professional/managerial and the underemployed to labour ratios at equilibrium are given in table 1. It can be seen that the second modification has reduced the number of underemployed within the city by over 50%.

For equation (iii) (table 1) the proportion of underemployed to labour is approximately the same at equilibrium as it is in Forrester's freely growing city (that is, up to 100 years in figure 2), and the ratio of underemployed to professional and managerial is only 10% larger.

Figures 2, 3 and 4 indicate that the level of underemployed population still grows exponentially although at a slower rate. This is because the labour force equations are unchanged and therefore L grows exponentially; the in-migration of underemployed population is related to L, and hence U also increases exponentially. But figure 4 clearly shows a considerable change in the equilibrium level of the underemployed category, and

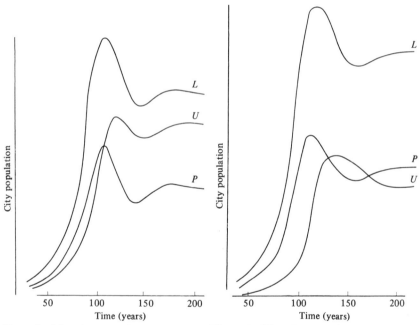

Figure 3. Migration equation:
$$I_u^{KM} = L^K A_u^K N.$$

Figure 4. Migration equation:
$$I_u^{KM} = (L^K)^{1/2} A_u^K N.$$

U = underemployed; L = labour; P = professionals/managers. (The vertical scale for P is one-third that of L and U.)

Table 1. Underemployed to professional and underemployed to labour ratios at equilibrium.

In-migration equation	U/P	U/L
(i) $I_u^{KM} = (U^K + L^K) A_u^K N$	5·4	0·96
(ii) $I_u^{KM} = L^K A_u^K N$	4·3	0·76
(iii) $I_u^{KM} = (L^K)^{1/2} A_u^K N$	2·5	0·47

demonstrates how the explicit form of the migration equations can affect this element of the evaluative criteria used by Forrester.

2.2.2 A linked-city model
The previous section has shown that the values of the evaluative measures implicit in the Forrester model are strongly dependent on the structure of the migration equations. Although important, these specific effects are expected to be secondary to the consideration that there is not a 'limitless source' of migrants upon which any one city can draw. This section describes how a start has been made on the modification of this style of model to include the interaction between city regions, and thereby to include an 'accounting' of migrants. An earlier section (2.1.4) discussed why policies aimed at improving conditions for the unskilled should be analysed and evaluated at a national level, and argued that Forrester considers a city in much the same way as a manager considers a firm—his objective being to maximise the well-being of that city in relation to an undifferentiated environment of other cities. But in evaluating policies it is necessary to consider their wider effects on other cities. The linked-city model aims to examine the feasibility of developing a model that evaluates policies at a regional or national level, which in the particular case envisaged here would be for 20 city regions covering England and Wales.

This development has been attempted so far by a simple modification of the migration equations. The number of people of the type U migrating from city region i to city region j in unit time is given by

$$U_{ij} = U_i \epsilon_i^U \frac{1}{A_i} \frac{A_j}{\sum_j A_j} \, , \tag{3}$$

where U_i is the number of people of type U in i, ϵ_i^U is some intrinsic mobility coefficient for the underemployed category, and A_i and A_j are the attractiveness of cities i and j respectively.

Equation (3) can be broken down into two parts, the expression $U_i \epsilon_i^U / A_i$ being the number of underemployed leaving i in unit time, and $A_j / \sum_j A_j$ is the probability of these going to city region j. They correspond approximately to the 'escape frequency' and 'capture cross sections' discussed in section 3.

These equations have been introduced into the Forrester model and preliminary runs have been made on a hypothetical 3-city region. In this case there is no longer an infinite source of migrants and as a result city growth occurs at a very much slower rate. In these preliminary runs the cities did not reach equilibrium within 250 years, even when a much reduced (one-tenth) land area constraint was introduced.

The initial runs were of two types:
1 Each city was given similar inputs for the population in the respective categories U, L, and P, and similar attractiveness multipliers. In these

two runs, out-migration and in-migration were almost equal and opposite
in magnitude, and city change occurred only through social mobility
through the various population categories, and by births and deaths.
City growth was in each case small and smooth, and an equilibrium
(or stagnation) was not reached.
2 In the second series of runs each city was given markedly different
inputs ($U_2 = U_3 = 300\,U_1$ and $A_2 = A_3 = 2A_1$). In these runs the
population totals take on a sharp oscillatory behaviour which requires
a long time to settle down. Although technically an interesting result,
this does produce problems because it is now difficult to distinguish if
population redistribution occurs because of unstable starting conditions
or as a result of the applied policies. A comparison of changes with
and without policies is of course possible and has been done in these
initial runs, but difficulties in interpretation still occur because the
effects of policies are often small in comparison to the nonequilibrium
settling down behaviour. Also it appears that the effects are too
sensitive to the specific time at which the policy was applied.

This work is in its very early stages and it is clear that further work is
required to investigate the correct/plausible starting conditions for each
city in this linked-city setup, and the characteristics of the interaction
between cities. Preliminary results on the latter are given in section 4.

Kadanoff (1971) has progressed further in a similar linked-cities
exercise. His work indicates that, when applied throughout a nation, both
clearance and training programmes are effective in reducing the numbers
of unskilled and of their unemployment. His conclusions suggest that a
combination of renewal, skilled job provision, and training will reduce
unemployment with a minimum of undesirable side effects. The analysis
was intended to demonstrate clearly that the choice and focus for a
particular model will strongly affect the policy conclusion reached.

3 Dynamic frameworks for spatial models

3.1 Introduction

Attempts at the dynamic simulation of urban processes of the type
considered in the last section are strongly structured on an ability to make
conditional forecasts. A formal prediction in time involves a statement of
the *initial conditions* combined with the *'equations of motion'* for the
development process. 'Equations of motion' translate information from
one time to another by considering the rate of change of a variable.
Dynamic simulation requires that these formal equations be known.
Often, plausible hypotheses for these can be made: for example, that the
rate of change of population within a region due to migration depends on
the relative levels of unemployment in that region and all other regions
(Hamilton *et al.*, 1969), or on the relative attractiveness of regions (Forrester,
1969; Kadanoff, 1972). But the last section showed that minor

modifications to the functional dependencies within the migration
component of Forrester's model give rise to markedly different values for
his evaluative criteria, and it is considered that there is scarcely sufficient
understanding of urban growth processes to specify these equations
adequately. Thus the numerical projections obtained from dynamic
simulation are of very doubtful value, but the potential strengths of such
models may lie in the explicit *exploration* of how urban and regional
systems work, of their behaviour modes, and how they may react to the
implementation of various planning policies. But it is important that such
dynamic simulation modelling be accompanied by a serious programme of
experimental research devoted to the formal understanding of urban
growth processes (essentially the experimental deduction of the equations
of motion). The purpose of this section is to obtain insights on how to
progress towards a framework and strategy for experimental research that
will best contribute to our formal understanding of urban development
processes. Much of the discussion centres around migration analysis
because this should form the important link between the demographic
and employment sectors of dynamic simulation models. An earlier paper
(Cordey-Hayes, 1972) explored in some detail which theoretical
frameworks provide a useful orientation for the experimental research, and
concluded that the Markov property and kinetic theory allow a structuring
of research by providing initially an accounting framework for the
description of change through time; but the paper then emphasised that
the experimentally observed transition parameters used in these approaches
must be related to the causal variables that influence this change. Kinetic
theory is briefly outlined here to illustrate this approach of hypothesis-
making within a time-oriented accounting framework as a necessary
accompaniment of dynamic simulation. Tomlin (1969) originally
developed the approach in a different context as "a kinetic theory of
traffic distributions and similar problems".

3.2 A kinetic theory approach
Kinetic theory is a dynamic theory of dilute gases which considers the
stochastic properties of a large number of intercolliding molecules; it
focuses directly on the collision processes themselves, and deals with
transport phenomena such as the interdiffusion of gaseous molecules and
the drift of ions in an electric field. The approach considers a system
which is initially not in equilibrium and explicitly considers the specific
interactions and processes that are effective in bringing about some
ultimate equilibrium of the system. It is thus a time dependent approach,
and the fundamental equation is the so-called 'transport equation'. This
formally describes the rate of change of the occupation number of a
'state' in terms of the probability of transition between states. Let n_i
denote the occupation number of category i and dn_i/dt its rate of change
over time. (For example, n_i may refer to the number of individuals

within a geographic region or socioeconomic group.) Denote the
probability per unit time of a transition from category i to j as a_{ij}.
Similarly n_j is the occupation number of state j, and a_{ji} the transition
coefficient which represents the probability of a j to i transition in unit
time. The rate of change of the occupation number of category i is
simply related to the difference between the inward and outward flows
for that category:

$$\frac{\mathrm{d}n_i}{\mathrm{d}t} = \sum_j (a_{ji}n_j - a_{ij}n_i) \,. \tag{4}$$

The same differential equation forms the basis of dynamic systems theory,
and Rosen (1970) describes how the solution of the equation has the
general form

$$\exp(u_i t)\exp(iv_i t) \,,$$

where $\exp(iv_i t)$ represents an undamped oscillatory function (u_i and v_i are
related to the transition parameters a_{ij}; they are the eigenvalues of the
a_{ij} matrix).

The time variation of the number of entities n_i in a 'state' i can thus
exhibit a variety of behaviours depending on the sign of u_i and its
magnitude relative to v_i. If u_i is positive and much larger than v_i, then
n_i increases almost monotonically with time; when u_i is negative and
larger than v_i, then n_i decreases; and when u_i is zero, then n_i exhibits
undamped oscillations as shown in figure 5.

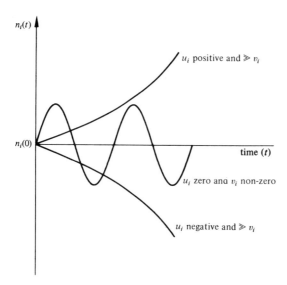

Figure 5. The variation of n_i, the occupation number of the state i, with time.

Given a specific functional form for a_{ij}, then it is in principle possible to obtain particular solutions of the basic equation (4), which would then, for example, describe the rate of change of population due to migration within a city region over time.

This analytic approach to urban growth and change processes suggests that a useful strategy for structuring *experimental* work (in this case, for migration analysis) would be:

1 to construct an accounting matrix comprising transition probabilities observed from past behaviour. This provides a *description* of the migration process through time in a useful summary form, but it should be followed by

2 an interpretation of these parameters in terms of causal variables; an example for migration analysis would be to interpret the transition probabilities in terms of hypothesised economic 'push' and 'pull' variables, and in terms of competition between alternative destinations (see also Ginsberg, 1972);

3 these tested hypotheses for the particular forms of a_{ij} could then give specific solutions to equation (4) which would, in principle, give the future distributions of population over time, or at least the 'behaviour modes' (approximate time path) of that system of city regions.

Considerable simplification of the solution procedure of equation (4) is possible if the a_{ij} can be decomposed into an 'escape probability' per unit time ϵ_i (or escape frequency) and a capture probability μ_j. This simplification separates the 'push' and 'pull' effects of the origin and destination categories. (For example, in migration analysis, intuitively ϵ_i is associated with the intrinsic mobility characteristics 'age and position in life cycle', and with zonal characteristics such as unemployment rates. Similarly μ_j would be associated with (say) economic structure, housing opportunities, and wage rates.)

Further theoretical research is required on this style of approach but some interesting results were obtained by adapting the solution procedures described by Tomlin (1969). These results are given in detail in the paper by Cordey-Hayes (1972), but in summary they include:

1 an equilibrium spatial allocation formula that implicitly contains time through the concepts of escape and capture frequencies; and

2 an equation that illustrates the description of the occupation number (n_i) of a state i during a nonequilibrium situation in terms of the relaxation time (τ) of the system (where τ is shown to be related to the mean time between moves).

3.3 Causal interpretation of the transition probabilities

The differential equations (4) are an accounting framework for changes through time, and in this respect the approach is similar to continuous-time Markov transition matrices (Ginsberg, 1972). However, kinetic theory, with its emphasis on the *processes* of change, focuses more closely on the interpretation of the transition probabilities. This paragraph aims to illustrate this by reference to an example from the physical sciences, and then to relate this to migration analysis.

It can be shown that, for a one-dimensional example, equation (4) can be rewritten in continuous notation as

$$\frac{\partial n_x}{\partial t} = \frac{\partial J_x}{\partial x} \, , \tag{5}$$

where $\partial n_x/\partial t$ is the rate of change of the number of entities per unit area at x, J_x is the mean number of entities crossing unit area at x in unit time, and $\partial J_x/\partial x$ is the gradient of the flow into and out of some infinitely thin slab located at x.

Equation (5) merely expresses the 'conservation of number' of entities, and in this respect is identical to equation (4). But this simple expression provides the framework for all of kinetic theory, and the 'physics' involved is simply to make hypotheses about the nature of J_x for particular situations of interest. For example, in the self diffusion of gases, it is hypothesised that J_x is proportional to the concentration gradient of the gas, $(\partial n_x/\partial x)$, that is,

$$J_x = -D\frac{\partial n_x}{\partial x} \, , \tag{6}$$

which from equation (5) gives

$$\frac{\partial n_x}{\partial t} = -D\frac{\partial^2 n_x}{\partial x^2} \, , \tag{7}$$

where D is a constant of proportionality (the diffusion coefficient), and can be deduced from physical arguments to be directly related to the mean time between collisions. Similarly, for the flow of charged particles in an electric field, the corresponding hypothesis is

$$J_x = \sigma E_x \, , \tag{8}$$

where J_x is the flow of charge carriers per unit time at x, E_x is the electric field at x, and σ is the conductivity (which is the inverse of resistance). Therefore

$$\frac{\partial n_x}{\partial t} = \sigma\frac{\partial E_x}{\partial x} \, . \tag{9}$$

From physical arguments it is possible to deduce an expression for the conductivity in terms of 'micro' variables, that is

$$\sigma = \frac{nQ^2}{m}\tau \, , \tag{10}$$

where n, Q, and m refer to the number, charge, and mass of the charge carriers respectively, and τ is the mean time between collisions.

Using this terminology for migration analysis, the equation (5) provides an accounting framework through time, and it could be hypothesised that the 'flow' of individuals per unit time is given by

$$J_x = \epsilon \frac{\partial v}{\partial x} = \epsilon \frac{\partial}{\partial x} \text{(unemployment)} ,\qquad\qquad (11)$$

where $\partial v/\partial x$ is the spatial gradient of (say) unemployment or income (or some 'attractiveness' concept), and ϵ is the intrinsic mobility of individuals which may be related to age, position in life cycle, and mean time between moves (τ), in a similar way to that represented in equation (10).

The above examples were given to illustrate more clearly the concept of hypothesis-making within a time-oriented accounting framework. The migration example is not intended to be rigorous, instead it aims to give useful insights and to summarise the features of the approach. In the next section preliminary results of an attempt to introduce this structured approach into the analysis of migration movements between 20 city regions in England and Wales are given.

4 A preliminary analysis of city region migration data
4.1 Introduction—the aims of the analysis
Section 2 attempted to demonstrate how the city growth process described in the Forrester model is markedly dependent on the explicit form of the migration equations. Minor modifications to the equation system gave rise to very different values for his evaluative measures, and at present there is insufficient understanding of urban processes to specify these equations adequately. In the present section the preliminary results of a study aimed at the deduction of these equations are given. The longer term aim of the study is to explain migration movements between city regions in terms of the economic structure of those regions; the analysis is guided by the analytic approach and concepts outlined in the last section, but the current lack of time series data means that the approach cannot be adopted rigorously and the transition probabilities are essentially notional.

The migration equations used by Forrester and also by Kadanoff contain two broad hypotheses. These are:
1 There exists a concept of 'city attractiveness' that can be used to explain migration movements between cities, and
2 The in- and out-migration to the city are respectively directly and inversely related to this concept of attractiveness.

The limited aim of the analysis given in this section is to test these hypotheses on the city region migration data recently presented by Fielding (1972). The intention is to structure the problem by firstly examining any systematic behaviour in the transition probabilities for movements to and from the city regions (in terms of the 'escape' and 'capture' probabilities), and then to consider if these suggest a concept of intrinsic

city attractiveness[1]. A later problem would be how to relate the
concepts to measures of job opportunity and housing availability.
The data, which were compiled for the Department of Economic
Affairs from the 1961 census returns, comprise a matrix of migration
flows between the 20 city regions (which are defined in terms of
employment, commuting zones, and retail turnover) and are disaggregated
into three age groups, but no socioeconomic disaggregation of the data is
currently available. Fielding (1972) has recently presented and given a
qualitative interpretation of the data. He emphasises that the value of the
data is that it is based on labour market areas, and argues that for these
functional regions there is a much better chance that recorded migrations
are movements of both house and job than is the case for standard regions
which often cut through commuting areas, and which may therefore
include moves over short distances associated with life cycle behaviour
rather than changes in employment.

4.2 The propensity to migrate

Figure 6 gives *gross in-migration per capita* $\left(\sum_i M_{ij}/P_j \right)$ plotted against *net*

migration per capita (where M_{ij} is the gross migration flow from city

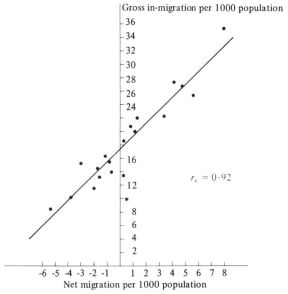

Figure 6. The gross in-migration *per capita* plotted against the net migration *per capita*.

[1] Most conventional quantitative analyses of migration flows appear to provide the
uninteresting result (from a policy point of view) that the escape probability is
proportional to the population within the region and the capture cross section related
essentially to the distance between regions. But Hart (1972) has recently obtained
good correlations between net-migration and employment opportunities.

region i to city region j, and P_j is the population of city region j). The results are as expected—city regions with a high gross in-migration *per capita* also have a high net in-migration *per capita*, and declining city regions have very low rates of gross in-migration. Rather more surprising is the strength (correlation coefficient $r_c = 0.92$) of the linear relationship over the 20 city regions, indicating the importance of data based on functional regions.

Similarly figure 7 gives the gross out-migration *per capita* $\left(\sum_j M_{ij}/P_i \right)$ against net-migration rates. It is clear that gross out-migration *per capita* is much more nearly constant than in-migration, but there appears to be a trend that areas with a *high gross out-migration per capita* have a *net in-migration*, and that net out-migration is more correctly associated with very low rates of in-migration than with a high out-migration *per capita*. That is, the areas with the highest gross in-migration *per capita* also have the highest gross out-migration rates. These are the Southampton, Plymouth, Bristol, Norwich, Nottingham, Coventry, and Leicester city regions, which also have the highest net in-migration. Attractive (growing) areas therefore have high out-migration *per capita* and very high in-migration rates, whilst declining areas have *low* out-migration *per capita* and almost zero in-migration rates.

These results are clearly demonstrated in figure 8, in which gross out-migration and gross in-migration *per capita* are plotted together. The 45° line indicates migration balance, points below this line indicate growing city regions and points above indicate declining regions. It is seen that

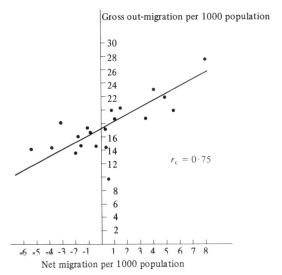

Figure 7. The gross out-migration *per capita* plotted against the net migration *per capita*.

M.Cordey-Hayes

the growing areas (which are at the extreme right of the figure) have both the highest in- and out-migration *per capita*, whilst declining areas have the lowest values for both in- and out-migration. This is clearly contradictory to the hypotheses of Forrester and Kadanoff (and those in the linked-cities model, section 2.2.2) in which it is assumed that in- and out-migration rates are inversely related, which would give an in–out relationship as shown in figure 9.

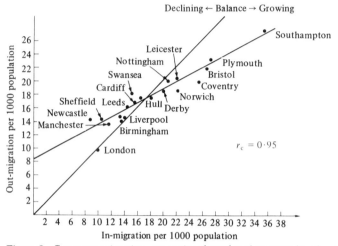

Figure 8. Gross out-migration *per capita* plotted against gross in-migration *per capita*.

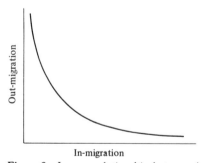

Figure 9. Inverse relationship between in- and out-migration rates.

4.3 The concept of intrinsic attractiveness

The distinctive feature of these migration results is that they are based on labour market areas (city regions) and the data has been normalised to allow for variations in population size. This has enabled an observation of regularities in migration behaviour over the 20 city regions that were outlined in the last paragraph. However, the strong relationship between in- and out-migration *per capita* was not expected; one would expect that cities with the same net-migration *per capita* may have very different

mixes of gross in- and out-migration rates. [A net migration of +10 per
1000 resident population may comprise in- and out-migration rates of
(say) 150 and 140, or 20 and 10, etc.] A trend in which cities with a
high net out-migration *per capita* would have large gross out-migration
per capita may have been hypothesised, but a strong relationship was
observed which was not consistent with this hypothesis.

The results show that cities with a particular net-migration *per capita*
also have almost specific values for the in- and out- rates of migration.

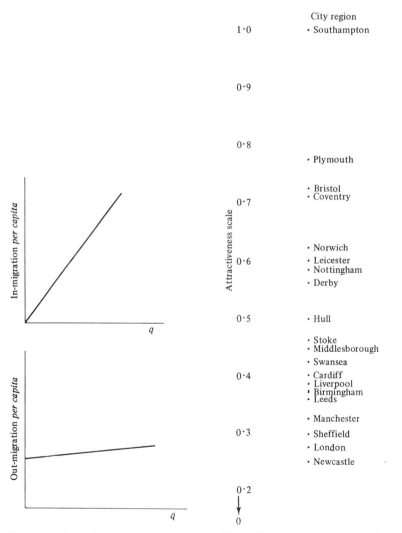

City region

1·0   · Southampton

0·9

0·8
           · Plymouth

           · Bristol
0·7   · Coventry

           · Norwich
0·6   · Leicester
           · Nottingham
           · Derby

0·5   · Hull

           · Stoke
           · Middlesborough
           · Swansea
0·4   · Cardiff
           · Liverpool
           ı Birmingham
           · Leeds

           · Manchester
0·3   · Sheffield
           · London
           · Newcastle

0·2

0

Figure 10. In- and out-migration *per capita* related through an unspecified variable q.

Figure 11. Attractiveness scale for the 20 city regions studied.

This implies a causal relationship between the latter two that is consistent
over the 20 city regions. That is, it implies that both in- and out-migration
are consistently related to a third variable (q) and the results given in figure 8
indicate that the relationships are of the form shown in figure 10.

For low values of q, the out-migration *per capita* is greater than the in-
migration and therefore there is a net out-migration. But since the in-
migration against q relationship has a steeper slope than the out-migration
relationship, then in-migration dominates for higher values of q. Thus q
has the properties that may be associated with a concept of intrinsic
attractiveness of the city region. From the details of the observed
relationships given in section 4.2, it is possible to extract the implied q-
values and grade the city regions accordingly, as shown in figure 11.

At this preliminary stage it is important not to overinterpret the data;
however, a number of important points emerge:

1 There is the possibility of interpreting the 'attractiveness index' in
terms of economic structure variables, which would then produce a
quantitative experimentally based link between the demographic and
economic sectors, and this is considered to be essential for the
development of dynamic urban simulation models.

2 The relationship between migration and attractiveness does not have the
form used by Forrester nor as used in the more serious studies of
Kadanoff (see figures 8 and 9).

3 City regions with balanced in- and out-migration rates have in- and out-
mobilities of $1 \cdot 75\%$ of the resident population (exemplified by Stoke,
Hull, and Derby). Cities with the largest net in-migration rates
(Southampton and Plymouth) have a gross in-migration rate of
approximately double this ($3 \cdot 5\%$), whilst cities in decline (Newcastle,
Sheffield) have out-mobilities of approximately half those of Derby
and Hull, and approaching zero in-migration *per capita*. (See figure 8).

4 If further analysis of the migration *flows* confirms that in- and out-
migration can be described in terms of an intrinsic attractiveness
concept (as given in figure 10), then this encourages an effort to
explore the characteristic features of the 'attractive city regions' and
suggests that policy-oriented interregional simulation models may be a
feasible proposition.

Acknowledgement. The work described in section 2 was carried out in collaboration
with Andrew Matheson; a more detailed description of the various modifications
made to the Forrester model are described in Centre for Environmental Studies
Working Notes 309 and 310.

References
Cordey-Hayes, M., 1972, "Dynamic frameworks for spatial models", *Socio-Economic
Planning Sciences,* **6** (4), 365–385 (and WP-76, Centre for Environmental Studies,
London).
Cordey-Hayes, M., Matheson, A., 1972, "Policy-oriented simulation models", WN-310,
Centre for Environmental Studies, London.

Fielding, A. J., 1972, "Internal migration in England and Wales", UWP-14, Centre for Environmental Studies, London.

Forrester, J., 1969, *Urban Dynamics* (MIT Press, Cambridge, Mass.).

Ginsberg, R. K., 1972, "Critique of probabilistic models", WP-73, Centre for Environmental Studies, London.

Hart, R. A., 1972, "The economic influences on internal labour force migration", *Scottish Journal of Political Economy,* 19, 151–174.

Hamilton, H. R., Goldstone, S. E., Hilliman, J. W., Pugh, A. C., Roberts, E. B., Zellner, A., 1969, *Systems Simulation in Regional Analysis* (MIT Press, Cambridge, Mass.).

Ingram, G. K., 1970, Book review in *Journal of the American Institute of Planners,* 36, 206–208.

Kadanoff, L. P., 1971, "From simulation model to public policy: an examination of Forrester's *Urban Dynamics*", *Simulation,* 16, 261–268.

Kadanoff, L. P., 1972, "From simulation model to public policy", *American Scientist,* 60, 74–79.

Rosen, R., 1970, *Dynamical System Theory in Biology, Volume 1: Stability Theory and Its Applications* (John Wiley, New York).

Tomlin, S. G., 1969, "A kinetic theory of traffic distribution and similar problems", *Environment and Planning,* 1, 221–227.

Space Allocation Methods in the Design Process

B.HARRIS
University of Pennsylvania

In recent years I have been sporadically concerned with the design process, which I arbitrarily define in a very general way as being the selection of a group of decisions or elements to satisfy a group of goals or objectives. This definition is broad enough to encompass in design not only genuine design activity such as architecture, but also planning, policy-making, and legislating of the most general nature. The unique quality of design applied to complex problems is that the design decisions interact with each other, and their effects are not independent either as to cost or as to their effectiveness in achieving goals. Because design decisions are interacting, there are apt to be multiple optima. Consequently design becomes a very large combinatorial problem which is in general highly resistant to direct solutions.

With the advent of the computer, a fair amount of attention is being paid to design methodology in the hope that if design methods can be formalized, they can be transferred to the computer, thus relieving the human designer from a large amount of drudgery, and possibly resulting, in many instances, in improved designs. At the current writing this hope has been continuously disappointed, and it is clear that further insights into the design process will be required before these efforts meet with even moderate success. My own limited efforts in this field differ to an extent from the mainstream of activity. I believe that this difference is well-founded on a logical basis, but I should not hope to change greatly the direction of the search now going on nor to discourage any of it. I hope only to be able to make my views quite clear and understandable. With this in mind, I will first briefly discuss what I believe to be three major points of difference between myself and others.

The first of these differences concerns the definition of problem-solving. I believe that definitions drawn from theorem-proving puzzles, and other similar activities, and extensions of these definitions into the realm of problem-solving behavior, are apt to be deceptive. One is tempted to ask where there is any problem in designing a new town or a home or an office building. Quite evidently there are abundant examples in which each of these problems has been solved, and it would be simple enough to adapt one of these solutions—as indeed is often done. But simply to ask this question immediately suggests that what is wanted is a *better* solution. The 'problem' is therefore not one of finding any answer, but of finding an optimal answer. Some may quibble over the question of optimality, but I will leave that discussion for some other time and place (Harris, 1968). It is entirely possible, and I believe likely, that the solution of optimizing problems differs radically from the solution of what I call feasibility problems, and that the two should not be jointly discussed except perhaps to draw contrasts between them.

My second point of difference with current approaches toward automated design is, I confess, somewhat more a matter of instinct than of reason, except insofar as it overlaps substantially with the third point. There is currently, I believe, something of an overemphasis on the semantics and vocabulary of the design process, on information retrieval, and on memory in the same process. In my view undue attention to these aspects of the design process may tend to obscure its basic structure and the structure of the problems with which it deals. Since these matters are to a large extent peripheral to the definition of structure, and since I believe that the structure of problems is a principal difficulty in design and that its solution is an urgent necessity, I believe that this emphasis is incorrect. It is of course quite possible that approaching the problem from opposite directions in this regard may lead to mutually reinforcing discoveries of different kinds.

The third difficulty arises out of my reluctance to accept human design protocol as the proper starting point for the automation of the design process. In mitigation of this view, I could observe that the human race has had many millennia of experience in solving combinatorial problems, and that good solutions have probably had a high survival value. Hence there must be a protocol which is possibly applicable to the problem at hand, and we may very well find it useful to observe human behavior for clues as to what that protocol may be. I suspect, however, that there may be three basic difficulties with this procedure. First, the very best designers and problem-solvers may be the most difficult to observe, which would bias our sample in the direction of inferior protocols. Second, it may be that the most important portions of the mentation and behavior which go into design are only partially conscious, and that these are not captured in the observation of the work of designers. Third, I consider it most likely that different problems have different structures, and that an important part of successful design is to adapt the structure of the solution method to the structure of the problem. This means that there is, or ought to be, a battery of solution methods which are all structurally different from one another, and that a most important step in automating design should be to explore the structure of problems and the fitness of different algorithmic or processual methods of solving them. There is of course a good chance that investigating protocols will once again lead to the same conclusion as an investigation of the problems themselves, but my hunch is that the latter will be more productive.

For this reason, and by way of an illustration of my thesis, I propose to discuss in this paper the problem of space allocation. I shall start with the relatively simple case of a given number of activities to be assigned to a given number of locations. This could apply equally well to the layout of a factory building, of a new town, or of a regional system of cities. It is thus a planning problem *par excellence*, although a relatively limited one. I shall first discuss the problem in its simplest form. I shall discuss the complete solution and various heuristic approaches which are not complete but which may be more feasible. I shall then expand the discussion briefly to include some slightly more complex examples, and finally I shall attempt to indicate some very important design issues which are not approached by the methods discussed so far. The fact that the methods for solving very limited problems are still quite cumbersome and expensive suggests the magnitude of the difficulty of solving the large problems in which they are embedded.

The simplest problem in space allocation is the case where we have N activities and N locations to which they are assigned. If each activity incurs a certain possible cost or benefit in each location, the problem of an optimal assignment is a special case of the transportation problem of linear programming, called the assignment problem. This problem can be solved expeditiously for very large numbers, and has a single locally optimal solution which is therefore also globally optimal. When we take into account the interaction between locators, the problem changes drastically. Suppose, for example, that activities are mutually interdependent, with some volume of interaction between them which is defined by the quantity v_{ij}. Suppose also that the pairs of possible locations in which activities may be located are separated by a distance d_{kl}. Finally, suppose that the *cost* of interaction between activities i and j, placed in locations k and l respectively, is the product of these two quantities, $v_{ij}d_{kl}$. The problem of locating activities in a pattern which minimizes total interaction costs can now be formulated as the zero–one quadratic assignment problem (Koopmans and Beckmann, 1957):

$$\min \sum_i \sum_j \sum_k \sum_l v_{ij}d_{kl}X_{ik}X_{jl}$$

such that

$$\sum_i X_{ik} = 1, \qquad (k = 1,2,...,N)$$

$$\sum_k X_{ik} = 1, \qquad (i = 1,2,...,N)$$

where $X_{ik} = 0,1$.

There is no difficulty in expanding this problem to include a linear term corresponding to the cost (or negative benefit) attached to a specific location for a specific activity.

Lawler (1963) has shown a reasonably simple method for solving the quadratic assignment problem using a branch and bound procedure, together with a very large number of solutions of the linear assignment problem. This linear problem is specially devised to conform with the terms of the original quadratic problem. This branch and bound procedure requires essentially N^2 solutions of an $N \times N$ problem and is therefore very time-consuming. We may note parenthetically, however, that this represents a gigantic gain over the direct enumeration of all possible solutions, which is $N!$. This would be utterly impractical beyond about ten locators. Lawler's method is practical up to about twenty-five or fifty locators.

A characteristic of the formulation of the problem so far set forth, which leads to very substantial practical difficulties, is the fact that there is exactly one locator in each location. This implies essentially that the locations are uniform in size. It is possible, however, to exclude a single locator from selected locations by placing a very high cost on his utilization of them.

In architectural applications of this formulation, whether solved by quadratic programming or not, the problem may be formulated in either two or three dimensions. The space must be divided up into more or less uniform rectangles or parallelopipeds, and the appropriate distances for interaction between them must be calculated. The activities in their turn must be divided up into units which will just about fit into these uniform cells, and the volumes of interaction between pairs of activities must be calculated. If a department or activity is too large to fit in a single cell, it can be divided into parts. One of these parts will be assigned all of the interaction costs with other activities, and the parts will be given high interaction costs with each other. As a result these activities locate as a unit in a compact space, and their location with respect to other activities is determined in the usual way. Unfortunately, if there is a wide variation in the space occupied by various activities, this device leads to an inappropriate multiplication of cells, which greatly increases the size of the problem. As we shall see at a later point, the procedure also creates difficulties with some heuristic algorithms.

There is a converse difficulty which is not so immediately apparent. Certain activities may have real interaction costs and may present locational problems, even though such activities may not be unique and may have to be located in a number of different places. Examples are washrooms and shopping centers. The difficulty is that we have no way to assign to these activities, fixed interaction costs with the other activities. Depending on their location, they interact with some and not with others. This pattern of interaction leads to a linear programming problem of a quite different type which cannot easily be joined to the quadratic programming problem, because the latter depends on an exhaustion of available space and locations, while the approach for this pattern requires vacant space to provide for choices of location.

While the application of this formulation of the problem to matters of building design and layout may be fairly obvious, its application to city planning and the layout of new towns is somewhat more novel.

An interesting and fruitful experiment in this regard has just been reported by Gordon and MacReynolds (1972). They divided a metropolitan region, very much like Los Angeles, into twenty-seven roughly uniform areas corresponding to identifiable communities and topographic subregions, whilst dividing the activities of the metropolis into twenty-seven packages, such as middle-income housing, large-scale shopping, and so on, in such a way that each package could approximately fit into one of the twenty-seven areas. Some packages like low-income housing were replicated more than once. Gordon and MacReynolds used this formulation of the problem, and the quadratic programming solution, to explore both the realism of the assumptions of the model and (with a 10 × 10 problem) the general impact of changes such as improving the transportation system and relocating the port. The results conformed with intuition, and suggested that valuable extensions of the technique might be developed. In my view, the second difficulty above—of activities such as low-income housing, which should seek several different locations—was not resolved by Gordon and MacReynold's approach.

So far, I have employed the example of quadratic programming to define the problem as clearly as possible. Partly because of the difficulties mentioned, but principally because of the computational requirements, quadratic programming is not very much used for solving problems of this type. We now devote a certain amount of attention to the principal heuristic means which are used to attempt a solution of the same problem. By a heuristic procedure I mean a procedure which is well-defined and systematic, which searches for a problem solution (in this case an optimum), but which is not guaranteed to produce more than an approximate solution. The obvious trade-off here is between computing time or planning effort and the completeness of the results. A major object of study in work of this kind should be the determination of more or less exact relationships between the amount of effort and the 'goodness' of results for different problems, under different heuristics.

The basic approach, which has been used in many places and has been set forward as a fundamental heuristic for discrete optimization in a wide variety of contexts, is swapping. Suppose that we have a tentative solution for the locational problem under consideration. We now take, let us say, the first activity and consider swapping it with each other activity. We either immediately execute any swap which improves the objective function, or we wait until some class of possible swaps has been examined and execute the best of the class. Possible classes of swaps are all swaps of one item, or all swaps of all pairs of items. This process is constantly repeated in a systematic way until no further improvement from a swap is possible (Reiter and Sherman, 1962).

The principal difficulty with swapping procedures of this kind is that frequently an improvement could be found if sets of items could be swapped, but it is blocked off if we are limited to single items. However, the number of swaps of single items to be explored is of the order of N^2, while the number of swaps of two items is of the order of N^4, and in general, if M out of N items are to be swapped, the number of possibilities is of the order of N^{2M}. In principle, however, true optimality cannot be guaranteed unless M is as great as the total number of elements which can be included in a feasible plan. As far as I know, no adequate explorations of this matter have been made, but higher-order swaps are undoubtedly better pursued by other means such as Lawler's solution to the quadratic programming problem. If, as was suggested earlier, certain activities have to be treated as groups of activities with high interaction costs, to locate members of the group together, then low-order swaps cannot possibly change the location of these groups, and the group as a whole may never be optimally located. This is a basic difficulty with the swapping heuristic which cannot be overcome.

A second and somewhat less commonly used approach, which can be combined with the swapping heuristic as a preliminary to it, is a constructive approach which combines activities sequentially according to some predetermined scheme. One such scheme is to provide a central location for one or more activities which have generally high levels of interaction. Then additional activities are added one at a time, in the order of the extent of their interaction with activities already located. Each of these added activities is placed either in the best incremental location, or in the best location which can be achieved by displacing, outward from the centre, one or more of the activities already located. This latter step is simple in one dimension but conceptually difficult in two or three dimensions. An alternative constructive method is to combine those activities exhibiting the highest pairwise interaction, then to combine pairs of pairs, etc. There might be some difficulty in providing a scheme whereby these clusters as they were formed would be given locations. This second scheme would be superior to the first if no particular activities were salient in total interaction, but there were large numbers of groups of 'local' interactions.

A third heuristic which could be applied to this problem is in a sense another view of the last one mentioned and has a relation to it through the theory of clustering. This is to take the universe of activities and decompose them hierarchically, separating them into groups which have major interactions, while minimizing the interactions between groups. This is a variation of methods proposed by Alexander (1969) and by Manheim for hierarchical decomposition, and it is closely related to clustering. In this particular instance, after the decomposition has been carried to a certain point, some additional methods have to be proposed for optimizing within and between clusters. One could, for example, decompose a set of activities into groups which would each occupy one floor of a building, and then optimize different floors and shuffle the plans to optimize between floors. Either quadratic programming, or one of the other heuristics being discussed, could be employed for this purpose. A particular advantage of this method is that those activities which were discussed above as having locational requirements, but not a universal range over all areas, could be assigned on some rational basis to various major clusters, and their location within these clusters could be optimized. This assignment would be distinct from the operation of this heuristic.

A fourth approach, which is not actually an independent heuristic but a device of some significance in the application of most of them, is the recognition of the desirability of randomizing starting configurations. True randomness may not be necessary, but a systematic perturbation of solutions is highly desirable. This perturbation gives hill-climbing approaches, such as the swapping procedures, an opportunity to search for new configurations, and possibly for them to come up with optimal solutions which could not be reached from any point in the previous explorations. We shall return to the question of the perturbation of starting points, in a somewhat larger context, later in this paper.

If we relax the somewhat rigid assumptions in which the problem has so far been framed, the difficulties multiply enormously, at least as far as optimal solutions are concerned, and to an extent for heuristic methods. In order to illustrate this problem, I will briefly mention two examples.

The first example was propounded by Simmons (1969). It is the problem of arranging along a corridor a number of rooms of various widths, with various propensities for interaction, so as to minimize the cost of interaction. Because the choice of intervening rooms influences the cost of interaction between predetermined pairs of rooms, this is a more complicated problem than the previous one. Viewed strictly as a combinatorial problem, it has almost exactly the same nature, having $N!/2$ solutions. Finding the optimal solution, however, requires more complicated programming, and, in my own branch and bound procedure, the time required is at least exponential in N, varying roughly as 4^N. It is possible to formulate this as a cubic assignment problem with h, i, and j referring to activities, and k, l, and m referring to locations, with the following objective function:

$$\min \sum_h \sum_i \sum_j \sum_k \sum_l \sum_m v_{hj} w_i X_{hk} X_{il} X_{jm} \;,$$

where

$$k = 1, 2, ..., N-2,$$
$$l = k+1, k+2, ..., m-1,$$
$$m = k+2, k+3, ..., N.$$

In the above, w_i refers to the width of the room required for activity i.

It is not known, however, whether this substantially reduces the computational difficulties. Since I have above pointed out the realistic need to allow for locators of different sizes, it is of interest to note that this realistic consideration greatly complicates the solution of problems. I can also report, however, that the Simmons problem yields to a combination of heuristic methods including a variety of starts, a constructive solution, and a hill-climbing procedure which swaps locators (Harris, 1971). Unfortunately it is not easy to see how this could be extended to two or three dimensions.

Various persons interested in architectural and structural design problems have attempted to develop heuristic solutions to similar problems such as the arrangement of machinery in a single space. In an example put forward by Eastman (1969) a very large number of constraints had to be satisfied, and there was probably only one solution. In cases of this nature, theorem-proving methods and adaptations of them are applicable. Even very simple examples prove to be highly intractable, partly because of the complex problem of satisfying and checking all of the real-world constraints, but primarily because of the explosive combinatorial nature of the problem.

Having shown that the combinatorial aspects of very simple and clearly defined locational problems grow extremely rapidly, I now wish to point out that these problems are embedded in a set of larger design problems whose nature may very well be even more complex than those which we have just discussed. Even assuming for the moment the realism of the quadratic assignment problem, and the possibility of solving it for large problems in reasonable times with heuristic means, we must examine the other assumptions of the problem. The first of these is that the configuration of spaces into which the locators must be put is fixed. The second is that the cost of interaction between locations is fixed. Neither of these assumptions is realistic.

It may be useful to discuss the second assumption first. In city planning, to arrange a transportation system for a fixed array of land uses planned for the future is a standard problem which is in itself highly intractable. But even this difficult problem is limited by the assumption that the land uses are known and the transportation system must in some sense be optimally designed to serve them. By focusing first on the locational problem, we have removed that assumption and the total problem is now ill-defined. If we provide a transportation system as a hypothesis, then we will be able to solve the locational problem. Once we have done that, it is not clear that all of the transportation provisions which we have made will be justified. For example, patronage may be at too low a level on some of the mass transportation facilities. We then have to readjust the transportation system and rerun the locational problem. This, however, is not all. There are many completely distinct configurations of transportation facilities which could be designed to serve any given area.

Even if the process which we have just described converges, it may not be optimal because we have started from the 'wrong' initial transportation design configuration. To overcome this problem we need to perturb, or vary at the large scale, the proposed transportation systems. This generates a much larger and more difficult search problem.

We may note that the architects have to an extent to face 'transportation' problems of a similar but less exacerbated nature. The relative economy and utility of elevators, escalators, slideways, and pedestrian movement must be resolved in the design of a building or building complex. These issues interact strongly in architecture, however, with the second set of configurational problems.

When we remove the assumption that the space to be filled is predefined, we open the door to a new level of genuine design activity. The relaxation of this assumption gives a greater freedom to the architect than it does to the planner.

For the architect very few spaces are wholly predetermined. He has very considerable latitude in the selection of size and shape for the envelope of any building, and as to the framing and arrangement of the interior space. It might well be contended that these decisions, constrained by site, zoning, cost, and technical feasibility, represent the true decision space of the architectural designer. In my view, it should not, however, be permissible for the designer to neglect cost and effectiveness considerations. In this context, therefore, the assignment of the activities to be housed in a structure becomes an important subproblem which must be solved in order to evaluate each design. The search for viable and effective designs, however, is once again a different and quite possibly more complex problem than the one with which I opened this paper.

The city planner works with three-dimensional configurations, as does the architect. Control of the height, or more generally the density, dimension establishes one of the constraints within which the architect must work. The constraints on the planner are more elementary, having to do with insolation, air movement, congestion, and amenity. Given some treatment of density, the configurations which will evolve on a two-dimensional plan may be regarded as a specialized locational problem of the type we initially discussed. This can be done by regarding open space, land reservations, and other specialized uses as simply another locator. Stylizing the problem in this way may throw some light on its nature, but there are too many marginal adjustments required on the space allocation model to make it a feasible way to proceed. In this case, the interaction between city planning, space allocation, and the transportation system is strong and perhaps dominant, and it seems unlikely that they can effectively be treated as separate problems.

The sequence of ideas which I have developed here suggests two principal conclusions about design, based on a rather superficial survey of physical planning and architectural problems. I have not discussed the policy planning problems as they might arise in education, health care delivery, welfare, and public protection, but I believe that these problem areas could be fitted into very much the same framework. The most elementary operations for these policy areas would not be space allocation, and they would probably be much simpler and more susceptible to direct attack than some of the larger and more complex issues which would have a 'configurational' aspect in the policy sense.

The first major conclusion of this review is that the relatively simple paradigms for problems like space allocation, which tend to be generated in the search for a theory of automated design, may be of considerable practical importance, and may become integrated into larger search procedures as an evaluative mechanism, but they do not lead systematically, or by some enlargement, into a consideration of the problems with which architects, planners, and policy-makers are primarily concerned. These problems are of a nature at least partially distinct, and they require a new set of planning models which do not yet exist.

A second and corollary conclusion is that the hierarchical nature of the kinds of decisions which we have been discussing is probably in principle distinct from the types of hierarchical decomposition discussed by Alexander (1969) and others. The concepts of hierarchical decomposition may be interpreted as dealing with a large number of decisions, all at an equal level. The hierarchy which has emerged in this paper depends on the fact that there is a dependency, or sequencing of relationships, between various design choices. The location of offices in a building cannot be elucidated until the shape of the building is known. This hierarchical relationship does not deny the interaction between the different levels in both directions, but it suggests that certain decisions are more salient than others, and that in an exploratory process these salient decisions will be the least frequently changed. Hierarchical decomposition of lower-level decisions and activities may still be very important in structuring and simplifying the problem, and in providing small bundles of decisions which can be jointly resolved.

Finally we may observe that the usual difficulties are once again evident in dealing with large-scale design problems. The necessity, or at least the desirability, of finding quick and reliable estimates of the optimal locational pattern within a fixed configuration is here emphasized from a somewhat unconventional point of view. Many believe that the solution of space allocation problems is a technique which produces valuable results in its own right. This is undoubtedly true to an extent, and hopefully both architects and city planners will accumulate a great deal of additional experience in this field. The point made in this paper, however, is that such procedures are a necessary part of evaluating and testing large numbers of configurational schemes. Such schemes are probably sketch plans, but to call them that raises a number of issues of planning procedures which are not the topic of this paper. Clearly, however, when we try to evaluate the worth of a trial plan, we blunt our judgment if we cannot estimate something like its optimal performance in a number of different respects. One of these respects is controlled by the efficient allocations of users of the scheme to the spaces available, and we must be able to estimate this efficiency. The ponderousness and complexity of methods for making these estimates is a barrier to sound sketch planning.

References

Alexander, C., 1969, *Notes on the Synthesis of Form* (Harvard University Press, Cambridge, Mass.). (Alexander later developed unpublished computer algorithms for this decomposition in collaboration with Marion Manheim.)

Eastman, C. M., 1969, "Toward a theory of automated design", Institute of Physical Planning, Carnegie Mellon Institute, Pittsburgh, Pa., mimeo.

Gordon, P., MacReynolds, W. K., 1972, "Optimal urban forms: toward a complete modeling of urban interdependencies", undated ditto, received spring of 1972 from Gordon at Department of Economics, University of Southern California, Los Angeles.

Harris, B., 1969, "People, problems and plans: the purpose and nature of design", *Transactions of the Bartlett Society, 7*, 11-53.

Harris, B., 1971, "Branch and bound in space allocation", Institute for Environmental Studies, University of Pennsylvania, Philadelphia, Pa., mimeo.

Koopmans, T. C., Beckmann, M. J., 1957, "Assignment problems and the location of economic activities", *Econometrica, 25*, 52-76.

Lawler, E. L., 1963, "The quadratic assignment problem", *Management Science, 9*, 686-699.

Reiter, S., Sherman, G. R., 1962, "Allocating indivisible resources affording external economies or diseconomies", *International Economic Review, 5*, 108-135. (This appears to be the basic paper on swapping as a heuristic. Many later applications have been made.)

Simmons, D. M., 1969, "One-dimensional space allocation: an ordering algorithm", *Operations Research, 17*, 812-826.

The Development of an Activity-Commodity Representation of Urban Systems as a Potential Framework for Evaluation

R.BARRAS, T.A.BROADBENT
Centre for Environmental Studies, London

1 Introduction

This paper does not discuss a formalized theory of evaluation for urban or regional planning nor a practical method for testing alternative plans. It attempts firstly to outline some recent trends in the theory and practice of evaluation and to suggest that these trends represent a real shift in concept. It is asserted that a clear distinction must be made between the formal descriptive representation of system behaviour and the normative representation of the evaluation process. A descriptive representation of the urban system is built up from general system principles, using commodities as the basic entities and activities as the relations of the system. The use of this representation within a conceptualized plan generation and evaluation process is then discussed. The paper is thus not a rigorous treatise but reflects its own view of the nature of the evaluation process as a semi-formal procedure.

2 A view of the evaluation process

2.1 Introduction

In the USA and UK in the last 10 to 15 years there has been considerable concentration on formal cost benefit analysis (CBA) linked to descriptive-behavioural models. In this section, some of the practical and theoretical limitations of CBA (particularly when applied to the evaluation of comprehensive schemes) are documented together with some of the positive lessons that might be drawn from its use with forecasting models. Other approaches to evaluation are also discussed, and the aims of an activity-commodity approach within the context of the overall planning process are then outlined.

2.2 Cost benefit analysis

Standard references on CBA are Prest and Turvey (1965), Lichfield (1970), Mishan (1971), and Pearce (1971). CBA is grounded in the microeconomic theory of the firm (Hill, 1968), and in the concepts of welfare economics. Thus a firm compares the worth of alternative investment projects by calculating the profit from each over a future time period, on the basis of expected revenues and costs, and in relation to the initial capital invested. If resources are limited, the firm invests in its chosen projects until marginal revenue equals marginal costs. If there is a perfectly competitive market involving infinitely small units, welfare theory indicates that their profit maximizing behaviour leads to an equilibrium and a maximization of welfare throughout society. When these principles are used to calculate the worth of investment to a *public* authority, several immediate problems arise. The analysis should ideally take into account the fact that the flows of money and goods between the public sector and the rest of the system is not as free as it is in a competitive market; also there is often no way of directly quantifying benefits and costs in terms of prices in a competitive market, and various external economies, or diseconomies, and interdependencies may exist. It is not often possible to take account of all these in a satisfactory manner, but some attempts to do so are usually made. The following specific drawbacks of CBA are those most relevant to the purpose of this paper but do not constitute a general critique.

Firstly, as a very general point about the notion of the existence of competitive markets, at many levels, ranging from the national down to the local or urban, there is some doubt about the concept of a competitive market as a useful approximation to the real world even in those spheres where goods are directly manufactured, bought, and sold. This means generally that prices at equilibrium do not necessarily reflect any general welfare maximum. Even at the national level, the actors in the system are often not the infinitely small operators, with no individual effect on the general price levels or quantities produced, that the competitive market model demands. When we come down to the urban scale the deviation from the ideal case is even more marked. The public authority is a major factor throughout the urban economic system; to equate its carefully limited but pervasive role with that of a profit maximizing firm in a local area can be misleading. Similarly a single firm in a local area can have a position of total dominance in terms of employment, and therefore in terms of the journey-to-work, housing, and other effects connected with employment. Even the theory of urban spatial structure is partly connected with notions of spatial monopolies. Thus, in this sense, the competitive market which provides much of the basis and justification for CBA appears as an elaborate but at the same time abstract theoretical construct. It bears little relationship to empirical evidence on urban structure, and as such provides few tools for direct influence over these structures.

The second point relates to the measurement of benefits and to the implied system model generally used to represent them. They should necessarily be *social* benefits. For the users of a public investment (for example, a new bridge), these benefits are again tied directly to the notion of the behaviour of individuals competing with each other in a market. The benefits to them, either of goods or of new behaviour (for example, a different journey pattern), are measured in terms of 'willingness to pay' for them. This picture of isolated individuals, each with a budget, buying his individual way around the system in accordance with his 'utility', may be a useful apologia for the consumer society, but as a general model it is not a 'society' at all. A society, whether national or urban, is a social *organisation*. Whether or not expressed in terms of interest groups or classes, to be of use, any general model must include some notion of how the whole organisation links together and functions. This immediately raises the question of the relationship between the microanalysis of individuals or small groups, and the total structure of the urban system with which we are dealing. Generally this is done in CBA by firstly measuring the individual's consumer surplus from new investment. A demand curve is posited which specifies the quantity of a good that would be bought at a given price; the lower the price, the more will be bought. Secondly the surplus is measured from what consumers actually pay for the goods they are getting, compared with what they would be prepared to pay for them following the new investment. Finally these surpluses are added together for all individuals. Even if we were prepared to accede that what consumers pay for is what they want, there is no simple way of proceeding from individual preference or behaviour to the system as a whole. Theil (1965) shows the general difficulty of aggregating micro relationships into macro ones, and Lange (1965) puts forward the general systems-analysis case against such a naive procedure. A system is more than the sum of its individual parts, and the full analysis needs not only a model or description of individual behaviour but a model of the linkages between individuals or groups in order to get a satisfactory description of the total system.

Most applications of CBA and most of the standard texts on the method stress its essentially partial nature even when viewed from its own philosophical and theoretical standpoint. Prest and Turvey (1965) touch upon this question at several points. At the outset it is clear that the method is not appropriate for 'large-scale' investment decisions—large, that is, relative to a given economy. If one is interested in comprehensive strategic planning for an area, then clearly one is discussing major structural changes in that area which do indeed alter "the constellation of relative outputs and prices over the whole economy" (Prest and Turvey, 1965). Again, in discussing projects which are large enough to affect some prices, Prest and Turvey cite the difficulties of measuring meaningful costs and benefits on the basis of demand and supply curves which are essentially artificial, partial constructs, and not observable anyway. Finally, in discussing urban renewal, they stress the inherent complexity of the problem where many groups and institutions interact, and the consequent need to disaggregate costs and benefits to identify who gains and who loses (see also Lichfield, 1970).

Prest and Turvey further note that where two projects, A and B, are interrelated, they must be assessed as three different projects—A alone, B alone, and A and B together. Also some projects might by definition exclude others and this must also be allowed for.

A comprehensive strategic plan for an area must necessarily encompass very many combinations of this type, and it would be extremely difficult to evaluate such a large number of them in traditional CBA terms. Little (1957) stresses the drawbacks of using a partial demand curve which only refers to a single good, and with which it is impossible to take account of the effect of the project on prices of other goods and thus of cost-benefit effects elsewhere in the system. Scitovsky (1941) shows how such a partial demand curve, which does not take account of wider effects, can lead to an absurd situation, where, after beneficial investment on the basis of a prior CBA, another CBA can show it worth returning to the original situation.

More recently, and particularly in the transport and land-use planning field, there have been direct attempts to marry CBA to formal behavioural models which do cover a wider system. Thus gravity models, which are widely used to predict the trips between zones in an urban area in terms of variables defining zonal characteristics and travel cost between zones, have been derived by maximizing utility functions and from consumer surplus criteria (see Neidercorn and Bechdolt, 1969; Neuberger, 1971). Since the gravity model tends to reproduce observed trip patterns fairly satisfactorily, the fact that it can be derived from a demand curve seems to lend credence to the notion that rational microeconomic behaviour of individuals in the market is a satisfactory starting point for urban system analysis. Secondly it supplies a direct connection between the straightforward descriptive model of trip making in an urban system and the evaluation of changes in travel costs arising from alternative plans. For each plan the gravity model describes the new distribution of trips, and the surpluses or benefits can then be calculated more or less directly.

Interestingly, Neuberger shows that some forms of gravity model [which after all is a system-wide model with many 'goods' (trips) and 'prices' (travel costs), and therefore many partial demand curves] do satisfy the restrictive criteria, and allow the calculation of a multidimensional or system-wide surplus. However, this will not necessarily be true for many system-wide models. But the major interest from the point of view of this paper is in the nature of the link between the formal behavioural model and the formal evaluative model. To show that a model which satisfactorily reproduces observed trip-making behaviour can be derived from an individual utility model does not necessarily justify the utility model as the relevant tool for providing social preferences in plan evaluation. Indeed the gravity model can be derived from much more empirical criteria about the random behaviour of a large number of identical system elements, with no notion of individual 'utility' (Wilson, 1967). The major point remains—that the choices individuals make provide no direct and straightforward guide to the way society may choose to plan the future. What society has to do is to observe the aggregate patterns of behaviour, say as represented by the gravity model,

and plan a strategy accordingly. This implies an evaluation framework
external to the descriptive model; one which makes a separation between
description and evaluation.

2.3 An alternative approach to evaluation

To sketch an alternative approach to CBA, let us suppose it is possible for
society, and hence planners on behalf of the public authority, to
formulate general aims and goals, and express them in terms of variables
which describe the urban system. This would be what might be termed a
'conscious' decision-taking framework, and contrasts with CBA in which
the individual consumer, taking his own decisions in the market as it is
presented to him, is in effect making the evaluation between possible
alternative plans which the planner might formulate. From the point of
view of society this latter type of decision-taking is 'unconscious'—it
happens automatically and so there is no need for the society as a whole
to try to formulate explicit goals.

The so-called 'goals-achievement' approach (Hill, 1968; Lichfield, 1970)
represents one attempt at a conscious evaluation method. In this
method, benefits and costs are measured in terms of progress towards
achieving desired objectives. An accounting framework is built up, showing
how each alternative strategy affects the different goals (for example, by
increasing accessibility, reducing capital costs, etc.). A major drawback
with these methods as they are currently used can be observed
immediately. When an analysis attempts to take account of the effects
of a large-scale project or plan on the rest of the system, that is, it
attempts a comprehensive coverage of the system, then the need for some
'model' or formal representation of the interactions between different
parts of the urban system becomes apparent.

In a typical goals-achievement account the actual mechanics and
interaction between the sectors of the urban system (that is, the system
model) are represented in an extremely rudimentary form. Any index of
achievement for a given objective (say accessibility) must embody an
implied system model involving system-describing variables such as distance,
activity locations, and levels. Again, an index for one objective must in
general imply something about other indices for other objectives.

However, with goals-achievement methods, these indices tend to be
calculated separately and not within a general system-wide model which
interrelates the variables in a consistent manner. Thus one index may be
calculated using a particular relation between variables, and another may
use a quite different, conflicting relationship. Even where identical
variables do not appear in different indices there may still be implied
inconsistencies involving the relationship between index variables and
other variables. The use, as just illustrated, of gravity models within CBA
shows how much further advanced CBA is in this respect, since there is an
overall consistency between the descriptive and the evaluative analysis.

The 'objectives' used in CBA—the utility criteria—are unambiguous, general criteria which clearly apply across the whole system. And here also the methodology is clearly far in advance of goals-achievement methods, where objectives are rarely formulated unambiguously in terms of direct system variables. Nevertheless goals achievement, at a very minimum, represents a valid aspiration to make planning decisions more conscious, and at the same time amenable to formal description and analysis.

2.4 The nature of the planning process

Before suggesting an appropriate method or procedure for evaluation in urban planning it is necessary to specify the planning process within which the evaluation is to proceed. Clearly, what is suitable for a short-term choice between two alternative single projects which only affect the urban system at the margin is not appropriate for a larger-scale problem involving a comprehensive and significant change in the whole system.

One view of the planning process is that of a cyclical procedure in which there is a continual and successive refinement and redefinition of several explicit stages. These are: the formulation of goals and objectives; plan generation; plan elaboration through formal models; partial evaluation, including a choice between alternatives; then, possibly, back to reformulation of objectives; the generation of new alternatives and the refinement of existing strategies, and so on. Such a view has been put forward by Boyce et al. (1970) in a review of the major land-use transport studies in the USA. Bellman (1965) describes a similar procedure when discussing the use of models as exploratory tools for any real-world process. It has been taken up by some researchers in the UK (for example, Massey and Cordey-Hayes, 1971; Barras et al., 1971). The process involves a continuous relearning, so that the technical requirements, understanding, and data become more detailed and systematized at each cycle.

The present paper adopts this conceptual view of planning and argues therefore that it should be an ongoing process; it should incorporate specific goals and objectives; it should be based on analysis, and it should embody some notion of a refinement procedure which proceeds from a coarse level of resolution to a finer one. The new UK development plan system (see the Development Plan Manual, 1970) embodies some of these concepts. The basis of the new planning system is a written statement which has to be based on argument and analysis. This statement, the 'structure plan', defines the high-level strategy for an area—its social, economic, and physical subsystems—and it is intended that it should be regularly updated. Within this overall strategy there will be both local plans, to be used for detailed development control, and special subject plans, dealing with particular sectors.

It can be said that this is an embryo version of the ideal planning process outlined above. There is a notion of clearly defined goals and objectives, the need for which arises out of the requirement for a written statement of strategy. There is a recognition that alternatives have to be tested and that there must be formal analysis of plans. There is an explicit evaluation stage, the idea of constant revision, and, perhaps most significantly, the idea of progressive refinement from general broad statements of strategy down to detailed development control, and finally a clear recognition of the need to partition the systems of interest; the overall strategy is submitted to central government through the structure plan and the detail is settled at local level.

2.5 The aims of the activity–commodity approach

This type of comprehensive strategic planning demands a strategic level approach to evaluation, in the spirit of 'goals achievement' if not in its actual form. Plans have to be explicitly related to stated aims, and conscious choice should be built into the process at every stage. Furthermore, as will be elaborated in section 4.1, in such a cyclical process the stages of strategy generation and evaluation are inextricably linked.

This paper presents some initial ideas for advancing the aspirations of goals-achievement methods in terms of the development of a macro framework that can both treat the urban system as a whole and at the same time provide for increasingly detailed partial analyses of different subsystems or sectors. A clear distinction is made between plan generation and evaluation as a *normative* framework, and the system representation as a *descriptive* model embedded into this normative framework, in such a way as to provide information to be manipulated directly by the generation/evaluation process. A formal descriptive representation of the urban system is developed in terms of commodities as the basic system entities and activities as the relations between them. Externally supplied objectives can be related to this activity–commodity representation in an explicit way, and externally supplied values can be incorporated through the interrelationships in the system to provide measures for evaluating changes in system states.

This approach is not intended to represent a direct alternative to CBA in the sense of an alternative set of rules to utility maximization. Rather, the suggested framework can be developed into a *means* by which choices are articulated. The use of micromodels of individual behaviour is avoided, but it is suggested that formal descriptive models might be used within the framework in an analogous but different way to that in which behavioural models are linked to formal CBA.

3 An activity–commodity representation as a formal description of the urban system

3.1 General system representations

As the first stage in developing the approach to evaluation suggested in the previous section, it is necessary to introduce a formalism that can bring out the overall structure and behaviour of the urban system while removing the less important detail. It is suggested that such a formalism can be evolved out of some of the basic concepts that have been developed in mathematical systems theory for the purpose of analyzing the common characteristics of complex systems. For some relevant applications of system theory to economics see Kuhn and Szegö (1969).

As the typical starting point in this approach the system can be characterized by a set of objects that act as the basic entities in the system definition. Various mathematical relations can be defined on this set of objects, and each relation constitutes a statement about the structure of the system. Thus a mathematical structure built up as an abstraction of the key entities and interrelations in a real-world system becomes a representation of the behaviour of that system. Such a structure can either be formulated so as to represent the system in static equilibrium, or it can be dynamic in form, reproducing explicitly the behaviour of the system through time. In this paper the urban system is expressed in terms of a static representation only.

Corresponding to any mathematical representation of system behaviour there can be constructed a compatible data structure, the elements of which are numerical values for the entities in the variable mathematical structure. For the purposes of this paper, each unique set of values for this data structure will be known as a distinct 'state' of the system and the complete set of such states that can be generated from a particular system representation will be known as the 'state space'.

3.2 The basic objects and relations in the urban system

In applying to urban systems and general approach outlined above we have drawn on the concepts of activity analysis originally developed in economics. The application of this approach to urban and regional systems has already been discussed by Broadbent (1970a, 1973).

Activity analysis starts with commodities as the basic system entities and activities as the relationships between them. In the urban system, commodities typically include goods, money, labour, vehicles, buildings, land, etc. Urban activities, such as industrial, service, residential, and local government activities, will be characterized as 'production activities' which produce or consume commodities. In this paper we shall only outline in general terms how mathematical systems theory might be used as a vehicle for a general activity–commodity representation of urban systems; a more detailed development of the formalism is to appear later. The mathematical structures outlined here are derived from basic principles in elementary abstract algebra.

We begin by identifying commodities as the basic objects in the urban system. This use of the term 'commodity' is a general one that identifies system objects as 'use values', presupposing no particular mode of production and exchange. Let it be assumed that each commodity or use value in the system is denoted by a set U_m, $m = 1, 2, ..., M$. At this stage nothing will be assumed about the real-world nature of these commodities, which in terms of the representation means that no mathematical structure is assumed for the sets U_m. The most general statement of the existence of the set of commodities as a whole is the Cartesian product given by

$$U^* = \mathbf{X}\{U_m : m = 1, 2, ..., M\},$$

which consists of the set all possible M-tuples drawn from the sets U_m. All relations on the set of commodities can be expressed as subsets of this Cartesian product.

Each production activity will be denoted by the set P_n, $n = 1, 2, ..., N$. As the basic relationships in the system, they can be formally expressed as a relation on the set of commodities, that is,

$$P_n \subset U^*, \qquad n = 1, 2, ..., N.$$

The total urban system S can now be defined as a second-level relation on the set of N production activities, given by

$$S \subset P^*,$$

where $P^* = \mathbf{X}\{P_n : n = 1, 2, ..., N\}$ is the Cartesian product on the set of activities.

3.3 Activity and commodity vector spaces

The system relations stated above can be the starting point for developing various types of mathematical structure for the system representation. These structures can be derived by the definition of rules and operations on the basic system sets. In this paper we shall confine ourselves to static linear representations and to this end, without presenting a formal derivation, let it be assumed that the commodity product set U^* be given the well-defined structure of an M-dimensional vector space over the field of real numbers $\mathbf{R}$. This linear commodity space will be denoted by U. Relative to a given basis of U, each element $u \in U$ can be represented by an M-tuple of coordinates drawn from the set of real numbers, that is,

$$u = (u_1, ..., u_m, ..., u_M); \qquad u_m \in \mathbf{R}, m = 1, 2, ..., M.$$

If each activity is associated with a set of labels Z_n, one label for each distinct vector u, then each activity relation P_n can be expressed as a functional mapping from the set Z_n into the commodity vector space U, that is,

$$P_n : Z_n \rightarrow U.$$

Each element $z_n \in Z_n$ of an activity set therefore defines a unique commodity vector u_n as

$$P_n(z_n) = u_n = (u_{1n}, ..., u_{mn}, ..., u_{MN}),$$

and can thus be characterized as the activity 'state' corresponding to a particular M-tuple of commodity values. A distinction will be introduced between that subset of commodities which is consumed by an activity (its inputs) and that subset which it produces (its outputs). Commodity inputs will be denoted by negative values, the outputs by positive values.

Now if $Z^* = X\{Z_n : n = 1, 2, ..., N\}$ denotes the Cartesian product formed from the set of activity state sets, then this activity product set can also be given the structure of a vector space over the field $\mathbf{R}$. This N-dimensional activity space will be denoted by Z and the total system relation S can then be defined as a functional mapping from a system state set Z^S into the activity space Z, that is,

$$S: Z^S \to Z .$$

Through this mapping S, each system state $z^S \in Z^S$ is defined in terms of an activity space vector z which relative to a given basis of Z can be expressed as an N-tuple of coordinates drawn from the activity state sets Z_n, $n = 1, 2, ..., N$, that is,

$$S(z^S) = z = (z_1, ..., z_n, ..., z_N); \qquad z_n \in \mathbf{R}, n = 1, 2, ..., N .$$

But each activity state value $z_n \in Z_n$ can, through the mapping P_n, in turn be associated with an M-tuple of commodity values. Any system state can thus ultimately be expressed as an $M \times N$ matrix of commodity values u_{mn} ($m = 1, 2, ..., M$; $n = 1, 2, ..., N$).

3.4 System boundary
The representation being developed should be broad enough to accommodate all the activities likely to be significant in the development of strategic plans for the urban system. The activity space Z should thus be defined to include the complete set of activities by which system behaviour will be described over the time period encompassed by the planning process. At any particular time t only a subspace Z_t may define the system state. In this way the system representation can be generalized to accommodate basic changes in system structure through time.

The definition of the activity space for the system implies a system boundary, across which the system may be linked to its environment by inputs and outputs of commodities. This can be formulated as a mapping between the activity space Z and the commodity space U, that is,

$$A: Z \to U .$$

The mapping A is a fundamental statement of the structure of the system in terms of its internal state (activities) and cross-boundary linkages (commodities).

3.5 Systems with fixed technology
We have now outlined the basic framework for a static linear representation of urban systems in terms of activity and commodity vector spaces. In

activity–commodity analysis it is usual to make the further restrictive
condition that the system has a fixed technology. For a linear system
this condition can be introduced into the mathematical structure by
making the mapping A, from the N-dimensional activity space into the
M-dimensional commodity space over the same field $\mathbf{R}$, a linear
transformation satisfying the two conditions:

$$A(z_1 + z_2) = A(z_1) + A(z_2) ,$$

$$A(kz) = kA(z) ,$$

for all $z, z_1, z_2 \in Z$; $k \in \mathbf{R}$. As a linear transformation the mapping A
can then be represented by an $M \times N$ matrix $\mathbf{A}$ relative to the given bases
of U and Z. By using V to denote the commodity space as it applies to
net commodity totals for the whole system, this gives the vector equation

$$v = \mathbf{A}z , \qquad v \in V, \; z \in Z .$$

The coefficients a_{mn} ($m = 1, 2, ..., M$, $n = 1, 2, ..., N$) of matrix $\mathbf{A}$ are an
expression of the fixed technology of the system, such that the amount of
commodity m produced (positive coefficient) or consumed (negative
coefficient) by activity n is a product of the technical coefficient and the
level of activity, that is,

$$u_{mn} = a_{mn} z_n .$$

Each row of the matrix equation, given by

$$v_m = \sum_n a_{mn} z_n ,$$

expresses the net total amount of commodity m for the system as a whole
in terms of the amounts of that commodity produced or consumed by
each activity in the system. Each column of matrix $\mathbf{A}$ is equivalent to a
vector of technical coefficients a_n for an activity n. The definition of an
activity as the mapping $P_n : Z_n \rightarrow U$ can thus be restated as the linear
transformation

$$u_n = a_n z_n , \qquad u_n \in U_n, \; z_n \in Z_n ,$$

where U_n is the set of commodity vectors defined by activity n and Z_n is
the set of activity levels.

Now the matrix of technical coefficients $\mathbf{A}$ constitutes a simple
statement of the structure of the linear system in terms of the relative
strengths of commodity linkages between activities. As an illustration
consider the special case of a system representation in which each
commodity is produced by one and only one activity. If the activities are
ordered so that the rth activity produces the rth commodity, then the
square $M \times M$ matrix of coefficients is in the form of an input–output
table, a special case of the general activity–commodity representation.

For a particular production activity P_r, the column of coefficients $(a_{1r}, a_{2r}, ..., a_{rr}, ..., a_{Mr})$ corresponds to the commodity inputs to P_r from all the other activities in the system with the exception of a_{rr} which represents the total output of commodity r. Conversely, row $(a_{r1}, ..., a_{rr}, ..., a_{rM})$ corresponds to the distribution of the commodity output expressed by a_{rr} to all the other activities in the system. Each activity in the system can thus be considered as the nodal element in a structure of commodity input and output linkages; see, for example, figure 1.

Lange (1965) has developed some interesting results on the behaviour of general linear systems using a structural representation of this type.

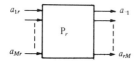

Figure 1. Input–output linkages of a production activity.

3.6 Hierarchical structure

To clarify the behaviour of complex systems, it is often useful to give the representation a hierarchical structure of interacting subsystems. For a fixed-technology activity–commodity representation, either the matrix of technological coefficients **A** or the full matrix of commodity linkages (u_{mn}) can be taken as the representation of system structure. Such a structure matrix can be used to determine a hierarchical partitioning of the system. The aim is to define relatively isolated subsystems within each of which there is a dense pattern of interactions. Different subsystems should be interrelated by a relatively simple pattern of aggregate linkages. Such a partitioning can be effected by the application of a lower threshold to the pattern of interactions in the structure matrix. By eliminating weak interactions, the strong clusters of interactions that show up help to indicate the most natural division into subsystems (see Simon, 1969).

Consider a simple case of partitioning into two subsystems. The undifferentiated structure matrix **S** is partitioned into two submatrices S_{11} and S_{22} along its main diagonal, corresponding to the internal structure matrices of the two subsystems, while the submatrices S_{12} and S_{21} are the coupling matrices that link them (Lange, 1965). This simple partitioning thus takes the form:

$$S = \begin{pmatrix} S_{11} & S_{12} \\ S_{21} & S_{22} \end{pmatrix}.$$

The subsystems defined in this partitioning can in turn be considered as relatively isolated entities in a higher order system representation, at a lower level of resolution. As a general principle, the basic entities at each level in a hierarchical system representation can be elaborated into subsystem structures at the level below.

With the system representation so structured, the different levels can be thought of as different levels of description or abstraction of the real-world system. Most simply, each level may be considered as a separate representation in its own right, with its own distinct structure and behaviour. When the different levels are considered as subsystems within the whole, because of their hierarchical ordering their functional interdependence is asymmetrical with the higher levels exerting control over lower levels (Mesarovic *et al.*, 1970).

3.7 Sectoral and spatial representations

So far the attributes by which both activities and commodities are categorized have not been specified, it being assumed merely that there were M different commodities and N different activities in the system. For a representation of the urban or regional system it is necessary now to identify these attributes. The aim should be to disaggregate system variables sufficiently to register the distributional effects of policies but at the same time avoiding excessive detail. Since this representation is intended to accommodate strategies that examine both the sectoral and spatial implications of resource allocation (see section 5.1), commodities will be categorized by both location and type, and activities by location and sector (for industry and services), or subgroup (for population). Thus Z_j^l will denote activity of type l at location j, and u_i^k commodity of type k at location i.

Then

$$u_{ij}^{kl} = a_{ij}^{kl} z_j^l ,$$

denoting the amount of commodity k at location i produced or consumed by activity l at location j, gives the basic commodity flows in the system.

The consistency equations for the use of commodities in the system, derived from the matrix equation $v = Az$, can now be stated as

$$v_i^k = \sum_{j,l} a_{ij}^{kl} z_j^l , \qquad v_i^k \in V_i^k , \quad z_j^l \in Z_j^l ,$$

where the v_i^k are exogenously supplied constraints that can either be taken as limits on the use of resources, or alternatively as desired levels of final demand for commodity k at location i. In some cases it may be necessary to introduce slack variables s_i^k into the representation as the balance between the exogenously supplied constraint and net output, that is,

$$v_i^k = \sum_{jl} a_{ij}^{kl} z_j^l + s_i^k ; \qquad z_j^l \in Z_j^l , \quad s_i^k \in S_i^k , \quad v_i^k \in V_i^k .$$

The technical coefficients a_{ij}^{kl} can either be derived exogenously, from measurements of the sectoral and spatial linkages in the urban system, or, alternatively, calculated by more detailed behavioural models embedded into the activity–commodity structure. For example, spatial interaction models could be used to calculate coefficients based on the spatial distribution of activities, as demonstrated in figure 3.

With a 'universal representation', based upon the most disaggregated commodity and activity spaces, now defined, a whole set of partial representations can be derived by the application of different sets of aggregation operators. The application of each set of aggregations corresponds to a particular projection of the universal representation. The theory of aggregation in models of the input–output type is an important area of current debate (see, for example, Carter and Brody, 1972). As will be discussed in section 5.1, two principal types of aggregation—sectoral and spatial—are of interest for the urban planning process:

(1) *Sectoral representation*
This can be derived from the universal representation by aggregating commodities k and activities l over their respective locations i and j, giving

$$v_*^k = \sum_l a_{**}^{kl} z_*^l \ .$$

Figure 2 shows the range of activities and commodities that could typically define the extent of a sectoral representation appropriate to local authority planning.

(2) *Spatial representation*
A spatial representation can be derived by aggregating the detailed sectoral categories of activities and commodities into much broader groups in order to concentrate on the spatial interaction behaviour of the system, that is,

$$v_i^* = \sum_j a_{ij}^{**} z_j^* \ .$$

Figure 3 shows a spatial interaction model, relating residential, industrial and service activities, cast into the activity–commodity framework. The coefficients in the table can be derived from behavioural models of the gravity type. This is fully explained in Broadbent (1973).

There is a considerable literature on models of general spatial equilibrium following the failure of Koopmans and Beckmann (1957) to obtain a unique equilibrium solution. At this point we are merely illustrating ways in which the categories in the urban system can be represented, and are not attempting to formulate a fully structured model of location behaviour.

The application of these spatial and sectoral aggregations introduces a basic hierarchical structuring to the universal representation. The manner in which these two partial representations are interrelated, through aggregate linkages with a sectoral upper level and spatial lower level, is discussed in section 5.3. Within each of these partial system representations further structuring can be introduced. Broadbent (1970b)

Commodities/resources	Activities																											
	Nonbasic															Basic						Slacks						
	Recreation	Retail: convenience	durable	Distribution	Office	Misc. Services	Local Govt: Social Serv.	Education	Other	Hospital	Transport	Residential				Construction	Office	Primary Industry	Manufacturing	Utilities	Hospitals	Shopping Out	Shopping In	Commuting In	Commuting Out	Unemployment	Rates balance	Constraints: base-year totals
Consumption: convenience	0	●	0	0	0	0	0	0	0	0	0	◇	◇	◇	◇	0	0	0	0	0	0							●
durable	0		●	◇	◇	◇	◇	◇	◇	◇	◇	◇	◇	◇	◇	0	0	0	0	0	0							●
Wholesale goods	0	◇	◇	●	0	0	0	0	0	0	0	0	0	0	0	◇	◇	◇	◇	◇	◇							●
Office services	0	◇	◇	◇	●		●	●	●	◇	0	0	0	0	0	◇	◇	◇	◇	◇	◇							●
Miscellaneous services	0	0	0	0	0	●	0	0	0	0	0	0	0	0	0	◇	0	◇	◇	◇	0							●
Public services: social	0	0	0	0	0	0	●	0	0	0	0	●	●	●	●	0	0	0	0	0	0							●
education	0	0	0	0	0	0	0	●	0	0	0	●	●	●	●	0	0	0	0	0	0							●
other	●	□	□	□	□	□	●	●	●	□	□	●	●	●	●	□	□	□	□	□	□							●
Local government: finance	0	●	●	●	●	●	●	●	●	●	●	●	●	●	●	●	●	●	●	●	●							●
Labour: category 1	●	●	●	●	●	●	●	●	●	●	●	0	0	0	0	●	●	●	●	●	●							●
at work other etc.	●	●	●	●	●	●	●	●	●	●	●	0	0	0	0	●	●	●	●	●	●							●
Construction	□	◇	◇	◇	□	□	□	□	□	□	□	□	□	□	□	□	□	□	□	□	□							●
Labour at home	0	0	0	0	0	0	0	0	0	0	●	●	●	●	●	0	0	0	0	0	0							●
Other adults at home	●	0	0	0	0	0	0	0	0	0	0	●	●	●	●	0	0	0	0	0	0							●
Children	●	0	0	0	0	0	0	●	0	0	0	●	●	●	●	0	0	0	0	0	0							●
Floorspace	●	●	●	●	●	●	●	●	●	●	●	0	0	0	0	●	●	●	●	●	●							●
Housing: category 1	0	0	0	0	0	0	0	0	0	0	0	●	●	●	●	0	0	0	0	0	0							●
	0	0	0	0	0	0	0	0	0	0	0	●	●	●	●	0	0	0	0	0	0							●
Households: type 1	0	0	0	0	0	0	0	0	0	0	0	●	●	●	●	0	0	0	0	0	0							●
	0	0	0	0	0	0	0	0	0	0	0	●	●	●	●	0	0	0	0	0	0							●
Land	●	●	●	●	●	●	●	●	●	●	●	●	●	●	●	●	●	●	●	●	●							●
Basic output: office	0	0	0	0	0	0	0	0	0	0	0					●	●	●	●	●	●							●

Figure 2. Activity-commodity representation of sector accounts. ● directly measured; ◇ national estimate; □ local estimate; 0 zero.

has described the development of a hierarchical spatial system, suitable for spatial interaction models of the type set out in figure 3, in which self-contained subregions are defined according to criteria such as journey-to-work closure. Fine zone interactions are modelled within the subregions, while interactions between subregions are represented by simple aggregate flows. A sectoral representation of the type illustrated in figure 2 could be similarly partitioned.

Commodities		Activities			
	Zone	Households 1 2 $\quad j \quad$ J $P_1 P_2 \quad P_j \quad P_J$	Basic industry 1 $\quad j \quad$ J $E_1^b \quad E_j^b \quad E_J^b$	Service industry 1 $\quad j \quad$ J $E_1^s \quad E_j^s \quad E_J^s$	Constraints
Labour at home	1 2 i I	$+\frac{1}{g}$ 0 . . . 0 0 . . $\quad +\frac{1}{g}$. $\quad\quad$. 0 0 . . . 0 $+\frac{1}{g}$	coefficient $-W_i\,{}^rB_j f_{ij}^r$	coefficient $-W_i\,{}^rB_j f_{ij}^r$	0 0 0 0	(a)
Service goods	1 i I	coefficient $-aW_i\,{}^sA_j f_{ji}^s$	0	+1 0 . . 0 0 . . $\quad +1 \quad$ . . $\quad\quad$. 0 0 . . 0 +1	0 0 	(a)
Basic	1 i I	0	+1 0 . . 0 0 . . $\quad +1 \quad$ . . $\quad\quad$. 0 0 . . 0 +1	0	E_1^b E_i^b E_I^b	(b)

(a) Constraints representing an internal balance.
(b) These constraints are the final output of basic goods.

Figure 3. An activity–commodity representation of a spatial interaction system. Household activities (columns P_j) output labour at j and input services from all zones. Basic activities (columns E_j^b) output basic goods at j and input labour from all zones. Service activities (columns E_j^s) output service goods at j and input labour from all zones. Each of the coefficients may be derived from a gravity model embedded into the activity–commodity framework. Functional values for the coefficients derived from a Lowry model are shown in the table (see Broadbent, 1973).

4 The use of the activity–commodity representation in the generation and evaluation process
4.1 The plan-making process
In the discussion of the evaluation process in section 2, it was suggested that a clear distinction should be made between the formal descriptive

model of system behaviour and the formal evaluation model. In section 3
we outlined the framework for a descriptive model of the urban system in
terms of activities and commodities. We shall now attempt to show, in
general terms, how such a descriptive representation can be embedded into
a formal conceptual model of the normative plan-making process. This
section consists only of some tentative first ideas that are considerably less
worked out than those used in the development of the descriptive activity-
commodity representation.

   To start with it should be stressed that any attempt to develop a
comprehensive conceptual model of the normative plan-making process
must recognize that the activities of plan generation and evaluation are
closely interrelated. In a sense one is the dual of the other—both phases
must be performed in the context of the exogenously derived objectives
for the planning process; the generation stage producing the alternative
strategies as outputs that become the inputs to the evaluation stage. This
duality has been recognized in a simple and straightforward manner in one
practical planning study already completed in Britain (Coventry-Solihull-
Warwickshire, 1971). The two stages of generation and evaluation can
perhaps most satisfactorily be linked through a cyclical or iterative process
in which the evaluation of the first set of strategies to be generated leads
to the refinement of some strategies and the generation of new ones, and
so on. Such a cyclical planning process has already been referred to in
section 2.

   We will thus consider plan-making as a process by which alternative
system states are generated and evaluated with respect to a given set of
objectives. Strategies for an urban system can thus be expressed in terms
of states or sets of states that as far as possible meet these objectives.
This does not imply a naive 'end-state' view of planning, solely concerned
with optimizing the achievement of a single goal state, but it does mean
that a direct relationship should be established between the statement of
planning objectives and the descriptive representation of system behaviour.
This is the aim of the normative process to be formalized in the following
sections of the paper.

4.2 The specification of the system
As the first stage in developing a conceptual model of the plan generation
and evaluation process, let us consider the function of any descriptive
representation of system behaviour embedded within this normative
process. In the most general sense we will characterize such a
representation as a set of rules such that, for any given specification of the
system, a particular system state is generated. If the set of all possible
specifications of the system is denoted by the set R, and the set of all
possible system states by Z^S (as in section 3.3), then the set of rules by
which the system representation or model operates can be stated as the

mapping

$$\theta : R \to Z^S .$$

This means that the set of rules by which the mapping θ operates must be sufficiently defined such that any particular specification of the system $r \in R$ defines a unique system state $z^S \in Z^S$. If this condition holds, then a complete statement of the system representation and its mode of operation is given by the triple $\Sigma = (\theta, R, Z^S)$.

To illustrate what such an approach might mean in terms of a particular system representation, consider the linear activity–commodity system with fixed technology developed in section 3.5. The operation of this representation was derived as a linear transformation between the activity space Z and the commodity space V, given by $v = Az$. The elements of any particular specification r for this system could thus be stated in the form of a triple (z, v, A), where $z \in Z$ is a particular vector of activity levels, $v \in V$ a particular vector of commodity constraints, and A the matrix form of the linear transformation, that is, the matrix of technical coefficients for the internal structure of the system. If A^* is used to denote the set of all possible linear transformations from Z to V, then the complete set of possible specifications of the system can be given in the form of the triple

$$R = (Z, V, A) .$$

Now any particular set of values for $r = (z, v, A)$ need only amount to a partial specification in order to define a unique system state $z^S \in Z^S$. Thus, if v and A are completely specified, then the linear transformation gives the set of activity levels z and thus the system state z^S. Alternatively, a particular specification may fix certain activity levels and leave other parts of the system to be determined by the mapping θ. Essentially the rules embodied in the mapping θ are therefore an expression of how different partial specifications of the elements of the system can be translated into a complete statement of system state, according to the basic operation of the system—in this case a linear transformation between two vector spaces.

4.3 The link between the normative process and the system representation

It can be seen from the previous section that the link from a normative model of the generation/evaluation process to the descriptive system model could be formalized in terms of the specification R: the output of the normative process being a specification $r \in R$ which through the descriptive model becomes transformed into an expression of a particular system state according to the mapping $z^S = \theta(r)$.

Now while in many cases it may be desirable to consider various system states in absolute terms, the planning process must always take into account that it is starting from a well-developed existing state. The alternative states considered by the planning process, however radical the change they imply, should always be seen in relation to previous or existing states. Expressed formally this means that, rather than an absolute specification $r \in R$ of the system, the link from the normative process should be expressed as a transformation of the existing or previous system specification r_1 into a new specification r_2. Such a transformation will be denoted by

$$\tau: R \rightarrow R \,,$$

where $\tau \in T$, T being the set of all such transformations that can be applied to the system specification. Thus, from an initial system specification r_1, implying a particular system state $z_1^S = \theta(r_1)$, the output from the normative process would be specified in terms of a particular transformation $\tau \in T$, giving a new specification $r_2 = \tau(r_1)$ from which a new system state $z_2^S = \theta(r_2)$ is derived.

On returning to the activity–commodity representation, with its specifications expressed in the form $r = (z, v, A)$, any transformation $\tau \in T$ applied to such a specification could be similarly expressed in the form of a triple (τ_z, τ_v, τ_A), where τ_z, τ_v, τ_A are transformations applied respectively to the activity vector z, the commodity constraint vector v, and the technical structure matrix A. Such transformations could take the form of an incremental change in certain system variables such as the commodity constraints or some activity levels, or a change in the structural linkages in the system through changing certain coefficients in the matrix A. Different levels of change in system state, as effected through different types of transformations, will be discussed further in section 4.7.

The search for alternative new system states in terms of transformations applied to the specification of previous states does not imply mere incrementalism as the objective of planning. In fact the aim is the opposite, for just as an overall view of a system requires an appreciation of its structural linkages, so the potential for radical change in a system can only be realized through an appreciation of its development as a continuous process. This implies a dynamic view of the system which, paradoxically, may in some senses be best achieved by embedding a static structural representation of the system into a normative process that focuses on the alternative possibilities for dynamic change. While an explicitly dynamic representation is useful as a means of exploring system behaviour as a process through time, such representations can be overconstrained with respect to the potential for alternative change in future system states.

4.4 Constraints
Certain constraints will operate upon the search for alternative system states. It is important that the constraints that are explicitly incorporated in the generation/evaluation process are kept to the essential minimum:

the more the constraints, the more restricted the search. Two types of constraint must be recognized:

1 Fixed constraints, such as physical or consistency constraints, that must be incorporated into the system representation. For example, in the activity–commodity representation, certain commodities such as land are in fixed supply—these can be incorporated into the representation through the vector of commodity constraints v.

2 Major exogenous changes in the environment of the system can impose conditions on possible change within the system itself. In the case of an urban system such changes are most likely to involve social and economic factors at national or regional level. These constraints can be formalized as a set of external transformations T^x, put exogenously into the generation/evaluation process, and incorporated into the transformations T that are applied to the system specification R. It is through this exogenous input T^x that significant uncertainty may be introduced into the process.

As far as possible other types of constraints, particularly behavioural constraints, should be introduced through the generation/evaluation process rather than by building them automatically into the descriptive system representation.

4.5 Objectives and values

It is the statement of goals, objectives, and values that provides the essential motive force behind the whole plan generation and evaluation process. As an expression of relative social preferences their formulation implies a political process involving conflicts and contradictions between different groups in society. Different sets of objectives and value systems can in fact be incorporated into the planning process, and various corresponding strategies generated, so that the consequences of adopting alternative social preferences can be evaluated.

The initial statement of goals and objectives must be sufficiently broad to allow full examination of all the policy issues of interest in the urban system. Given the range of issues that are important in the comprehensive planning of any urban system, the development of suitable strategies must inevitably be a heuristic process. A 'goal state' that is in any sense globally optimal cannot be meaningfully defined in a situation involving so complex a system as a city, and in relation to different sets of interrelated and often conflicting goals. Rather the generation/evaluation process must be seen as a search for improved states of the system that satisfy a set of explicit criteria defined in terms of the objectives. Such 'satisficing' solutions (Simon, 1969) can be defined with respect to the objectives in several ways: in terms of minimum levels of achievement measured against every objective; in terms of some overall measure of achievement against selected subsets of objectives, and so on. Such an approach to generation and evaluation based upon a search among a whole family of satisficing solutions can better provide the flexibility required to handle alternative and conflicting sets of values, and the problems of nonquantifiable objectives and variables.

In order for the stated objectives to be properly utilized within the plan generation/evaluation process, it must be possible to relate these objectives directly to the formal system representation embedded in the normative process. To this end it is necessary to transform the general statement of objectives into a specific set of values expressed directly in terms of the variables of the system representation. This transformation can be formally expressed by the mapping

$$\psi : \Sigma \times G \rightarrow C \, ,$$

where Σ is the triple (θ, R, Z^S), as an expression of the system representation and its mode of operation, G is the set of possible goal sets, and C the set of possible value sets derived from G.

With a value set $\bar{c} \in C$ expressed directly in terms of system variables, it is possible to go a stage further and 'process' these values through the system representation to produce a set of internal evaluative indicators which will be denoted by the set $\bar{w}$. The use of these indicators can ensure the consistency in the relationship between the system representation and its internal performance measures which is insufficiently developed in the goals-achievement methods currently used in planning (see section 2.3). To illustrate how such internal indicators can be derived by processing a set of values through the system representation, consider a solution analogous to a linear programming solution for the activity-commodity system. A linear objective function is supplied to the direct version of the model consisting of the weighted sum of the activity levels. The objective function is given by

$$\sum_j \sum_l c_j^l z_j^l$$

in the case of the 'universal representation' disaggregated by both sector and location (see section 3.7). The set of weights $c_j^l \in \bar{c}$ constitutes an expression of values, derived externally from the planning objectives, in terms of the activity levels in the system. A set of internal indicators can now be derived from the values $\bar{c}$ as the prices calculated in the dual solution of the model. Each commodity has a 'price' w_i^k determined from a general equilibrium solution which makes the total value of all the inputs to an activity equal to the value of the total outputs. This is done by solving the model down columns, that is,

$$\sum_k \sum_i a_{ij}^{kl} w_i^k + c_j^l = 0 \, .$$

By this means the externally supplied social preferences c_j^l are traced through the system of technical interrelationships a_{ij}^{kl} to determine the internal system evaluative indicators w_i^k.

The analogy with a linear programming solution can be pursued further. If the primal problem is

$$\max \sum_j \sum_l c_j^l z_j^l \,,$$

that is, maximize activity levels weighted by social preferences and subject to the constraints from section 3.7 that

$$\sum_j \sum_l a_{ij}^{kl} z_j^l = v_i^k$$

in which v_i^k are external resources in fixed supply or final demands, the dual is

$$\min \sum_k \sum_i v_i^k w_i^k \,,$$

that is, minimize the difference between the total value of final demands and the total value of resource inputs subject to the constraints

$$\sum_k \sum_i a_{ij}^{kl} w_i^k = c_j^l \,.$$

Thus in addition to suggesting a way in which evaluative indicators w_i^k can be consistently related to social preferences (through the fixed technology coefficients a_{ij}^{kl}), the dual shows that at the same time as maximal activity levels are being provided, resources employed in the system are being minimized.

One example of how these indicators might typically be used is in the situation where several new activities are being considered for introduction into the system. The w_i^k calculated from the equilibrium system can be used to determine the 'prices' of total inputs and outputs of these new activities, and therefore to compare their relative merit as new activities for the system. The overall achievement of the system is of course determined from the activity levels which enter into the objective function. Different weighting schemes expressing the value set $\bar{c}$ could be tried to test the effects of alternative social preferences. As a general rule, the statement of the objective function, while comprehensive, should be as straightforward as possible. It should not attempt to encompass complex trade-offs, for example between low density development and accessibility, that can more properly be handled within the system representation itself.

4.6 A formal representation of the generation/evaluation process

We are now in a position to construct a formal representation of the generation/evaluation process as a normative framework embodying a descriptive model of system behaviour. In outline the approach follows that suggested by Mesarovic et al. (1970) in specifying a 'decision-making system' consisting of a decision unit and an implementation unit. Two such subsystems can be identified for the generation/evaluation process as follows:
1 A decision unit can be specified as the mapping

$$\phi_D \colon Z^S \times T^x \times C \to T \times R \,,$$

taking as information inputs the existing system state $z_1^S \in Z^S$, the externally imposed transformations $\tau^x \in T^x$, and the value set $\bar{c} \in C$, and producing as output the transformation $\tau \in T$ to be applied to the system representation R.

2 An implementation unit can be specified as the mapping

$$\phi_1 : T \times R \to Z^S \, ,$$

taking as input the transformation $\tau \in T$ applied to the system representation $r_1 \in R$ to produce a new representation $r_2 = \tau(r_1)$, which in turn determines a new system state $z_2^S = \theta(r_2)$ as the output. The mapping ϕ_1 can be expressed as the composition $\phi_1 = \theta \circ \phi_T$, where $\phi_T : T \times R \to R$ is a general mapping for the transformation of the representation R.

The complete generation/evaluation process for plan strategies can thus be represented by the composition

$$\phi_S = \phi_1 \circ \phi_D \, ,$$

giving the mapping

$$\phi_S = Z^S \times T^x \times C \to Z^S \, .$$

The complete process is represented diagramatically in figure 4.

The feedback loop ensures that the process can proceed through any number of cycles by updating the input information on the current system state. This establishes the structure of the normative model as one that could form the basis for a cyclical planning process of the type outlined in section 2.4, with the successive generation and evaluation of strategies through several stages. The process can be further elaborated, for instance by introducing different value sets $\bar{c} \in C$ and alternative assumptions about the externally imposed transformations T^x.

The output of the process is a statement of plan strategies for the urban system. The formal statement of strategies could be made in various ways: in absolute terms as system states or sets of states, in relative terms as the transformations applied to an existing system specification, or as combinations of both. The transformations T provide a direct statement of the change implied by a particular strategy. One component of this change is exogenously imposed through the external transformations T^x and may determine the values of certain variables in the system specification over which the planner has little or no control. The other component consists of the planned change, applied to those parts of the

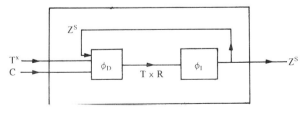

Figure 4. A notional representation of the generation/evaluation process.

system that can be controlled by the plan-making process. This
component of the transformation is a statement of the 'action' implied
by a strategy.

4.7 The structure of the plan-making process

Just as the system representation can be structured hierarchically (see
section 3.6), so can the whole decision-making process by which strategies
are generated and evaluated. Mesarovic *et al.* (1970) explores the hierarchical
structure of such decision-making systems in considerable detail. Only a
few observations will be made here on ways of structuring the plan
generation/evaluation system outlined in the previous section.

A central principal in evolving the structure of the normative process is
that it should directly parallel the structure of the system itself. The
upper levels should therefore be concerned with broad strategic issues
corresponding to the main structural features of the system representation.
Lower levels will be concerned with the more detailed treatment of partial
plans, within this strategy, corresponding to different subsystems within
the overall system structure. Such an approach has been adopted in the
new UK development plan system already referred to in section 2.4, with
structure plans at the strategic level incorporating local and subject plans
for lower level subsystems.

This type of hierarchical structuring of the plan-making process lends
itself to a 'top-down' approach to strategy generation and evaluation
within the space of possible future system states. The upper levels, where
the key system entities and interrelations are abstracted, allows the
different broad strategy areas to be partitioned for initial exploration.
Each strategy area can be considered to represent a neighbourhood of
solutions for subsequent tactical refinement at the lower levels and for the
elaboration of partial plans within the component subsystems of the overall
strategy framework. This hierarchical structuring of plan strategies can be
translated directly into different levels of change in the system state
through the transformations $\tau \in T$ applied to the system specification.
These transformations, as one form of the statement of a strategy, will
have their own internal structure mirroring that of the system representation
itself. Thus, with the activity–commodity representation, there are upper
level transformations of system structure, given by τ_A, and lower level
transformations, τ_z and τ_v, for the activity levels and commodity constraints
(see section 4.3).

This type of structure fits in well with the concept of a cyclical planning
process (see section 2.4) in which the broad strategy alternatives are
explored first, leading to the refinement and elaboration of final strategies
in the later stages. With this iterative process there is always a dialogue
between the different levels in the plan-making structure. The upper
levels of a strategy may impose transformations on the system specification
at lower levels, while relevant information on the system state at lower

levels is fed back as an input to decision making at the upper level. The next section presents a two-level example using the activity–commodity representation which indicates in very simple terms how such a multilevel plan-making process might proceed.

5 An example of a two-level system
5.1 Sectoral and spatial levels
In section 3.7 two partial activity–commodity representations, one sectoral and one spatial, were developed as aggregations of the 'universal representation'. They are illustrated in figures 2 and 3 respectively. These will now be used to form a simple two-level structure in order to illustrate some of the general ideas that have been developed in previous sections.

The two-level system is structured so that there is sectoral interaction at the upper level and spatial interaction at the lower level. This reflects the view that for the comprehensive planning of urban systems broad strategy alternatives should concentrate more on socioeconomic considerations, with spatial distribution effects at a secondary level. Investigations by Boyce *et al.* (1970) into the development of metropolitan strategies in the USA lend weight to this view. It was found that the alternative strategies, which were expressed principally in terms of physical patterns, showed less differences during evaluation that their spatial forms might have indicated.

The upper level of the representation concentrates on the distribution of resources between different sectors and groups. Strategies can consequently be evaluated in terms of the trade-offs between these different groups and sectors, and related back directly to the distributional goals and objectives of the planning process. The lower level of the model concentrates on the spatial distribution of resources and can be related to spatial and land-use objectives. There are parallels between this two-level representation and the distinction currently emerging in British planning between corporate planning, concerned with the sectoral allocation of local authority resources, and structure planning, concerned more with the spatial distribution of these resources.

Within the two main levels of the model, further hierarchical structuring could be introduced, as suggested in section 3.6. Subsystems composed of strongly interacting sectors in the upper level could be the focus of more detailed 'subject' plans, while at the lower level hierarchically ordered spatial systems could allow the development of more detailed 'local area' plans for particular subareas.

5.2 A normative framework for the two-level system
As was discussed in section 4.7 there should be a direct parallel between the structure of the normative plan-making system and that of the descriptive system representation. Consequently the formal generation/ evaluation model presented in section 4.6 will be adapted to a two-level structure into which can be embedded the sectoral and spatial levels of the

activity–commodity representation. This two-level normative framework is illustrated in figure 5.

For the upper (sectoral) level, the complete normative process is given by the mapping

$$\phi_1^S : (Z_1^S \times Z_2^S) \times T_1^x \times C_1 \to Z_1^S .$$

This assumes that as well as information about the state of the system at sectoral level (Z_1^S), information about system state Z_2^S at the spatial level is passed up to this higher-level generation/evaluation process.

At the lower (spatial) level, the normative process is given by the mapping

$$\phi_2^S : Z_2^S \times (T_2^x \times T_{12}) \times C_2 \to Z_2^S .$$

The link from the upper level is provided by the set of transformations T_{12}. These are determined as outputs from the sectoral process and consist of aggregate changes in system specification imposed on the spatial level. These can be taken together with the external spatial transformations T_2^x as exogenous transformation inputs to the lower-level generation/evaluation process.

Thus the two levels of this normative framework are interrelated with links in both directions in the manner already indicated in section 4.7. This allows the process of strategy generation and evaluation to proceed cyclically with a dialogue between the two levels.

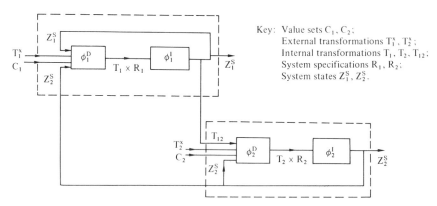

Key: Value sets C_1, C_2;
External transformations T_1^x, T_2^x;
Internal transformations T_1, T_2, T_{12};
System specifications R_1, R_2;
System states Z_1^S, Z_2^S.

Figure 5. The normative framework for the two-level system.

5.3 Use of the two-level system

Figure 6 shows a simplified version of the sectoral and spatial levels of the activity–commodity representation as shown in figures 2 and 3. It is related to the diagrammatic structure of the two-level plan-making process shown in figure 5. Thus figure 6 shows the activity levels (Z_1, Z_2) and prices (W_1, W_2) as the indicators of the general system state at each level, represented by Z_1^S and Z_2^S. The specifications of the system at each level,

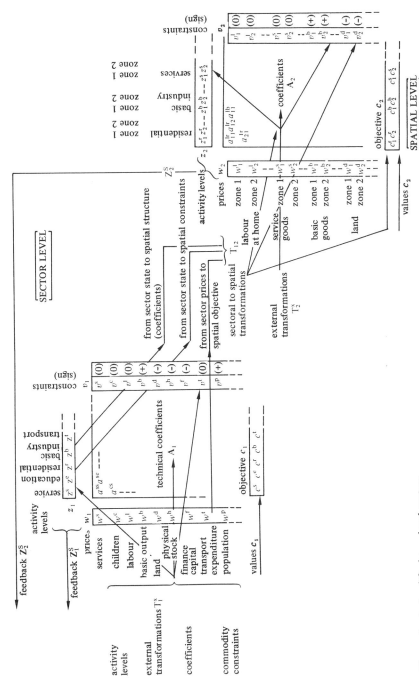

Figure 6. A simplified two-level system.

R_1 and R_2, are here taken to have as their components the sets of matrices of coefficients (A_1^*, A_2^*), the vectors of commodity constraints (V_1, V_2), and the activity levels (Z_1, Z_2). Normally the technical coefficients and commodity constraints would be specified and the system solved for the activity levels.

Figure 6 also shows the various transformation linkages (that is, the external transformations, T_1^x and T_2^x, the sectoral to spatial level transformations T_{12}) and the sets of values C_1 and C_2 externally derived for the objective functions at the two levels.

The indices used in the figure at sectoral level are given in table 1. At the spatial level the same indices of commodity and activity types are used, although some sectors are now aggregated.

To illustrate the use of this two-level system a suggested procedure based on the use of shadow prices as internal evaluative indicators will now be outlined. The general method by which these indicators can be derived, taking an externally supplied set of values $\bar{c}$ as activity level weights in an objective function and processing them through the system representation, has already been outlined in section 4.5. If these prices are derived as indicators of the existing system state, they can be used to provide information to guide the generation of strategies. This hierarchical process of generating future strategies will proceed through several stages. In early cycles, the strategies will be outlined in terms of the main structural features, lower levels of detail being brought in during later stages. It will be an experimental process, testing alternative future objective functions so that the successive calculations of system indicators (the prices) will provide greater and greater detail on the choice of strategy.

The suggested stages in a procedure that starts from the existing system state and proceeds to consider alternative future changes in state with respect to the two-level representation are as follows:

(a) Sector level
(1) Generalized technical change (T_1^x) (for example, car ownership rates, capital/labour ratios, labour/sales ratios, etc.). This would involve time

Table 1. The indices used in figure 6 at the sectoral level.

Commodities (k)	Index	Activities (l)	Index
Services	s	Service industry	s
Children	c	Education	e
Labour	l	Residential	r
Basic output	b	Basic industry	b
Land	d	Transport	t
Physical stock (houses)	h		
Finance capital	f		
Transport expenditure	t		
Population	p		

series analysis of the relationship between national and local change in such coefficients as the following:

Service activity: labour per unit sales in the retail sector, a_{**}^{ls}; land per unit sales, a_{**}^{ds}.

Basic activity: labour per unit output, a_{**}^{lb}; land per unit output, a_{**}^{db}.

Residential activity: the activity rate, a_{**}^{lr}; changing residential density, a_{**}^{dr}.

(2) Exogenous changes in constraints and activity levels at sector level (T_1^x). These would be derived from an external analysis of the demands on the urban system from regional or national level. They could be predictions, plans of large national enterprises, or alternatives to be tested. These changes are much more specific to the particular system and its external links than those in stage (1), and this stage could provide an opportunity for a feedback from urban-level impact studies to regional or national agencies. Examples in the simple representation are:

projected final demand for basic activity, v^b;

this may or may not lead to a choice of alternative activities, z^b;

projected total migration, determining total population v^p.

(3) Externally supplied social preferences (c_1). These have to be incorporated into an objective function which relates sector variables. In this simple example the relative preference could be between service and basic activity. In a more complex system the objective could be more generalized, such as the maximization of income.

(4) With the main technological and external influences accounted for, and their immediate impact on the system variables described, the next stage would be to concentrate upon those parts of the system under more-direct local-planning control. The aim would be to use the objective function in the search for 'satisficing' states (see section 4.5) for some future year, or along some time path. The major external transformations would already have imposed some kind of partial structure on the system for the future. Evaluation indicators (prices) could be calculated for this rudimentary future system, and used to choose between alternative plans (that is, new activities) for those parts of the system under local control.

(b) Links from sector level to spatial level

As previously stated, there is asymmetry in the linkages between the two levels. The sectoral resource distribution level, being the superior system, tends to take the major decisions as far as the spatial level is concerned, but at the same time the spatial level does provide the sector level with information. Three types of decision link, in the form of transformations T_{12}, are illustrated:

(1) Constraints. These can be accounting identities such as the total land consumption by sector. They are determined at the upper level and merely operate as control totals on the spatial level.

(2) Structure. The sector level analysis could, for example, involve a determination of total transport expenditure by households as against expenditure on other goods. Assume that the coefficients at the spatial level are determined through a gravity model, as indicated in figure 3. Now the travel parameter β in the trip function $\exp(-\beta c_{ij})$—where c_{ij} is the cost of travel between zones i and j—has been shown to be related to total expenditure on transport (Wilson, 1967). Thus any change in this expenditure, determined at the sector level, will change *all* the interaction coefficients at the spatial level—a structural change.
(3) Objective function. Some of the evaluation indicators at sector level (the prices) may act as weights (values) for the activities (or aggregates of activities) at spatial level. Thus the price of services as against residential activity could be fed into the objective function at spatial level.

(c) Spatial level
The general form of the analysis would be the same as at the sector level. Firstly, exogenous changes would be allowed for and special analyses carried out for major individual locators, for example, large factories for basic industry or regional shopping centres. This would be followed by the calculation of spatial indicators (prices) such as those associated with accessibility and densities (see, for example of this, Broadbent, 1973).

(d) Feedback from spatial to sector level
This would provide information for further resource and sector analyses, though these would be less strong than the decision links from the sectoral to the spatial level. Examples could include summaries of spatial states such as spatial distributions and densities. These measures could help to influence the allocation of resources in infrastructure. Similarly, changing the spatial distribution of the housing stock could influence decisions on the division of resources between renewal and development.

References
Barras, R., Broadbent, T. A., Cordey-Hayes, M., Massey, Doreen B., Robinson, Krystyna, Willis, J., 1971, "An operation urban development model of Cheshire", *Environment and Planning*, 3, 115-233.
Bellman, R., 1965, *Mathematical Aspects of the Theory of Systems: Proceedings of the Symposium on System Theory* (Polytechnic Press, Brooklyn, New York).
Boyce, D. E., Day, N. D., McDonald, C., 1970, *Metropolitan Plan Making, Monograph Series number 4* (Regional Science Research Institute, Pennsylvania).
Broadbent, T. A., 1970a, "An activity analysis framework for urban planning", WP-61, Centre for Environmental Studies, London.
Broadbent, T. A., 1970b, "A hierarchical interaction-allocation model for a two-level spatial system", WP-67, Centre for Environmental Studies, London.
Broadbent, T. A., 1973, "Activity analysis of spatial allocation models", *Environment and Planning*, 5 (6), forthcoming.
Carter, A. P., Brody, A. (Eds.), 1972, "Applications of input-output analysis", in *Proceedings of the 4th International Conference on Input-Output Techniques, Geneva 1968* (North-Holland, Amsterdam).

Coventry-Solihull-Warwickshire Subregional Planning Study, 1971, *A Strategy for the Subregion* (Coventry City Council, Solihull County Borough Council, Warwickshire County Council).

Development Plan Manual, 1970, *Development Plans: A Manual on Form and Content* (HMSO, London).

Hill, M., 1968, "A goals-achievement matrix for evaluating alternative plans", *Journal of American Institute of Planners,* **34,** 19-29.

Koopmans, T. C., Beckmann, M. J., 1957, "Assignment problems and the location of economic activities", *Econometrica,* **25,** 53-76.

Kuhn, H. W., Szegö, G. P. (Eds.), 1969, *Mathematical Systems Theory and Economics: Lecture Notes on Operations Research and Mathematical Economics, Number 11* (Springer-Verlag, Berlin).

Lange, O., 1965, *Wholes and Parts: A General Theory of System Behaviour* (Pergamon Press, Oxford; PWN, Warsaw).

Lichfield, N., 1970, "Evaluation methodology of urban and regional plans: a review", *Regional Studies,* **4,** 151-165.

Little, I. M. D., 1957, *A critique of Welfare Economics* (Oxford University Press, Oxford).

Massey, Doreen B., Cordey-Hayes, M., 1971, "The use of models in structure planning", *Town Planning Review,* **42,** 28-44.

Mesarovic, M. D., Macko, D., Takahara, Y., 1970, *Theory of Hierarchical, Multilevel Systems* (Academic Press, New York).

Mishan, E. J., 1971, *Cost Benefit Analysis* (Allen and Unwin, London).

Neidercorn, J. H., Bechdolt, B. V., 1969, "An economic derivation of the 'gravity law' of spatial interaction", *Journal of Regional Science,* **9,** 272-282.

Neuberger, H. N., 1971, "User benefit in the evaluation of transport and landuse plans", *Journal of Transport Economics and Policy,* **V,** 1-24.

Pearce, D. W., 1971, *Cost Benefit Analysis* (Macmillan, London).

Prest, A. R., Turvey, R., 1965, "Cost benefit analysis: a survey", *The Economic Journal,* **LXXV,** 683-735.

Scitovsky, T. A., 1969, "A note on welfare propositions in economics", in *Readings in Welfare Economics,* Eds. K. Arrow, T. Scitovsky (Allen and Unwin, London). Reprint of paper from *Review of Economic Studies,* 1941.

Simon, H. A., 1969, "The architecture of complexity", in *The Sciences of the Artificial* (MIT Press, Cambridge, Mass.).

Theil, H., 1965, *Linear Aggregation of Economic Relations* (North-Holland, Amsterdam).

Wilson, A. G., 1967, "A statistical theory of spatial distribution", *Transportation Research,* **1,** 253-270.